*Rh*

# Rh

## The Intimate History of
## a Disease and Its Conquest

### DAVID R. ZIMMERMAN

Macmillan Publishing Co., Inc.
New York

Macmillan Publishing Co., Inc.
Collier-Macmillan Canada Ltd.

Library of Congress Catalog Card Number: 72-90280

FIRST PRINTING

Printed in the United States of America

*To Ted*

# Contents

# List of Illustrations

# *Preface*

THIS BOOK IS about creativity in medical research. My aim is to unfold, from the participants' viewpoints, a strikingly productive series of observations, intuitions, and deductions that have led—within the career span of a single scientific generation—from the elucidation to the defeat of one extremely lethal disease. Rarely is a disease dealt with so effectively in so little time.

The disease is *erythroblastosis fetalis*, which is also called *Rh hemolytic disease*. Those whom it kills all die before birth, or shortly thereafter. Some of the survivors recover; others are left crippled for life in mind and body.

The conquest of Rh hemolytic disease has been filled with drama. The drama of achievement. The drama of surprise and conflict. The drama bred of frustration and bitter disappointment. Most striking of all has been the drama of ideas: the way that each individual scientist achieved the understanding that led him to take a great step forward. And the step itself.

This fruitful creative drama was what first drew my attention to Rh research nine years ago. I was a reporter for a medical news magazine. Rh was—and is—a "good story," which was the chief justification for covering it then, as news, as it is the prime justification for recreating it here, as history.

There is pleasure in observing an act of intellectual achievement

—a pleasure like that of seeing a ballet artist or athlete perform. For the professional observer, this pleasure carries the challenge of conveying the experience to others so that they can share vicariously in it. This I have attempted to do for the history of Rh.

For whom?

For the ordinary intelligent person who may enjoy sharing the scientists' labors and their triumphs. And for scientists who, while they may be familiar with one or another element of this account, are unlikely to have conceived of it as a whole.

Science, as it is written for the scientist and written about for the citizen, most often is concerned with experiments and results. Discoveries are reported, usually a fragment at a time, in widely scattered professional journals. Most often, the individual creative act that lies behind these discoveries is deliberately concealed, rather than displayed. Most often, too, it is the fragmentary progress reports that are the basis for what is reported to the public about science. This narrative account of the activity that lies behind such reports thus breaks ground that is rarely tilled in either professional or general circulation publications—it is written for the readers of both.

A word of warning may be in order. Several abstruse areas of scientific inquiry are rapidly traversed in this account, including immunohematology, genetics, and obstetrics. What is said of each area is not intended as a primer or outline of the science per se— and should not be so construed. Rather, each discipline is broached only to find important markers on the trail to the conquest of Rh disease. It is not the forest that I intend to illuminate, only a very narrow path that leads through it. Thus, a reader who feels himself lost in a thicket of technical matters will do well not to beat at the brush around him. Keep reading! The trail will soon reappear underfoot.

Erythroblastosis offers several important advantages to the journalist-cum-historian who attempts to expose the creative process leading to the conquest of a human disease. Most important is the perspective of hindsight, which is a potent selective tool. At a rough guess, ten thousand scientific reports have been published about erythroblastosis fetalis in the past forty years. But very few played any significant part in the successful attempts to defeat it. Standing at or near the finish line, it is possible to cast the eye backward to pick out those very few contributions that turn out to have been important; the balance can with confidence be ignored.

This could not be attempted in a book, say, on cancer, about which tens of thousands of papers appear annually—their issue remains in doubt.

Even the relatively short record of erythroblastosis would be difficult to synthesize from the published scientific literature alone; too much has been left out. Fortunately, the rapidity with which the work progressed has permitted most of the key participants— indeed, all but one—to be alive for the finish. I have had the privilege of interviewing in person virtually every one of them. I have been in touch with others by letter or telephone. All, with one or two exceptions, have been extremely generous with time, patience, and information. Although too numerous to thank individually here, each one's help is specifically noted in the Acknowledgments.

There are several men without whose generous help this book could not have been written. I would like to extend to them special thanks. Drs. Vincent Freda and John Gorman of the Columbia-Presbyterian Medical Center, New York City, found time in their always-crowded schedules to answer what must have seemed like an endless succession of questions. Dr. Freda was especially helpful in the years 1964–1968, when their work was newsworthy. Dr. Gorman has been especially helpful subsequently in the reinterpretation of that news as history. Both men have made available important unpublished letters and documents without which this account would have been far less accurate and complete.

The third member of the "New York team," Dr. William Pollack, has granted several interviews at the Ortho Pharmaceutical Corporation, Raritan, New Jersey, where he is now vice president and director of diagnostics research. These talks, while helpful, were usually held under somewhat formal and inhibiting circumstances; they were tape-recorded by Ortho, or were attended by a company information officer.

Ortho has provided some helpful information but has declined to make available any of its vast collection of documentary material, much of which is innocent of trade secrets. This is regrettable. In a decade in which drug manufacturers met unending criticism for practices that better served corporate profit than the public weal, Ortho's role in Rh research was a refreshing and exemplary exception. The interest of public understanding of the industry at its best might have been well served by a documented account of how Ortho made the corporate decision to gamble and support a risky, unproved research venture whose ultimate value could not then have been guessed. Because of Ortho's reticence, this story cannot be told here.

During the 1960s the group of researchers in New York City was one great fount of progress against Rh disease. At least as great a contribution was made by Dr. Cyril Clarke and his colleagues at the University of Liverpool, England. For a month in 1969, Dr. Clarke graciously permitted me to explore with him, and with his colleagues and associates, the history of their superb achievement. Especially helpful was Dr. Ronald Finn, who also provided manuscript copies of important early texts. Counsel and assistance came from Dr. Philip Sheppard and Dr. John Woodrow. Several key observations that bear on the historical assessment of the work in Liverpool were graciously provided by Dr. Richard McConnell.

Considerable controversy surrounds the events I will describe. If the Rh story shows anything, it is that scientific achievement is tightly bound to personal, human feelings. Since science writers may be as subject to bias as scientists themselves, it is perhaps fair that I state my own point of view and say where I believe I may be biased.

As a newsman first, and more recently in writing the present account, I have been in close professional contact with members of the New York group. Since I brought to this subject no special knowledge of my own, much of what I have learned and much of my own perspective is based on theirs. Moreover, much of this account is told from their point of view.

It is my hope now, having talked with all parties, that my viewpoint and narrative have attained a dimension and an objectivity of their own. The value of this account depends on my success at that task.

Whatever my point of view, and whatever my biases, I have attempted to be especially scrupulous in examining, without favor, the bitterly contested question of who is to get credit for certain key creative achievements. I have been encouraged in this effort by the thought that the only real reciprocation that I can extend to all those who have helped me is an objective, trustworthy record of their achievements. I believe it is accurate to say that I feel no bias for or against Liverpool or New York. Obviously, if I did not believe that both made important contributions, this book, in its present form, could not have been written. If I retain a bias, it probably is not a partisan one. Rather, as a "young writer," I have tended to identify with the struggle and achievements of "young scientists" who are only a few years older than I am. *Caveat emptor!*

A few notes on method: This is not intended to be a complete, formal history of erythroblastosis. Hence, it is not fully annotated. I claim authority only with regard to the 1960s, about which no other book-length account has yet appeared. As a result, for this period I have provided relatively complete documentation. For earlier periods in blood and erythroblastosis research, only key, controversial, or obscure statements are documented; the rest is common knowledge available in standard texts. This background appears in Chapters 1–5.

Almost without exception, the participants' later views of their achievements have been colored by their present perspectives—what Dr. Kurt Stern calls "retrospective memory." As a guide to the present reader, and to anyone who may later wish to consult this account as a research source, I have used the simple past or present tense when my source is a contemporary document or publication. When the source is an individual's memory, I have usually identified the individual and have indicated that memory was my source by using the conditional form "he would remember," or "she would later say." In only a few places have I taken that liberty for which Thucydides begged in his account of Pericles' Oration to the Athenians—which he had not been present to hear.

Documentary sources are keyed by number within each chapter, and appear in the Notes at the end of the book. A few historical issues of limited interest are also treated there.

The scientific nomenclature of erythroblastosis has changed rapidly and radically since 1930. A contemporary reader might fail to comprehend a report written several decades ago, so different is the language. To overcome this problem, I have arbitrarily chosen one contemporary set of terms, and have used it throughout—even in quotes taken from early workers. A Glossary is provided. In addition, there are text drawings by Geoffrey Nunberg and photographs.

Finally, several individuals in the publishing field have made this book possible. William H. White, the founding Executive Editor of *Medical World News,* and that magazine's late Managing Editor, Ted Stoil, aided and encouraged me in my coverage of Rh as a medical news story. The late David Segal was first to agree that Rh might make a good trade book—and encouraged me to write it. Mrs. Kathie Fried has carefully carried the editorial chores through to completion. Through many difficult years, Mrs. Carolyne Brooks has provided careful, thoughtful, and cheerful secretarial assistance, which I appreciate more than she will ever know. Dr. Fred Allen, Jr., has read the manuscript and offered numerous suggestions. My wife, Veva, lovingly has accepted, as shared, the enormous time burden this work required.

I am grateful to everyone who has helped. I, alone, am responsible for errors.

DAVID R. ZIMMERMAN
*New York, January* 1973

# Introduction

## By James D. Watson

THE FINAL NEATNESS, if not beauty, of many scientific achievements stands in great contrast to the day by day aspects of the human life that must create it. Probing into the unknown is generally a murky affair, and moments of analytical genius, of the type that we associate with high-powered chess, come only rarely and sometimes not at all. Most of the active hours of scientists are holding actions, waiting for the day when the reading of a newly arrived journal or book, or a chance conversation with someone down the hall, leads to a new way of thinking. And success in large part goes to those whose thoughts, both rational and irrational, are dominated by the importance of the final objective, even to the point of seeming one-sided, if not totally unbalanced.

These are attributes most easily taken up by the relatively young, marked only by responsibility to themselves, and not tied down to the day by day task of doing well a job that everybody knows can be done. Usually, some more established scientist must know them well enough to see that they are paid for not being busy, and occasionally to protect them when their love for offbeat ideas leads them to clash with the by now faded ideas of the men at the top.

And when a real idea does suddenly appear, its genesis is sometimes not that clear—often it emerges from a tortuous series of half-truths that are quickly forgotten when the whole is in. Yet these partial truths may have been very vital to the whole process.

Only by their possession could morale have been maintained toward a goal that all too often seems conquerable only by a brain more high-powered than your own.

Thus the reconstructing of the total life history of most scientific ideas is a very difficult task, with the real story almost always varying from one participant to another. So it is not surprising that very few people have taken up this task and most histories of science have the sanitized outlooks of high school textbooks of American history.

David Zimmerman's study of the conquering of Rh incompatibility is not of this genre. He writes of the scientific world as I know it and provides a most needed view of the complex interactions of idealism and the need for personal success. Let us hope we soon have more books like this. Science is now too much at the heart of our society for the illusion to persist that scientists are fundamentally different from other, more practical, people.

JAMES D. WATSON, PH.D.

*Rh*

# Prologue: Resolute Vince

VINCE HAD A cheerful, outgoing appearance that afforded no clue to his powerful creative bent. A large, strongly built young man with crew-cut hair and an amiable manner, he savored his professional obligations: delivering babies and attending to his patients' obstetric and gynecologic complaints. A friendly, boyish charm, combined with masculine professional self-assurance, enhanced his appeal to the women for whom he cared.

Obstetrics is a surgical discipline. Vince, like most good surgeons, enjoyed working with his hands. To cut, sew, pull, probe, and thus provide care—these were his workaday pleasures.

Unlike many surgeons and obstetricians, Vince was also drawn to the less concrete, more elemental aspects of nature and science. His craving to be a doctor—New York University awarded the Doctor of Medicine degree to Vincent J. Freda in June 1952—had foreclosed a competing career bent toward nuclear physics. But while perfecting his manual skills as a surgical intern at Bellevue Hospital in New York, and later as an obstetric trainee, Vince was again attracted to the elemental and arcane: *immunology*, the inquiry into biologic identity, difference, and defense; and *serology*, its subspecialty, which assesses blood compatability for the purpose of transfusion. New knowledge in these enigmatic sciences resists the direct grasp of hand or mind—its elucidation requires subtle thought and sophisticated experiments.

1

For all the self-confidence engendered by his professional skill and achievement, Vince, personally, was painfully shy. Likeable he was. He wanted to be liked. He feared that he failed to please. Yet he could sense that he was liked, and would become skillful in using this asset to further his aims. When crossed or frustrated in his pursuits, Vince could be astonishingly adamant in the expression of his anger and annoyance.

Vince's personal anxieties fueled a predilection to be at all times busy, professionally. Scheduled operative procedures. Office patients. Rounds. Research. Babies to be delivered, day and night. It was rare to see Vince when he had not been roused early or kept up late by a laboring lady. He suffered chronic fatigue with apparent good cheer. Yet it was less a sense of achievement that was brought out in Vince by sleepless nights than it was a chilling opposite sense of having failed to adequately achieve.

Vince had come to medicine without benefit of familial example or connection. He was born in New Haven, Connecticut, of parents recently arrived in the United States from a small Italian village. His father, a designer of men's clothes, had moved his family to a suburb of New York City when Vince was a child to be near the big Fifth Avenue stores for which he worked.

Vince attended St. Peter's Preparatory School in Jersey City, New Jersey, went to college on a scholarship at Columbia University in Manhattan, and then crossed town to the East Side, to the New York University Medical Center for his medical and internship training. Surgery had been his original aim. But his first exposure to patients, while still a medical student, was on the obstetrical service. The work and the warm regard which he came to hold for his teachers led him to choose their specialty as his own. Later, after two years of military service as an Air Force medical officer, Vince returned to New York University for the first year of his obstetrical residency training. He would complete his training at the Columbia-Presbyterian Medical Center, on Manhattan's upper West Side. Thereafter he would remain at Columbia for more than a decade, teaching at its medical school—the College of Physicians and Surgeons—and practicing obstetrics at its allied hospitals.

Vince adapted well to the political exigencies of the academic medical community. By carrying a fair clinical load, plus teaching, and by conducting some routine obstetrical research, he might comfortably have achieved more than most men can ever hope for: a secure, useful, and respected career. This route he eschewed—it would not suffice. While meeting all the expected professional obligations, Vince continued to feel somewhat apart and unfulfilled. His ambition was not being satisfied. For there was one other aspect of himself, as yet untested, in which Vince had extraordinary innate faith: the power of his own ideas.

He harbored a potent urge to find achievement in medical research. Daringly, he sought it not wholly within his speciality, obstetrics, but partly in areas of his avocational interest: immunology and blood.

Vince must have had a deep feeling that to do significant research in these areas he first needed further training—a preceptorship. One of his medical school professors at New York University, whom he knew, but not well, was a famous pioneer in the study of immunology and blood. Vince, while serving in the Air Force in Japan, had set up a laboratory and had conducted, by himself, an original immunologic experiment. The results, although they were equivocal, were just interesting enough so that, when he returned to New York, in 1956, Vince could bring them—and thereby himself—to this older scientist's attention.

# 1

## *Bitter Beginnings*

VINCE'S CHOSEN MENTOR, Dr. Alexander Wiener, was a brilliant, bitter, sensitive man. He had won recognition as one of two pillars upon whose research all progress against erythroblastosis fetalis, a deadly disease of unborn and newborn babies, had been built. The other pillar, and Wiener's rival—in an unabated enmity of many years' standing—was Dr. Philip Levine.

Levine's had been the more stolid, well-focused achievement, compared to Wiener's erratic, wide-ranging genius. Levine, now in his mid-fifties, was the older of the two by several years. Their contributions to blood research had been enormous. Their long-standing battle, which had all the inescapable bitterness of a family fight, now was fixated in a dispute over who had made the key discoveries that had bared erythroblastosis to medical intervention.

Both men had been protégés of the father of blood science and immunology, Dr. Karl Landsteiner. They continued, years after his death, to vie for recognition as his chosen disciple and scientific heir.[1] Landsteiner, with whom they had worked in the last period of his life at the Rockefeller Institute for Medical Research in New York, had won the Nobel Prize for Medicine in 1930 for his blood research. Levine and Wiener had also been nominated, jointly, for this honor, which colleagues felt they richly deserved, but had not received it; in part, perhaps, because of their unseemly rivalry.[2]

Landsteiner, a Vienna-born Jew, had been trained in the rigid, authoritarian, anti-Semitic tradition of German medicine. In 1900,

4

as a young man of thirty-two, he had discovered the Human Blood Groups, a discovery which for the first time made possible safe transfusion of human blood.

For centuries, attempts had been made to transfer animal or human blood to sick people as a therapeutic. Recipients occasionally improved dramatically, but more often than not the blood made them violently ill and they died.

Landsteiner discovered why:

He drew blood from himself and from his laboratory co-workers. He allowed each specimen to stand until it separated into two components. One was the blood's vital, oxygen-transporting *red cells*, which coalesced in a clot. The other was the *serum*, the clear

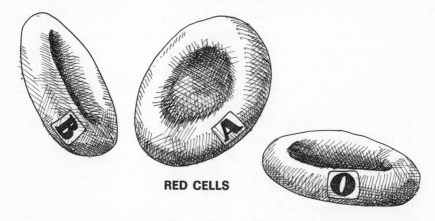

**RED CELLS**

liquid within which red cells flow through the bloodstream. Then Landsteiner mixed—one man's red cells with another man's serum.

In some instances, there was no observable reaction. The reconstituted liquid remained fluid. But in other instances, when he mixed the red cells of one with the serum of another, a destructive reaction could be seen. The red cells became glued together, or *agglutinated*, in easily visible clumps at the bottom of the test tube.

Sometimes, Landsteiner later observed, subjecting one man's red cells to another man's serum resulted in a different destructive reaction: The cells' thin outer membranes were ruptured, or *lysed*, so that their red stuff, the *hemoglobin*, seeped out and dispersed through the serum, staining it pink. Landsteiner deduced that blood transfusions often failed because comparable destructive reactions occurred when a donor's blood was mixed with the recipient's in his circulatory system.

The idea that led Landsteiner to make sense of these findings was a then-current biologic concept that a living organism cannot be poisonous, or destructive, to itself. An organism is alive only because its many constituent elements do not attack each other or the whole. This inner harmony of each individual life, its biologic identity, was seen as the basis of its continued existence—the basis of life itself. It followed that each person's red cells must be non-reactive with his own serum, for if they failed to coexist, even for a minute, the individual's red blood would be destroyed and he would quickly die.

If red cells from Individual A could be mixed, without reaction, with his own serum, and also with serum of a second individual, then it followed, Landsteiner deduced, that in some important way the two individuals' red cells and/or serums were identical.

In some mixes, on the other hand, where red cells from Individual A were destroyed by something in Individual B's serum, there also was a reciprocal destructive relationship: Red cells from Individual B invariably were destroyed by something in Individual A's serum. There was a fundamental difference between the two individuals' bloods.

Another individual had serum that would destroy the red cells of both Individual A and Individual B—which meant that in some essential way he was unlike both A and B. But, strangely, this individual's red cells could be mixed, without reaction, with the serum of either Individual A or Individual B.

If one individual's red cells were destroyed by a second individual's serum, there was an antagonism between them. Landsteiner deduced that some factor, or *antigen*, in the blood of the first was specifically provocative to some destructive substance, or *antibody*, in the serum of the second.

Since he had found two different types of reaction-provoking red cells, Landsteiner labeled their antigens, alphabetically, A and B. Individuals whose red cells carried these antigens belonged, he said, either to *group A* or *group B*. The third set of individuals, whose red cells were compatible with the serums of both group A *and* group B individuals, later were labeled *group o*, for *zero*, or no antigen; this *zero* was widely misread as the letter O, which became the group name. Landsteiner belonged to group O.

The blood factor in a group A individual's red cells that led them to be destroyed by the serum of a group B or group O individual was, by definition, the *A antigen*; it followed that the specific antibody that destroyed them should be called *anti-A antibody*. An

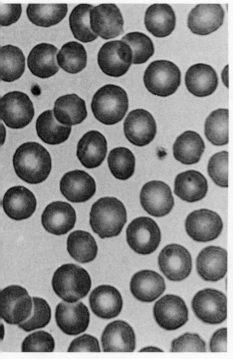
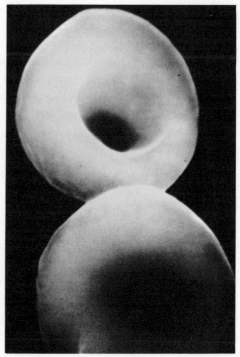

Normal red blood cells appear as flat discs (left) when seen through ordinary light microscope at 600 diameters magnification. Cells' rounded contours become visible (right) when photographed through recently developed scanning electron microscope at 5,600 diameters. (*Left: Wright stain; Courtesy Professor Ann Bell, University of Tennessee College of Medicine, Memphis. Right: Courtesy Drs. Carel van Oss and James Mohn, and S. Karger, Basel.*)

antibody that selectively destroyed only group B red cells was *anti-B antibody.*

Antibodies are contained in a small fraction of the serum called *gamma globulin.* Several different antibody-carrying gamma globulin molecules later were elucidated; only two are relevant here. They are designated 7S and 19S. The 7S is a lighter, smaller, two-armed molecule. The 19S is larger, heavier, and has five armlike projections. At the tip of each projection is a part that grabs and anchors to the antigen against which the antibody is directed.

Antigens are distributed over the red cell surface in a myriad of too-tiny-to-see dots, or *antigen sites.* It later was calculated that each group-A red cells has roughly one million A antigen sites on its surface.

Landsteiner had discovered three blood groups—A, B, and O—and associates soon found one more: Some individuals have both A and B antigens on their red cells; hence their serums have neither anti-A nor anti-B antibodies. There are thus four—and only four—ABO blood groups, and every human being belongs to one of them:

If he is in group A, his red cells carry the A antigen and his serum contains anti-B antibody.

If he is in group B, his red cells carry the B antigen and his serum contains anti-A antibody.

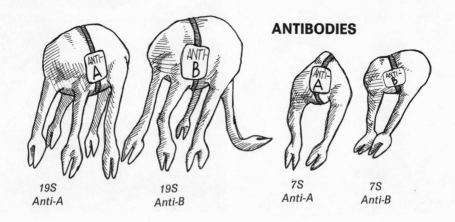

**ANTIBODIES**

| 19S | 19S | 7S | 7S |
| Anti-A | Anti-B | Anti-A | Anti-B |

If he is in group O, his red cells carry *no* antigen, and his serum contains both anti-A and anti-B antibodies.

If he is in group AB, his red cells carry the A antigen and the B antigen, and his serum has neither anti-A nor anti-B.

These findings, later called "Landsteiner's Rule," would be summarized thus: Those, and only those antibodies, are present in the serum for which the corresponding antigens are lacking in the red cells.

By using serums containing known antibodies to test unknown red cells, and by using red cells of a known blood group to test an unknown serum, each and every person's ABO blood group could now be quickly determined. By testing large numbers of individuals, it was possible to determine the proportion of individuals of each blood group in a given population. In the American white population, for example, 45 percent are group O; 41 percent are group A; 10 percent are group B; and 4 percent are group AB. Blacks have more group B's and fewer group A's. Among the Chinese there are many more group AB's.

Landsteiner's discovery made possible the safe use of blood for transfusions. Dangerous transfusion reactions now might be avoided by testing the blood of the potential recipient and his prospective donor. If the donor's red cells carried an antigen against which the recipient carried the corresponding antibody—as, for example, a group A donor and a group B recipient, whose serum contains anti-A—then the transfusion would be *ABO-incompatible*, and hence dangerous; another donor had to be sought. If, however, the prospective donor's red cells would meet no antibody attack in

**ANTIBODIES ATTACK GROUP A CELL**

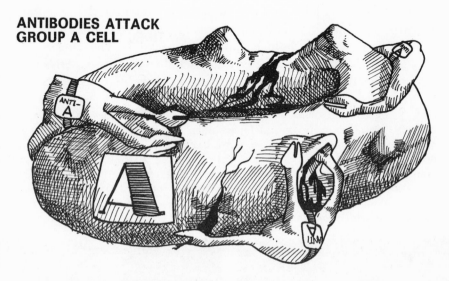

the recipient—a group O donor for a group B recipient, for example—then the donor's blood was *ABO-compatible* to the recipient. The transfusion might safely be given.*

\* These rules ensure compatible blood transfusions:

Group A blood can be given safely to other group A individuals, and to AB individuals, none of whom have anti-A antibody in their serums. Group A blood cannot be given to group B or group O individuals, both of whom have anti-A antibodies.

Group B blood can be given safely to other group B individuals and to group AB individuals, since neither group has anti-B. But it can cause fatal transfusion reactions in group A and group O individuals.

Group O blood can be given to other group O individuals and to groups A, B, and AB, since the red cells do not carry any antigen against which anyone would react. Group O individuals hence are called "universal donors." But a group O individual can take blood only from another group O individual, since his natural anti-A and anti-B antibodies would react against all other bloods.

Finally, group AB blood can be given safely only to other AB individuals, since all other blood types have either an anti-A or an anti-B antibody or both. But group AB individuals are "universal recipients," because their serums contain neither anti-A nor anti-B antibodies. Hence they can accept blood that is group O, group A, group B, or group AB.

Landsteiner had opened the way. But the promise of safe therapeutic use of blood transfusions would be fulfilled only later, by others. "Medicine wasn't ready to put the revolutionary discovery to work," his disciple Wiener said later. "The world paid not the slightest attention. Ignored, Landsteiner continued his [other] research projects."[3]

Levine, writing of the same period, adds: "Notable contributions which flowed freely from his active and fertile mind were interrupted by World War I. There followed a series of frustrations, loss of facilities in the laboratory, personal deprivation, and starvation. In 1919, with the aid of friends, he was given space in a corner of a laboratory in a small Roman Catholic hospital in The Hague."[4]

A year or so later Landsteiner was invited to the United States to work at the Rockefeller Institute—now Rockefeller University—in

Clear picture of antibodies' effect on red cell surface was achieved by microbiologists Drs. Carel van Oss and James Mohn at the State University of New York School of Medicine, Buffalo, in 1970. Under scanning electron microscope, at magnification of about 5,000 diameters, group A red cells clumped by 7S anti-A antibody (left) and by 19S anti-A (right) are entangled and grossly distorted. Their surfaces are scalloped and raised into blisterlike points. Antibody molecules are invisible at this relatively low magnification. (*Courtesy Drs. van Oss and Mohn, and S. Karger, Basel.*)

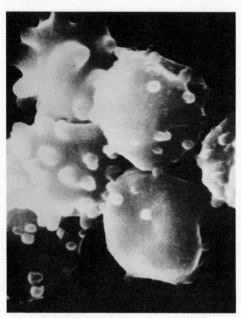

New York. He began in 1923 and was to remain there until his death in 1943.

Living in America did not bring Landsteiner happiness. Levine, Wiener, and others who knew him paint a picture of a morbidly shy, alienated man who rarely felt comfortable outside his laboratory. "He never completely adjusted himself to life in a New York City apartment house," Levine later recalled. "Noises he abhorred, and in anticipation of neighbors' complaints he disposed of his piano, which he played exceedingly well." A contemporary who

**ANTI-A IGNORES GROUP B CELLS**

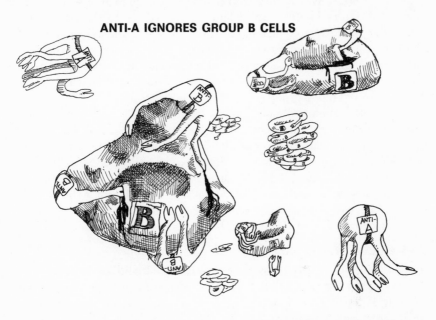

perhaps was less worshipful than Levine elucidated Landsteiner's peculiar reason for denying himself the pleasures of his piano: " '[If I play,] neighbors will play too and disturb me.' "[5]

"In public," Levine was to say, "he was shy and endured an obvious discomfort when presiding at the weekly seminars at the Rockefeller Institute." But in the laboratory Landsteiner was quite another man: "He was an active, enthusiastic, tireless worker," the admiring Levine commented. "His assistants had no choice but to follow the pace set by the master." Landsteiner was "never satisfied with the report submitted by an assistant; the work was repeated and all essential experiments, especially those which might lead to publication, he carried out himself."

Landsteiner told young men whom he hired that he—Landsteiner—would be listed as the senior author of all papers published on the basis of their joint research efforts in his lab.

Another of these young men who labored at the laboratory bench alongside Levine, Dr. Jacob Furth, later would say, succinctly: "Landsteiner was a genius! And a slave driver!"[6]

Wiener, as worshipful as Levine, would long recall his own first encounter with Landsteiner:

My knees wobbled that day in 1929 as I made my way to the Rockefeller Institute. I was a very frightened young medical student. A telephone call [from Philip Levine] had summoned me to the laboratory of one of the great research men of our age—Dr. Karl Landsteiner.

At the time there were two main theories on how the various types of blood were inherited. I had written a mathematical analysis of the theories, and for good measure had thrown in the statement that the Chinese had discovered blood groups in the thirteenth century.

Now I stood before Landsteiner, a six-footer with dark piercing eyes, bushy eyebrows and drooping mustache. Where, he asked, had I learnt that the Chinese had discovered blood groups? I cited my source, a brief mention in a paper I had read. A flicker of a smile passed over the no-nonsense countenance. 'I think you will find it better, young man,' he said, 'always to consult original sources.' I would find a book in the library—he gave me the exact reference—that I might read. The Chinese, of course, hadn't discovered blood groups: Landsteiner had.[7, 8]

And Landsteiner now felt called upon, thirty years afterward, to summon an unknown medical student to his office to tell him, in no uncertain terms, of that fact. This obsessive concern for recognition and credit would not be lost on Wiener, who was to carry it forward through forty more years of blood research.[*]

"After my initial chastisement," Wiener adds, with evident relish, "we became good friends." Wiener was never a paid worker in Landsteiner's lab. But he worked close by, in the blood lab of New York City's Chief Medical Examiner—a job he still held when Vince Freda sought him out three decades later. Wiener, like Levine, collaborated with Landsteiner on several research projects.

"For ten years," he later reminisced, "I spent Wednesday evenings with him. He would sit at home at the dining-room table munching apples while we discussed current research, or worked on papers." Levine, who also spent "many evenings at [Landsteiner's] home on preparation of papers," concurred that "his military

---

[*] Landsteiner could not tolerate criticism of himself, contemporaries say, and carefully avoided situations that might provoke it.[9]

bearing and sternly flowing mustache failed to conceal an underlying but frequently suppressed spirit of warmth, gentleness and sincerity."

Landsteiner had dropped his blood research in 1901, after publishing his ABO discoveries. But in the United States, twenty years later, he had returned to the red cell—with a new and unusual purpose. He was, perhaps, prompted by a refugee's sense of alienation and deracination.* He conceived the idea that a new system of human identity could be forged in the laboratory—where he was Master—on the basis of individual differences in the antigens that occur on red blood cells.

Fingerprinting had already demonstrated that each human being could be assigned a unique identity on the basis of skin whorls and curves, and the notion that individual differences among people could be explained by chemical differences in their bodies was much in the air. "Each individual human blood may have a particular biochemical structure," Landsteiner said. Whether Landsteiner understood that a chemical identity is different, and unrelated to personal individuality, is not clear.

His early work, which he now would extend, had divided mankind into four hitherto unknown groups, based on affinities of blood. Landsteiner believed, however, that red cells had more antigens than A and B. The problem was to find them. To do so, he proposed to use antibody-containing blood serums from rabbits, rather than humans, for his tests. He would first inject group A human red cells into a rabbit. This would *immunize* the rabbit to the A antigen, so it would produce anti-A antibody. It would also immunize it against any other, weaker, antigens, or *blood factors*, that might also be present on the human red cells.

Landsteiner then would draw blood from the rabbit. He would isolate the antibody-containing serum, and then mix it with group A human red cells. All the rabbit's anti-A antibody would attach itself to these red cells. Then the group A cells, with anti-A antibody attached, could be removed from the rabbit serum.

With the anti-A gone, the serum could again be challenged with group A red cells. If the serum reacted with some but not with

---

* He had already repudiated his Jewish identity, by converting to Catholicism. Later Landsteiner sued the editor of a Jewish *Who's Who* who planned to list him in it, saying, according to news accounts of his legal deposition, that he would "be greatly distressed and humiliated and exposed to ridicule and contempt" if identified as a Jew. To be so designated, he added, would be "highly detrimental to my American mode of living and my family."[10]

Dr. Landsteiner resumed his blood group research in the United States. (*Courtesy Rockefeller University.*)

others of these red cell samples, then clearly those with which it did react carried a hitherto undetected red cell antigen, X. Persons whose red cells were clumped by this serum, or *reagent*, would be *X-positive*, because they had the X factor. Persons whose red cells did not react with the anti-X antibody in the reagent would be *X-negative*. Clearly, if enough factors could be found there would be enough possible combinations of factors A, B, X, etc., for each individual on earth to have a red cell antigen profile all his very own—an identity based on blood!

Despite its philosophical shortcomings, the procedure for finding unknown X factors was relatively straightforward. But the work was tedious and demanded meticulous laboratory technique. Landsteiner wanted an assistant to do it. Philip Levine was his man.

Levine, who had been born in Russia in the year Landsteiner discovered the ABO blood groups, had trained at Cornell Medical School, where he had taken an M.D. and then an M.A. His early motivation had been vague—"to help people."[11] But he did not want to go into medical practice, and a job with Landsteiner was an acceptable alternative.

Landsteiner taught Levine blood typing techniques—"indoctrinated him," Levine's co-worker Furth later would say: "He made Levine into a faithful and a very meticulous supertechnician."

Levine's duties included some that other M.D.-M.A.s might have found beneath them. Landsteiner, for example, did not trust nurses to draw bloods needed for their researches. So Levine was sent, by ferry boat, across the East River to Welfare Island, where there was a mental hospital whose inmates were bled to provide specimens for Landsteiner's lab. "Levine was almost a slave," Furth would later recall. But Levine was willing. He had submitted to another of Landsteiner's rules, which was, as Levine himself later interpreted it: "If you want to work with me, you have to work on my research problem."[12]

**ANTIBODY SPECIFICITY**

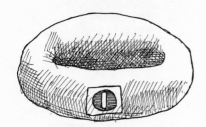
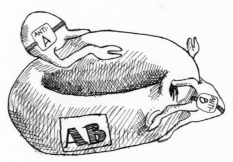

Together, they soon succeeded. In 1927, Landsteiner and Levine announced their discovery of three new red cell factors, which they designated *M, N,* and *P.* These were of little clinical importance, since the M, N, and P antigens were too weak to cause transfusion reactions. But they carried Landsteiner significantly toward his goal of subdividing mankind into groups and into individualities based on blood. All group A persons, for example, might now be further divided into those who were M-positive and those who were M-negative. And the group A individuals who were M-positives might be further divided into those who were P-positive and those who were P-negative. The prospects were promising—and endless.

At about this time, Wiener entered Landsteiner's orbit. Wiener had been born in Brooklyn in 1907. He received his M.D. at Long Island College of Medicine in 1930.

In November 1930, Landsteiner won the Nobel Prize for his ABO blood discovery. In his laureate address, Landsteiner said of the blood genealogy research: "Very numerous individual blood differences exist in man. . . . Whether each individual blood really has a character of its own, or how often there is complete correspondence [between individuals' bloods], we cannot yet say."

A year later, Levine's term at Rockefeller ended. The Institute hired many promising young men but promoted only a few to tenured positions. Those who were not promoted after five or six years were expected to leave.

*For every antigen . . . there is an antibody*

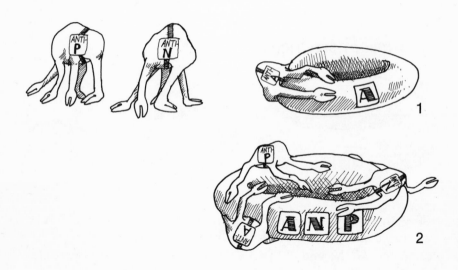

Levine was not among the chosen. Landsteiner could not—or would not—use his influence to keep him. Levine got a job at the University of Wisconsin. As he left, Landsteiner demanded from him a promise that he would not, on his own, do any further blood group research. "We agreed," Levine said later, "that I was to embark on new vistas rather than to continue with studies on blood groups. To abandon [them] . . . was not a simple matter for me."[13]

Torn between worshipful devotion and bitter disappointment, Levine nevertheless consented to Landsteiner's unintentionally flattering demand—and dutifully went into exile in the Midwest.

Wiener now became Landsteiner's number-one blood research associate. He soon plotted a fresh tack in the search for new blood factors. As Landsteiner had elucidated new human bonds based on blood, so man's close biologic kinship to animals was being established through the discovery that men and monkeys have many blood factors in common. The higher a monkey's perch on the phylogenetic ladder, the closer was his blood profile to man's.

Wiener, working by himself at first, proved that monkeys have the M factor that Landsteiner and Levine had found on human red cells. Then Weiner had an idea. Certain otherwise undetectable variants of the A antigen had recently been identified by challenging human red cells with an antibody that reacted specifically to red cells from sheep. The test serums, made by injecting sheep red cells into rabbits, contained antibodies against antigen variants that also were present on human red cells—albeit in amounts too small to provoke antibody production when the human cells themselves were injected into rabbits. When the rabbit test serum, containing potent antibodies against the antigen variants on sheep cells, was mixed with human red cells, it would reveal the same antigens' presence in human blood by clumping the cells.

Wiener perceived that he could make an analogous new test

Rh-positive red cells clumped by 7S anti-Rh antibody (left) and 19S anti-Rh ( right ) are packed densely together. But cell surfaces remain smooth, unlike similar cells attacked by anti-A (see page 10). The reason for the difference is unknown. (*Courtesy Drs. van Oss and Mohn, and S. Karger, Basel.*)

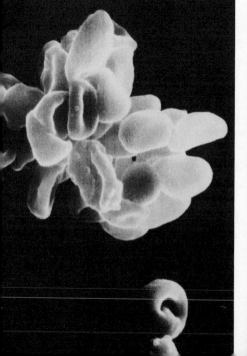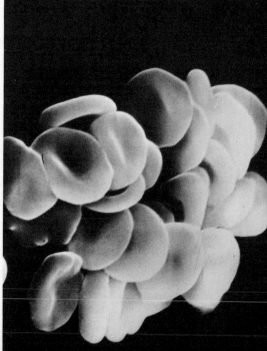

serum by injecting rhesus monkey red cells into rabbits and using the anti-rhesus antibodies in the rabbit serums to test human blood for the presence of rhesuslike blood factors that might be too weak to be brought to light in any other way.

Landsteiner approved the plan. He and Wiener now made test serum against type M rhesus monkey red cells and exposed it to type M human red cells. They then strained out and discarded the type M cells, with all the anti-M antibody stuck to them. The remaining serum, now free of anti-M antibody, was mixed with a new batch of red cells from type M humans.

## Rh INCOMPATIBILITY

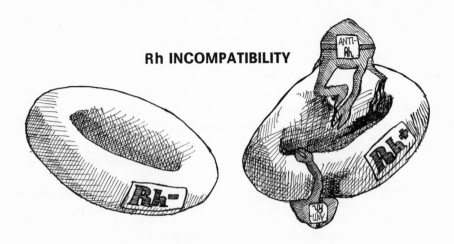

Fulfilling their every hope, the test serum reacted with the red cells of most individuals, but not with all. This was a definitive sign that the test serum had detected a hitherto unidentified antigen that was present on those specimens of red cells that had reacted, but not on the others.

With all human bloods, in fact, when the A, B, M, N, and P antigens were eliminated from consideration, the anti-rhesus serum still clumped the majority of specimens of human red cells, but failed to clump the balance. Statistically, Wiener and Landsteiner found that the anti-rhesus serum reacted with red cells of 85 percent of the white population, but failed to react with red cells of the remaining 15 percent.

Wiener and Landsteiner had shown that the red cells of most white humans—and, in fact, of most humans of all colors—carried

Structures of individual antibody molecules as revealed in enormously magnified scanning electronmicrographs made by Dr. Sven-Erik Svehag at Sweden's National Bacteriological Laboratory in Stockholm. Micrographs like this first were achieved in 1967. The circular configuration of the 19S antibody molecule (*left*), here magnified 235,000 diameters, first was depicted by Dr. Svehag. It has five double projections. The 7S molecule (*right*), here magnified 325,000 diameters, is smaller, and shaped like letter Y. (*Courtesy Dr. Svehag.*)

the mysterious new blood factor, or antigen. Because humans possessed this factor in common with rhesus monkeys, Wiener named it the *Rh factor*. Persons on whose red cells this antigen appeared he designated *Rh-positive*. The minority who lacked it were *Rh-negative*.[14]

Of what importance was the Rh factor? It gave Landsteiner a new tool to subdivide mankind into smaller, closer groups based on their blood factor profiles; each previously discovered blood group could be divided into two, based on whether members did or did not carry the Rh factor.

The Rh antigen-antibody reaction appeared to be weak and difficult to elicit, and it later was to be calculated that there were far fewer Rh antigen sites than A or B sites per cell—ten thousand, perhaps, compared to one million. There was absolutely no reason to believe that Rh played a part in human disease. Wiener had not the slightest notion that it might have a role in the deadly disease of unborn and newborn babies that was then called erythroblastosis fetalis. In fact, while he and Landsteiner were doing their first Rh experiments at the end of the 1930s, there was perhaps only one researcher anywhere in the world who felt strongly that erythroblastosis could be blamed on an antigen-antibody reaction in blood. Her name was Dr. Ruth Darrow. Unbeknown even to himself, however, one other researcher had embarked on a path that would lead him to a similar conclusion. His name was Philip Levine.

# 2

# Bad Blood and Sick Babies

IN 1930, the year Landsteiner won his Nobel Prize, the disease that was to be known as *erythroblastosis fetalis* hardly existed, although unborn and newborn babies long had suffered and died of it; some of its symptoms had been described by the ancient Greeks.[1]

As distinguished from symptoms of a sickness, which are events, a *disease* is an intellectual concept that exists in doctors' minds. It is their method for rationally comprehending symptoms and sickness as parts of distinct, recognizable patterns of events due to a specific cause or causes—whose identity they hope to discover. If they understand a disease's destructive process and can also pinpoint its cause, their chances of finding effective ways to treat it and prevent it become vastly improved. Thus, the accurate description of a disease and the discovery of its cause are among medical science's most creative achievements—and are the bases for most subsequent progress.

In 1930, there was not one disease. There seemed to be four. Each was regarded as a separate and unique problem, although a few reports, widely scattered through the medical literature, had suggested that two or three of them might be related. None of the four was clearly understood. "The[y] . . . have been known for a long time, and have constituted a mysterious and highly fatal group of diseases afflicting the newborn infant," pioneer researchers were soon to say.[2] Each of the four was identified, cumbersomely, by the descriptive name of its most prominent characteristic. These names are cited here for identification purposes only. They are unimportant in the later history of the disease.

In one of these disorders, babies were born extremely misshapen, their bodies swollen by fluid. Most had died before birth. Occasionally, one would be liveborn—a pale, limp baby, with a distended belly. "Respiration is initiated with great difficulty, if at all," observers noted. "During the brief period that life remains [breathing] is characterized by great irregularity and gasping inspirations."[3] Fetuses and newborn babies that died of this sickness —and die they invariably did—were said to have *hydrops*, which means, roughly, to be waterlogged, or *universal edema* (swelling).

A second, seemingly different, sickness sometimes struck liveborn babies who at first seemed relatively healthy. A few hours after

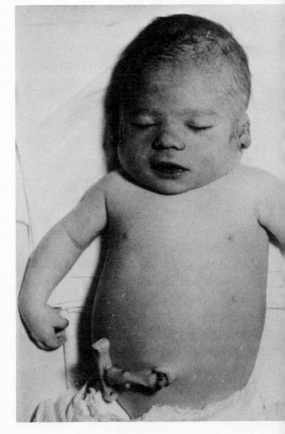

Grotesquely swollen newborn has severe, hydropic form of erythroblastosis which is usually lethal within hours after birth. (*Courtesy Infant Disease Research Foundation.*)

birth, their bodies began to change color. Their skins became deep yellow, golden, or bronzed. When they were examined carefully, their little bellies were found to be swollen—due to enlargement of the liver, spleen, and other organs. Underneath yellowing skin, the flesh became pallid and bloodless. Some of these babies died in heart failure, apparently for want of red blood cells. For others, death came a different way. They grew lethargic, moving their limbs only in rigid, stiff motions. Their eyes looked squinty. Their cries became feeble and high-pitched. They fed poorly. Convulsions followed, and the most fortunate, perhaps, soon died. "Surviving infants," a textbook author later remarked, "are physically helpless, unable to support their heads or to sit. Walking is delayed or never acquired and marked [mental] retardation is present."[4] In fatal cases, these babies' brains were found to be stained bright yellow by *bilirubin*, a substance made in the liver from the remnants of damaged red blood cells. In some less severe cases, if the brain was not damaged, the baby might fully and spontaneously recover. This condition was popularly called "yellow jaundice"—a redundancy, since "jaundice" means yellow. Its technical name was *icterus gravis neonatorum*—severe yellowing of the newborn.

The third seemingly unrelated sickness was an especially severe

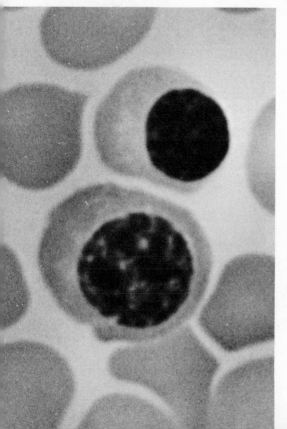

Blood smear from erythroblastic baby is stained to show nuclei in immature red cells, or erythroblasts, which are present in abnormal numbers. (*Wright stain. Courtesy Professor Ann Bell.*)

anemia. This deficiency in red blood cells sometimes was complicated by inexplicable episodes of hemorrhaging into the baby's lungs, gut, or spinal column. Whatever its cause, which was unknown, this condition seemed to be triggered by events before birth, and so was designated *congenital anemia*. Usually it became critical in the second or third week of life. Some babies died; most recovered.

The fourth disorder was a disturbance of the blood and blood-forming tissue in fetuses and newborn babies. It had been named *erythroblastosis fetalis*, meaning the presence of too many *erythroblasts*, or immature red cells. Erythroblasts are unable to do mature red cells' regular work of carrying oxygen to the body tissues and carrying away carbon dioxide. They could be identified and counted on a blood smear under the microscope because they possess cell nuclei—which disappear as red cells mature. A normal newborn's blood contained at most one or two erythroblasts per hundred red cells. But in erythroblastic babies these inadequate cells might account for a quarter of all the red cells. Not surprisingly, the surfeit of erythroblasts occurred in babies who had an enormous excess of blood-forming, or *hematopoietic*, tissue. Instead of being largely confined to the bone marrow, as is normal in the newborn, in erythroblastic babies this tissue had spread through the entire body. It filled and caused swelling of the liver and spleen, and extended into the kidneys, along blood vessel walls, and even encroached upon the brain.

The four disorders—*hydrops*, *icterus*, *anemia*, and *erythroblastosis* —had been described in the medical literature as essentially separate and discrete disorders. In 1930 this view was about to change. The young researchers who were to change it were all associated with the Harvard Medical School in Boston.

One of them was an instructor in Harvard's pathology department, Canadian-born Dr. John Ferguson. He was studying red cell production before birth. His method was to slice into thin sections, for microscopic examination, blood-forming tissues taken from babies who had died of blood disorders at or before birth.

Early in gestational life, red cells are made by the fetus' liver and spleen. But, normally, blood-making in these organs ends before birth; red cell manufacture shifts to the marrow of certain bones. Ferguson was struck by the fact that several of his autopsy cases were in this respect grossly abnormal. These dead babies' livers and spleens were filled with patches of blood-making activity; erythroblasts were present in extraordinary numbers.

Perhaps as a result of this abnormal blood-making activity, the livers and spleens were enormously enlarged. One baby had a liver that was four times the normal weight; another, a spleen that was tenfold too heavy. "The most striking features of these cases and the one common to all," Ferguson observed, "is the hematopoietic activity in the liver and other organs . . . [which] must be considered quite abnormal."[5]

But erythroblastosis was not all that was wrong with these babies. Two that had died before birth had hydrops. Three of the four that had died afterwards had icterus. Both disorders were uncommon. Yet here were five cases, in each of which the baby also had erythroblastosis.

"In studies of this nature," Ferguson would say, years later, "you have to collect the data, get it together, and see which way it points." His data, he felt, pointed to the conclusion that his cases were "probably representative of a definite disease entity of the newly born, and . . . the underlying cause is undoubtedly the same in each instance, whether the individual case is characterized by jaundice [icterus] or edema [hydrops], or whether both . . . are lacking."[6]

Feeling that he had pushed his investigation as far as it would go, Ferguson wrote down his findings and submitted them for publication. They appeared in May 1931, and caused a stir:[7]

"Some of my friends thought it was guessing!"

Guessing or not, Ferguson was right on target. He had correctly related three of the four mysterious disorders of the newborn that so perplexed his colleagues. His picture was incomplete, however, for he had worked exclusively with autopsy material, and had, in fact, ventured a guess, which was wrong, that the disease was wholly incompatible with life outside the womb.

The contrary already was being proved, in another Harvard lab, at nearby Children's Hospital. The man who would win major credit for the work there was a dark-featured, handsome young pediatrician, Dr. Louis Diamond. After graduating from Harvard Medical School, he had gone to Children's for postgraduate training in pediatrics. Like Ferguson, he was interested in blood diseases, especially anemias. With the help of a colleague, Dr. James Baty, he set up a research laboratory for the study and treatment of children's blood diseases.

Several times in the years 1929–1931 Diamond was called to treat newborn babies suffering from severe anemia. He gave them blood transfusions—which then was a highly innovative thing to do. Unlike most pediatricians of that day, Diamond had equipped himself to study these babies' bloods. Before transfusion, he found, some of them were extremely short of mature red cells, or *erythrocytes*, but often had enormous numbers of "nucleated reds," or erythroblasts. After transfusion, the babies usually pinked up and recovered. Except for the many erythroblasts in their blood, which usually soon vanished, they might not have seemed unusual. Anemia, like jaundice—which also appeared in some of these babies—was not uncommon in newborns. Diamond nevertheless kept track of the cases, and made a point of investigating the babies' parents—for some specialists suspected that the anemia might be related to a dietary deficiency in the mother, or to congenital syphilis.

"Much to my surprise," Diamond later would say, "an odd fact began to emerge: The parents of these babies had previously had children who died of severe newborn jaundice [icterus gravis]. Or had had one or more stillborn babies. Or both.

"It didn't ring any bell until we'd collected about twenty cases."

The bell-ringing cases came from a single Boston family. Diamond's professor of pediatrics, Dr. Kenneth Blackfan, described this family for Diamond at the Massachusetts Medical Society's annual meeting in June 1932, which Diamond was unable to attend. (Blackfan's remarks are slightly abridged):

This mother had already given birth to four healthy, normal babies. Her fifth pregnancy resulted in the birth of a liveborn infant. Shortly after its discharge from the maternity hospital, it was noticed that the baby was very pale. Despite measures to relieve the anemia, which increased rapidly, the child died.

The sixth pregnancy also resulted in the development of a severe anemia. The child was brought to Children's Hospital at about 17 or 18 days of age. As a result of frequent, small blood transfusions, the anemia finally was brought under control. The child is living and well.

The seventh pregnancy also resulted in the birth of an anemic baby, who was brought to Children's Hospital, and likewise was returned home well.

The mother, having had this experience with her last three babies, refused to go to a maternity hospital when next she was pregnant. She said she was going to be delivered at home so that she could see for herself what was happening with the baby when it was born.

At five hours of age, the baby presented evidence of icterus gravis. When 9½ hours old, it was brought to Children's Hospital with all the characteristic signs and symptoms.

With transfusions and other measures, the child made a satisfactory recovery; the jaundice disappeared. When it was the same age as the previous children had been when they took sick—about 17 or 18 days— it was found that its blood picture was identical to theirs: a picture that has been regarded as typical of congenital anemia of the newborn.

*This instance seems to connect very clearly in our mind the relationship between the two disorders as that of two different stages of the same disease, with the icterus usually being seen shortly after birth, and the signs of what is regarded as anemia coming on later.*[8] (Emphasis added.)

While Diamond was working on these cases, two close colleagues at Boston's Lying-in Hospital, pediatrician Dr. Stewart Clifford and obstetrician Dr. Arthur Hertig, who had been stimulated also by Ferguson's discovery, found eight more babies in whom icterus or hydrops occurred with erythroblastosis. Thus, by early 1932, Diamond had related anemia to icterus. Ferguson already had linked icterus and hydrops to erythroblastosis. Clifford and Hertig had confirmed this. All probably accepted Diamond's assertion that anemia was part of "the same underlying [disease] process."[9]

Diamond stated his conclusion in a long paper that he submitted for publication early in 1932. In June, his key cases were described to the Massachusetts Medical Society, along with Clifford and Hertig's, which were published in July.[10] Diamond's more definitive report—with his chief, Blackfan, and his contemporary, Baty, as coauthors—appeared in September.[11] Diamond's conclusion that erythroblastosis was one disease encompassing hydrops, icterus, and anemia would slowly win universal acknowledgment. In time his report would come to be regarded as a landmark: the start of the modern era of erythroblastosis research.

How did the three Harvard investigators influence each other? Diamond later acknowledged no indebtedness to Ferguson—who had been first to publish.[12, 13] Diamond's co-worker Baty would say later that "all three papers were essentially from the same department, and our ideas evolved together." Baty would also indicate, and Clifford and Hertig would say explicitly, that the pathfinding role had been Ferguson's. According to Clifford: "Ferguson was the guy at pathology conferences who was demonstrating these cases. He was the guy who set us thinking about it [the inclusiveness of eryth-

Forgotten figure in Rh history, Dr. Ferguson made key discovery that abnormal red cell production occurs in both hydropic and icteric babies. (*Circa 1960, Courtesy Dr. Ferguson.*)

roblastosis]. I think he's the guy who brought it into being. He's really the guy who deserves the credit."

Diamond, who was to make further important contributions to progress against erythroblastosis, later became famous for having been first to elucidate the disease, along with his coauthors Baty and Blackfan. Clifford and Hertig's role was largely forgotten. Ferguson, who went on to work in other research areas, has been completely ignored in historical accounts.

If the scope of the disease was now certain, its underlying cause was not. Clearly, there were too many immature red cells, and too much tissue making them. But there also was too much red cell destruction—and it was for want of mature red cells that many babies died. Was the problem ultimately too many immature red cells and/or their failure to mature? Or was it too rapid red cell destruction, which could not be compensated for, even by abnormal proliferation of the blood-making apparatus? In short: Too much immature blood and blood-making? Or too much blood destruction?

Diamond favored the first—and, it would turn out, wrong—alternative. "The disease," he said, "appears to be a disturbance of the metabolism of the hematopoietic system, resulting: first, in either a failure of maturation of red cells or in an overgrowth of immature forms of red cells; second, in the[ir] delivery . . . in large numbers to the peripheral circulation; and third, in the increased destruction of red cells."[14]

When the disease reached its climax before birth, in hydrops, the proliferation of blood-making tissue and erythroblasts was strikingly apparent at autopsy. This overabundance of erythroblasts and compensatory destruction of all red cells, including mature ones, resulted in a fatal scarcity of functional red cells. The fetuses died of heart failure, oxygen starvation, and other consequences of their anemia.

In the disease's late form, congenital anemia, the red cells' failure to mature, combined with their undue destruction, could similarly account for the severe, sometimes lethal consequences. Icterus, the disease's middle stage, occurred because the body destroyed its surfeit of erythroblasts faster than it could get rid of their yellowing remains. In each situation, Diamond felt, the cancerlike proliferation of blood-making tissue and cells—erythroblasts—lay at the head of the clinical disease.* Why this might happen, Diamond did not know.

Among the questions he did ask himself was whether an incompatibility between the mother's blood and the fetus' might play a role in the disease. He tested the bloods, and found that as a rule each mother was ABO compatible with her sick baby. So he decided—possibly to his later regret—that the disease was not caused by a blood incompatibility between mother and child.

One other earlier observation that later would prove to be of enormous value was noted, in passing, by the Boston researchers; it appeared in Clifford and Hertig's report but not in Diamond's. It was that while erythroblastosis tends to recur from pregnancy to pregnancy in the families in which it strikes, it never occurs in a woman's first pregnancy: *The first baby is always spared.*

No greater contrast in approach to a problem can be imagined than that between Louis Diamond and the doctor, later all but

---

* Ferguson leaned, speculatively, to the opposite view that it was anemia that triggered the erythroblastosis, on the basis of the disease's resemblance to other anemias. He could adduce no direct evidence for this view, partly, he would say later, because anemia, which is a lack of or defect in red cells, could not be diagnosed from autopsy material.

forgotten, who made the next great advance. The one had trained at Harvard. The other graduated from Rush Medical College, a faltering, small school in Chicago. The one was a highly trained specialist; the other, a G.P. with an office in the basement of her home. Finally, one was a man, challenged professionally in his work to make sense of some provocatively suggestive clinical material. The other was a woman and a mother, whose interest in erythroblastosis arose suddenly, in the anguished moment when the disease claimed the life of her son.

Ruth Renter, born in 1895, had graduated from a college in Cleveland with a no more specific aim in life than to be of service to others. She went to work as a telephone operator. One day, while on a train trip, she chanced to observe a painfully crippled child. On the spot, according to family accounts, Ruth resolved to become a doctor whose work would relieve such suffering.

She enrolled at Rush and moved to Chicago. She married a young physiologist, Dr. Chester Darrow. In 1930, the year she won her M.D., their first child, a girl, was born. Two years later came a second daughter. Ruth Darrow, at thirty-seven, already was far along in her childbearing years. But she wanted a son.

On July 22, 1935, she gave birth to a baby boy. He was named Alan.

In the delivery room, Alan appeared healthy and vigorous. The Darrows exulted. A few hours later, the baby's skin turned yellow. Beneath it, his flesh paled for want of effective red blood cells. Within a day, Alan's skin was deeply bronzed; his movements grew listless; his cry, feeble. The diagnosis was made: erythroblastosis fetalis.

Blood transfusions by now were a standard treatment. Alan was given two ounces, followed by two subsequent transfusions of about three ounces each. He was too weak to nurse. Prepared formulas, then much the rage among pediatricians, were available for bottle-feeding. Ruth Darrow apparently objected: It was *her* milk that should nourish her son. Her breasts were pumped; her milk was fed to him from a bottle.

By the end of a week, Alan had rallied. The jaundice was fading. His flesh pinked up. He could nurse normally—he seemed well on the road to recovery, and so was discharged from the hospital. After several more weeks of apparent steady improvement, Ruth Darrow is reported by a family member to have said proudly to her husband Chester: "It looks like our baby is going to pull through!"

The next day Alan became violently ill. Breathing was difficult. He vomited and could not eat. He grew pale and stuporous. Brought to the hospital, he was found to be bleeding into his spinal column and intestinal tract. Alan died, convulsing, two days later.

When an autopsy was done on the body, it was found to be filled with patches of abnormal blood-forming tissue. They had filled and grossly distorted the liver and spleen. The brain was badly damaged, and the skull was filled with blood—the immediate cause of death.[15]

The Darrows were anguished. Compounding Ruth's grief was a horrifying sense that somehow she, as Alan's mother, had been responsible for his death. Hadn't he seemed to become worse at just those times when his reliance on her milk for sustenance had increased? Could she have poisoned Alan with her mother's milk?

It was a moment of intense pain and of courageous resolution.

Ruth Darrow knew from Diamond's report, and others, that the disease's familial occurrence meant she probably could not bear another child who would live unless a cure could be discovered. She resolved that she would find one. Previously, she had fulfilled her vow on the suffering of the crippled child through her clinical practice, the care of her patients. Now she would complete her vow by undertaking research that would relieve a childhood disease whose horror she had intimately experienced. In so being of service, she might redeem her own chance to be mother to a son.

"I was fairly certain," one of her daughters would later say, "that she didn't want another baby until she could be certain of its survival." Concurs a colleague of Darrow's of that era: "Knowing her, I'd say it was so." Thinking about erythroblastosis, working on it, trying to unravel its cause and how to deal with it would come to "consume her," this colleague, Dr. Irene Shmigelsky, would recall. "It filled her sleeping time and her daytime." Ruth Darrow herself would say, a decade later, that since Alan's death "the study of this disease has been my chief avocation."[16, 17]

She asked for, and received, the autopsy report on her son's body. She consumed dozens of published reports covering hundreds of cases in an attempt to deduce, from the disease's multiplicity of confusing traits, the basic cause against which corrective measures might be most successfully mounted.

In her dedication to her patients, her family, and her research, Darrow was unsparing of her own comfort. Her family's living room was also the office waiting room for her patients. Nights, she often slept on a couch in her basement office, to be close to the telephone for emergency calls. It was at night, also, that she worked on erythroblastosis. "She'd think her thoughts at two o'clock in the morning," Irene Shmigelsky would later say. "Then, the next day, she'd talk them out. She did her thinking by talking."

Her thinking was complex; its expression, prolix; and to many of her colleagues at Women and Children's Hospital, where Darrow had staff privileges, it was too tedious to hear. They tended to avoid her in the corridors, according to Shmigelsky, who did listen, and who would later recall Darrow saying, apologetically: "I'm sorry, it's my way of thinking, to think out loud."

Darrow did her thinking quickly, pressed by the sense that her chance to bear another child was rapidly passing. In two years, she had internalized the literature on erythroblastosis, resynthesized it in her mind, and talked out—to others, and onto paper—a whole new theory of the disease's causation. At its core, her theory confirmed her initial, shocked sense, when Alan died, that in erythroblastosis, the mother poisons her infant.

Whatever it was, this poison might reach newborn infants in mother's milk, but, clearly, it must have a more direct route to the fetus during intrauterine life, since many were gravely stricken long before being born. The mother "seems to be the primary source of the influence," Darrow deduced, "since she is the one constant factor to be found when this pathologic state appears in a series of offspring."[18] Whatever the toxic substance, she continued, it had the unique characteristic of harming the child, but not the mother—since pregnancies producing erythroblastic babies ordinarily were symptom-free.

Darrow deduced that the toxic agent first attacked the fetus' red blood cells and/or liver. Since the red cells alone were affected in the disease's mildest form, congenital anemia, it followed that they were the toxic substance's primary target.

What form of destructive agent would act specifically against red cells? One specifically formed against them: an antibody. "If, now, [all] the possible mechanisms giving rise to destruction of erythrocytes are reviewed," Darrow said, "all may be eliminated from consideration save one, *the destruction of red cells* by some form of immune reaction."[19] (Emphasis added.)

It seemed improbable that the baby was immune to itself. So, Darrow reasoned, the immunity must be between mother and child:

If the destruction of red cells by the action of specific immune antibodies is tentatively considered to represent the pathologic mechanism underlying this disease, one may reconstruct the etiologic events as follows: The mother is actively immunized against fetal red cells or some component of them. The immunization may conceivably occur as a result of an accident within the placenta whereby the fetal cells or their hemoglobin gain entrance to the maternal blood. . . . The antibodies formed in the maternal organism may then pass to the child through the placenta. . . . In the operation of such a mechanism the mother would show no symptoms, yet she would transmit a destructive influence to successive offspring through the placenta. . . .[20]

Darrow had succeeded, almost perfectly, in elucidating the disease process in erythroblastosis through which a mother, inadvertently, kills her baby. Its red cells, leaking across the placenta into her bloodstream, trigger an antigen-antibody response. The antibody made in the mother leaks back through the placenta to the fetus—or, later, is transmitted to the newborn in mother's milk— where it encounters more red cells like those against which it was formed, and destroys them. If it was the red cells that first were destroyed, then, Darrow reasoned, it must be an antigen in or on the red cells themselves that triggered the fatal reaction.

Based on all that subsequently would be learned about erythroblastosis, these were brilliant, albeit unproved, deductions. At the moment she reasoned that the disease's basic cause must be an antigen-antibody reaction of the mother against her fetus' blood, Ruth Darrow was virtually 100 percent right—and, as it would turn out, as right as she would ever be; her subsequent deductions would carry her further from a correct appraisal rather than closer to it.

Darrow's primary error was to pick the wrong red cell antigen upon which to hang her theory. She knew—from Diamond's study —that erythroblastic infants for the most part appeared to be ABO compatible with their mothers, and so she echoed Diamond, saying, offhandedly: "This mechanism, incidentally, bears no relation to a difference in blood groups in mother and child."[21] Instead of blood group incompatibility, she focused on the fact that the stuff of fetal red cells, the *fetal hemoglobin*, differs slightly in chemical makeup from the hemoglobin of adults. She decided that the antigen that triggers the mother's immune response must be her fetus' hemoglobin—and she later would spend several years trying vainly to prove this proposition. Darrow said: "The assumption that fetal

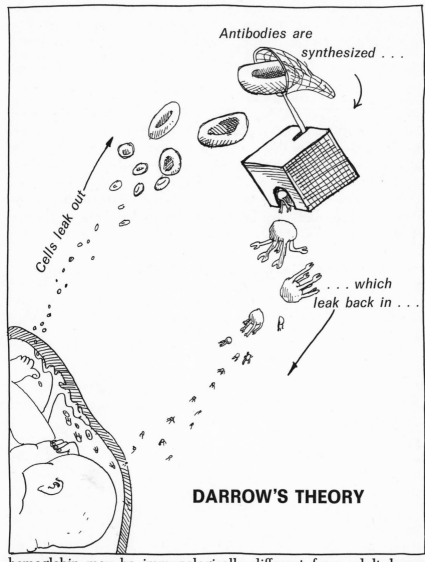

Antibodies are synthesized . . .

Cells leak out

. . . which leak back in . . .

**DARROW'S THEORY**

hemoglobin may be immunologically different from adult hemoglobin, and thus, possibly the antigen involved, amplifies and completes the hypothesis that an antigen-antibody reaction is responsible not only for one but for all forms of this malady."[22]

Darrow published her theory, prominently, in the *Archives of Pathology*, in March 1938.[23] But, due perhaps to its great length (forty pages), its dense prose, and its novel conclusions, it attracted little favorable comment. The fact that she was a woman contributed to its neglect. Darrow despaired; her theory still needed to be proved. But meanwhile, her own opportunity to make use of it was fast vanishing. She quickly set her mind to work on a treatment regimen based on her deductions that might serve erythroblastic babies like Alan, and she began to look for babies on whom to try it.

To help her find cases, a colleague wrote her a letter of introduction to the chief of Chicago's Board of Health, saying: "Dr. Ruth Darrow is very much interested in erythroblastosis of the newborn. Her own baby died of that condition and she has been studying the subject intensively since. She is anxious to get hold of mothers who are going to have a baby in which an erythroblastosis has occurred in a previous pregnancy inasmuch as it is a familial condition. She is very capable and very serious in this undertaking and I can vouch unreservedly for her responsibility in a matter of that sort."[24]

Meanwhile, the action had shifted back to New York City.

# 3

## Mothers and Doctors

LEVINE HAD RETURNED from Wisconsin in 1935 and had taken a job as transfusionist at Beth Israel Hospital in Newark, New Jersey, a few minutes by train from Manhattan. He is remembered at Beth Israel as a perfectly selfless man of science. A student nurse there, whose task it was to bring him patients' blood specimens, later would depict him as having been wholly wrapped up in his work: "Seven days a week he labored, day and night—he sometimes slept in his laboratory—so that he seemed to have no other life; rather than leave his lab to eat and mingle with colleagues, he might send someone to the hospital cafeteria to fetch him a cheese sandwich."

Blood transfusion was coming into wide use, thanks to the application of several technologic breakthroughs, not the least of which was the *refrigerator*. Another was *anticoagulation*: a method for treating whole blood with the chemical sodium citrate, which prevents it from clotting and spoiling when kept in a bottle.

Donor blood now could be collected and could be reliably preserved, cold, a week or longer until needed. Blood banks were established to keep it. No longer did donor and recipient have to be brought together so that one's blood could be transferred directly into the other.

The rise in transfusions had created a rise—to a now undeniably high level—in inexplicable transfusion reactions. They occurred, mysteriously, in patients who were given blood that was apparently perfectly matched in terms of the ABO blood groups. These so-called "intragroup" transfusion reactions could be painful and dangerous, and sometimes proved fatal. They thus were a growing worry to physicians who ordered blood and to serologists and transfusionists who tested and gave it.

Levine, in Newark, and Wiener, in New York, had two of the area's best serology labs, and, having both been trained by the Father of Blood Science himself, knew more than most about blood typing and matching. They thus were the experts of choice when consultation was needed on a difficult transfusion problem. These problem cases were raised and discussed at meetings of the Blood Transfusion Betterment Association of New York City, a body of transfusion specialists who later founded the city's first community blood bank.[1]

In the summer of 1937, another of these disturbing intragroup reaction cases, this one at Bellevue Hospital, was referred to the Association. A twenty-five-year-old woman, Mary Seno, had recently delivered a badly decomposed dead fetus. This was her second unsuccessful attempt to become a mother. Mrs. Seno had started to bleed before the dead baby's birth, and had continued to bleed afterwards. A transfusion was ordered. Her blood was group O, as was her husband's, so, following the practice of the time, a pint of his blood was infused into her; it was her first transfusion. Moments later, she began to shake and shiver with chills, complaining of pain in her head and legs.

The bleeding from her vagina would not stop. So her doctors took out her uterus. She now passed dark urine—a clear sign that the blood she had received from her husband had caused a transfusion reaction that had compromised her kidneys.

Mary Seno was quite weak from delivery, blood loss, and surgery, and her doctors, concerned for her safety, wanted to give her more blood. They performed a direct cross-match, mixing in the test tube her serum with her husband's red cells. Although ABO "compatible," her serum clumped his cells. He could not be a donor.

The Blood Transfusion Betterment Association kept on tap a number of group O donors. The cross-match was repeated on each of them. Disturbingly, one after another red cell sample was destroyed by Mary Seno's serum. Fifty samples of group O blood were tested. Only eight proved compatible. She got six more transfusions from these safe donors, and recovered. There remained for her doctors to solve the problem of why her group O blood was strongly incompatible with that of most other group O's.

To answer this puzzling question, Levine was now asked to study

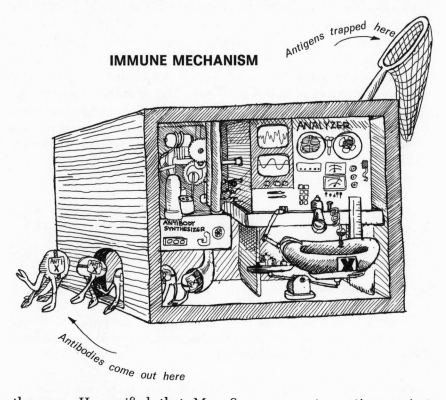

IMMUNE MECHANISM

Antigens trapped here

Antibodies come out here

the case. He verified that Mrs. Seno was not reacting against human blood factors A, B, M, N, or P, which were all that then were known. He tested her serum against 54 more samples of group O blood; only 13 were compatible. Thus, of a total of 104 samples of group O blood, Mrs. Seno was incompatible with 83, and compatible with but 21. Clearly, hers was an intragroup reaction. But unlike most such cases, she had reacted to her very first transfusion. Usually intragroup reactions did not occur until after a person had had two or more transfusions.

When ABO-incompatible blood is given, the recipient will react immediately, even if it is his first transfusion, because anti-A and anti-B antibodies are present virtually from birth; they thus are called *natural antibodies*.

Intragroup reactions, however, usually occurred in individuals who had been transfused at least twice. This strongly suggested that a natural antibody was not the cause. Rather, it made sense that the blood recipient had become sensitized, or immunized, to an unknown antigen, or *X factor*, the first time he received blood from someone who carried that factor on his red cells. While this first exposure immunized the recipient to the X factor, it did not trigger a visible transfusion reaction. But the next time he was given blood from the same donor, or from another carrier of the X factor, his now-primed immune system responded by producing enormous amounts of anti-X antibody. This *immune antibody*—as distinct from the so-called *natural*, anti-A and -B antibodies—was believed to be the cause of intragroup reactions. In each case, two transfusions of X-positive blood were required to cause an anti-X adverse reaction.

Mary Seno was an exception. Levine said:

> It is evident that the unusual antibody must have been present at the time the patient was given her first transfusion with the blood of her husband. . . .
> In view of the fact that this patient harbored a dead fetus for a period of several months, one may assume that the products of the disintegrating fetus were responsible . . . for . . . immunization [of Mrs. Seno against it.] Presumably the immunizing property in the blood and/or tissues of the fetus must have been inherited from the father. Since this dominant property was not present in the mother, specific immunization [against it] conceivably could occur.[2]

Levine had deduced, from the fact that Mary Seno had responded to an unusual X factor after a first transfusion rather than a second, that her stillborn baby also carried the X factor, and that it had acted, in her, as the initiating, or *immunizing*, stimulus. He also had deduced that the fetus had inherited this unknown X factor from its father.

Levine had done something else, which his former lab partner, Jacob Furth, felt was causing him great inner torment. By using Mary Seno's blood as a test serum to challenge some 100 potential group O donors, he had identified a new blood group—the carriers of the factor X whose red cells her serum clotted. Moreover, unlike M, N, and P this new factor clearly was clinically important, having almost killed Mary Seno.

Five years earlier, however, Levine had acceded to Landsteiner's demand not to continue the search for new blood groups. Publishing the Mary Seno case would benefit science, and perhaps also Levine's ego. But it would violate his agreement with Landsteiner.

"He was torn between bitterness for the way he had been treated and his loyalty to Dr. Landsteiner," Furth would recall many years later. "It was quite a feat for Dr. Levine to make up his mind and go ahead with it—despite his promise."

Levine did publish the case, more than a year later. It appeared under his name, and that of a co-worker, Dr. Rufus Stetson, in the *Journal of the American Medical Association*, on July 8, 1939. In this report, Levine does not offer a name for the antigen present in Mary Seno's dead fetus and on her husband's red cells—and present also on the red cells of about 85 percent of blood donors tested with her serum. Perhaps the omission was intentional—in deference to his promise to Landsteiner.

Events now were moving quickly. Six months later, in January 1940, Wiener and Landsteiner were to publish their discovery of the Rh factor (described in Chapter 1).[3] In the interim between July and January, Wiener had come to the realization—not from the Mary Seno case, but from an intragroup reaction case of his own—that the Rh factor, which at first encounter had seemed weak and benign, could cause lethal transfusion reactions.

A physician in Baltimore, Dr. H. Raymond Peters, was caring for a woman who, after an operation, was transfused with ABO-compatible blood. After the fifth transfusion, she suffered a severe transfusion reaction, and on August 30 she died. Peters sent Wiener a tube of her serum.

It was in working with this serum that Wiener made his creative leap. He tested it with red cells from several ABO-compatible persons. The serum reacted, incompatibly, with about six of every seven red cell specimens, but failed to react with about one in seven. This was about the same ratio of reactors to nonreactors—85 percent to 15 percent—that he and Landsteiner had found when they used anti-rhesus monkey antibody in rabbit serums to test human red cells. This was also about the same proportion of reactors to nonreactors that Levine had found when he tested Mary Seno's serum with supposedly compatible group O blood donors.

Could the serum of the dead woman in Baltimore and Landsteiner and Wiener's rabbit anti-rhesus monkey serum be reacting to the same blood factor on the red cells of most human beings?

To find out, Wiener set up an experiment. He used the dead woman's serum to test red cells of 14 ABO-compatible persons. At the same time, he used some of his rabbit serums, containing anti-Rh antibodies, to test red cells from the same 14 persons. "The coincidence of the positive number of reactions led us to compare the two serums," Wiener would say later. "If we didn't have the [similarity in] frequency, it would never have occurred to us to compare them!"

When, two hours after he had mixed serums and red cell samples in test tubes, Wiener examined the tubes, he discovered himself to be richly rewarded. "Remarkably," he exclaimed, "the woman's serum and the anti-rhesus serum reacted with precisely the same red cells."[4] Both clumped 10 out of the 14 red cell specimens—the *same* 10—and, identically, both failed to clump the remaining 4.

Could this be a coincidence? Wiener calculated the odds. The chances were 16,000 to 1 that it was not. "It is reasonable to conclude, therefore, that the agglutinable property [blood factor] demonstrated with the patient's serum is identical with Rh."

Wiener went on to lay down the logical—and clinically momentous—explanation that the dead woman was Rh-negative, and had died after receiving repeated transfusions of Rh-positive blood. The first Rh-positive blood she had been given served simply to *immunize*, or *sensitize*, her to the Rh factor. Subsequent infusions called forth massive production of anti-Rh antibody, which reacted with the donor cells and killed her.

Wiener reviewed the literature on intragroup reactions. Most had occurred after a second or subsequent transfusion. Some, perhaps many, might be due to Rh incompatibility.

There was one small exceptional group, which included Mary Seno. All had had intragroup reactions after just one transfusion. "Remarkably enough," Wiener said, "in all of these cases . . . the patients were women who had recently given birth or had had a miscarriage." Wiener agreed with Levine's reasoning, apropos Mary Seno, that a fetus might sensitize its mother to a blood factor. He said: "It does not seem improbable, that, for example, a Rh-negative woman carrying a Rh-positive fetus might react by producing [anti-] Rh antibodies."

The clear importance of his new discovery, Wiener said later, prompted Landsteiner and him to quickly submit to a journal their original Rh experiment, which they had until then withheld from publication. When it appeared in January 1940, their short report

In amicable moment, Rh pioneers Drs. Levine (left) and Wiener chat at party honoring Levine's retirement as Ortho immunohematology chief. (*Al Giese, 1965, Courtesy Medical World News.*)

gave no clue to the Rh factor's clinical role. But Wiener meanwhile was writing a full report on his findings, and in March he mailed it to the *Annals of Internal Medicine*, which published it in June. Peters was coauthor. A new, lethal blood factor had been described, and a method—tests for Rh compatibility between donor and recipient—had been proposed to control it. Wiener clearly had made the most important contribution to blood grouping and transfusion safety since Landsteiner's discovery of ABO.

The next great moment would be Levine's—with an assist from an obstetrician who was familiar with one thing that Levine was not: erythroblastosis.

Mary Seno's dead fetus, and others like it, may well have had the severe, hydropic form of erythroblastosis. But Levine did not know that. He had not examined it, and it had not been autopsied. More important, Levine's concern was not with what killed a fetus, but the threat that its antigens posed to a mother in need of blood. The fetus' death might have been due to any number of causes. Still-births were not remarkable. Neither, for the most part, were they rigorously studied. To blood researchers especially, they were of little intrinsic interest.

Such was not the case for obstetrician Dr. Lyman Burnham, recently moved from New York City to the nearby suburban town of Englewood, New Jersey. A private practitioner who was eager to make a mark by contributing to science, Burnham was put in touch with Levine in June 1940, when the mother of a dead baby he had delivered died after a transfusion of her husband's blood. Burnham said later that "the association of erythroblastosis and transfusion accidents was first suggested" by this case, but he neither autopsied nor did blood studies on the baby;[5] nor is this idea mentioned in a report on the case that Levine wrote with Burnham as one co-author.[6]

A similar case four months later, in October, brought matters to a head. The mother had no living children, and an attempt was made to give her one by delivering her early, by cesarean section. Burnham was called in as a consultant to look after the baby.

It was alive at birth, but severely ill, and died within twelve hours. This time an autopsy was done: erythroblastosis. Meanwhile, the mother, having lost blood during the operation, was given one, then another transfusion of her husband's apparently-compatible blood. She had a violent transfusion reaction and lapsed into a coma.

Burnham, because of his previous dealings with Levine, now called him again on the phone to ask help in selecting truly compatible donors. Burnham later would recall: "I said that the baby died. It died of erythroblastosis. Levine said, 'Well, what is erythroblastosis?' I told him. He said, 'I know about this—they told us about it in medical school—that's when the baby gets jaundice.'"

Burnham's recollection would be that after explaining the wider, more contemporary notion of erythroblastosis, he sent Levine, along with blood specimens from mother, father, and dead baby, reprints from his files of three papers on the disease. Included was Diamond's, but not Darrow's, which Burnham would say later he was not aware of.

Burnham continues: "A few days later, Levine called me on the phone and said, 'We've found anti-Rh antibodies in the mother's serum. They must be the cause of erythroblastosis!'"

The key connection had been made. Fetal antigens provoked an

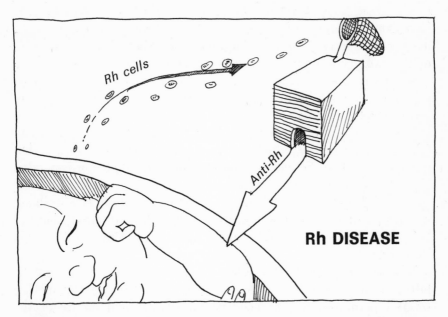

antibody response in the mother. The antibody would destroy transfused blood from the father, which was like that of the fetus. It could also destroy the fetus' blood before birth. Levine wrote:

It is probable that there is a connection between the occurrence of these [fetal] complications and the presence of immune antibodies in the mother. This relationship lends itself readily to form a theoretical basis for the etiology of at least some cases of erythroblastosis fetalis. . . . The hypothesis of immunization [of the mother by her fetus] can readily explain the familial incidence of this condition.

The blood picture characteristic of erythroblastosis fetalis, i.e., destruction of red cells and compensatory reaction of the bone marrow, can also be explained in terms of the immunization theory. One may assume that the antibodies in the mother's circulation under certain conditions are capable of penetrating the placental barrier . . . [and] by their continual action on the blood cells and perhaps tissue cells of the fetus, induce erythroblastosis fetalis, and its several manifestations. . . . The fetus may die in utero. . . . There is sufficient evidence to indicate that most of these [women's] serums contain an antibody which parallels the anti-Rh antibody of Landsteiner and Wiener.[7]

Levine published his theory, and data to support it, in the *Journal of the American Medical Association* on March 1, 1941. Burnham and a third co-worker, Dr. Eugene Katzin, are coauthors.

Levine, unlike Ruth Darrow, who had published her similar

theory three years earlier, could adduce evidence from his blood laboratory to support his theory that Rh incompatibility between mother and fetus caused erythroblastosis: Many, though not all, mothers of erythroblastic babies were Rh-negative. Their husbands usually were Rh-positive. The sick infants themselves for the most part also had Rh-positive blood, which their mothers' antibody would quickly destroy.

Corroboration was available. In a moment of rare cooperation, "in tests done jointly with Dr. Wiener," Levine had showed that one mother whom he had studied had antibody that "corresponded to the anti-Rh [antibody]" that Wiener had made in rabbits.[8] Levine also retested Mary Seno. She was Rh-negative. Her husband was Rh-positive—a strong indication, if not ultimate proof, that her baby had died of erythroblastosis due to Rh incompatibility with its mother.

Levine's ability, in other cases, to prove that the fetus and its father both possessed the blood factor against which the mother reacted permitted him to account for the familial nature of the disease more satisfactorily than could Darrow, who had failed to see that it was inherited.* The Rh factor was a genetic trait, which each ill fetus had inherited from its father, and which, since she was Rh-negative, was absent in the mother, who made antibody against it. Destruction of the fetus' red cells by this antibody in the womb and immediately after birth seemed to Levine an adequate basis for explaining the rest of the disease's complex of symptoms.

As the mother's anti-Rh antibody leaked across the placenta and

---

* Levine owes no debt to Darrow. He says he became aware of her paper only early in 1941, after his own paper had been submitted for publication.[9] Darrow believed him, her first daughter, Virginia—who assisted her mother in her laboratory, and who was conversant with her work—would say later. Burnham's account confirms this, for he says that only a few days elapsed between the time he raised the issue of erythroblastosis with Levine and the time Levine specified the mother's antibody as its cause.

Among his associates, Levine asserted that rule of ownership he himself had so painfully learned from Landsteiner. Obstetrician Burnham felt that his own contribution—the linking of the clinical diagnosis *erythroblastosis* to intragroup transfusion reactions—would win recognition only if he published his cases in a paper of his own. A half dozen papers establishing Levine's commanding contribution already had appeared, each with Levine as senior author. But Levine objected to Burnham's plan. "I remember arguing with Dr. Levine," Burnham would say years later, "and him saying, 'No! No! You can't put it down—that's my contribution.'" Like Levine before him, Burnham disobeyed the injunction in a paper that appeared late in 1941. But he says at the outset: "All of the serologic studies in these cases were carried out by Dr. Philip Levine."[10]

destroyed its red cells, the fetus produced more and more new red cells—erythroblasts—to replace them. Thus, while Diamond's description of the disease remained essentially correct, he had been dead wrong about its cause. Erythroblastosis was an effect. The cause was anti-Rh antibody from the mother, which destroyed the fetus' red cells more rapidly than it could effectively replace them.

The name for the disease, erythroblastosis fetalis, thus no longer accurately reflected the new understanding of its cause. More accurate designations, *hemolytic disease of the newborn*, and *Rh hemolytic disease*, were coined. However, erythroblastosis would continue to be used as an equivalent.

Levine's theory would prove to be correct. Upon it would be built an immense clinical effort that would revolutionize many areas of medicine, some of them far from the blood lab, and lead directly to the salvage of thousands upon thousands of lives.

Levine's explanation of erythroblastosis shattered a long-cherished myth that the fetus was sealed off and isolated from the mother by the walls of the womb, and could not harm or be harmed by her. Subsequent erythroblastosis research would transform the fetus from an unreachable, medically untouchable isolate in the world of as-yet-to-be into a living human being, interacting with its mother—and amenable to medical diagnosis and life-saving treatment. Levine also established the startling idea that immune reactions were not limited, as a hazard, to blood transfusions —which, after all, are a human artifact—but could also be the cause of naturally occurring lethal diseases.

All this, however, belonged to the future. In the spring of 1941, when Levine first published his theory, few believed it. Medical historian Dr. Edith Potter of the University of Chicago, who was to become one of the world's leading experts on the pathology of erythroblastosis, later would recall that her colleagues greeted Levine's new theory with "enormous skepticism."

One of the most skeptical was another Chicagoan, Ruth Darrow.

Ruth Darrow was pregnant. Wondrously so, in a way, for she now was forty-five years old.

Since Alan Darrow's death, one pregnancy, in 1939, had ended in miscarriage. Now, as her due date approached, Darrow confided her hopes and fears to her family and colleagues. The odds seemed terribly against her. The death rate for babies diagnosed as having erythroblastosis approached 90 percent—and this baby was bound to be ill. Since each successive infant usually was sicker than the last, Darrow's two previous pregnancies boded especially ill for the one now ending. Could she redeem it?

Levine's theory, which was so close to her own, would be no help—because she rejected it! She doubted that an inherited blood factor, an antigen on the cell membrane, caused erythroblastosis. A complex immunologic experiment, which she recently had completed, confirmed her in her view that immunologic differences between fetal hemoglobin and adult hemoglobin might be responsible.

Darrow had a more compelling reason for rejecting the Rh theory. She arranged to have her blood typed for Rh. The test showed, incorrectly, that she was Rh-positive, and hence compatible with her husband and children, who were also found to be Rh-positive. While it is not clear whether she had this misinformation before she delivered, it is evident that when she did get it, it reinforced her feeling that neither her family's erythroblastosis, nor perhaps anyone else's, was due to Rh. Only three years later, in 1944, did a second test show that the Darrows were Rh-incompatible: Ruth definitely was Rh-negative.[11]

Ruth Darrow went into labor on September 21. She put her lifesaving plan into action when she felt her first contraction. She breathed deeply, deliberately, throughout labor to superoxygenate her own blood and thus increase oxygen transport across the placenta to combat the fetus' anticipated anemia.

For this baby, Darrow had switched hospitals. She delivered at Women's and Children's Hospital, where she was an attending physician. One of her young interns, Dr. Josephine Chapin, was nominally in charge of the case. But Ruth Darrow gave the orders.

The baby was a girl, Gail. She appeared healthy at birth. Despite a high count of inefficient erythroblasts in her circulation, her blood oxygen level was initially normal. The deep breathing had worked. So far, Darrow had succeeded.

To continue the effort, now that the cord was cut, Darrow ordered oxygen administered every three hours.

Within an hour after birth Gail became jaundiced. The antibodies brought with her from the womb were attacking. Darrow knew no specific antidote. Perhaps these poisons could be diluted and so be rendered less harmful. She ordered that plasma, blood minus only its red cells, be given as a diluting and detoxifying agent.*

By day's end, Gail was considerably worse. Three more ounces of plasma were given.

On day two, she was worse than before. Her body was deeply bronzed by jaundice; she was listless and took fluids poorly.

A crisis was at hand. Gail was very sick, and the plasma appeared to be making her sicker. "As the evidence for increasing liver injury seemed unequivocal," Darrow said later, "it was deemed inadvisable to continue further with plasma."

Darrow was desperate. Her plans were failing, and with them her hope. As an alternative treatment, there remained only whole blood, which Alan also had had. Gail was given three ABO-compatible blood transfusions, each larger than Alan's had been; each was equivalent to about one-third of her total blood volume. Equivalent amounts simultaneously were removed from another blood vessel. Gail was also given medicine to prevent bleeding attacks, which Alan had suffered, and diet supplements of injected sugar solution. Her mother denied her the breast milk that she felt had helped to poison Alan.

Ruth Darrow passed her forty-sixth birthday working over her ill baby. Miraculously, a day or two later, Gail rallied. Ten days later, the jaundice was gone.

Gail Darrow went home, fully recovered. Ruth Darrow, mother and physician, had triumphed.**

---

* Plasma contains the natural clotting material, *fibrinogen*. Serum is plasma with the *fibrinogen* removed.

** It later would be difficult to ascertain if Gail had been as sick as Alan at the start. A death like his, in the fifth week of life, is unlikely to be due directly to erythroblastosis. Later, on the basis of Alan's case report, neonatal jaundice specialist Dr. Lawrence Gartner of New York City attributed his death to a rare aftereffect of erythroblastosis, a liver disorder, *inspissated bile syndrome with biliary cirrhosis*. Theoretically, Gartner adds, anti-Rh antibody in mother's milk could harm a breast-fed erythroblastic baby like Alan—but no such case has ever been reliably documented. Ruth Darrow's false premise had pointed her toward a correct conclusion!

# 4

## *Progress*

LANDSTEINER DIED in 1943. In an obituary, a colleague wrote: "There are military heroes, it is said, who go into battle trembling with fear; this was a hero of science who fought without optimism, unable to exult in his superb achievement."[1]

Landsteiner's quest for a new, pure human genealogy, based on the certainties of blood groupings and sanctified in the religion of science, had led to the discovery that the closest of all blood bonds, between mother and child, might be lethal. A mother could kill her unborn or newborn child because their bloods were incompatible! Here was a dramatic disease—which was to call forth some dramatic cures.

Erythroblastosis menaced a multitude: 12 percent of all American marriages paired an Rh-negative woman with an Rh-positive man; their offspring were at risk of their Rh incompatibility, although the disease did not strike in every family. Precise counts would never be made of how many babies actually died each year, but educated estimates for the United States alone were: 5,000 to 10,000.[2, 3] The loss of a stillborn or a newborn baby might be less than the loss of a long-loved child or an adult. But erythroblastosis, or *Rh hemolytic disease* as it now was called, imposed added burdens. Once it had killed, usually all who followed would die. Childbearing, for the parents, became a highly predictable recurring tragedy.

Elucidation of the Rh factor and its role in transfusion reactions

and erythroblastosis spurred an enormous scientific effort. Paced by
Levine and Wiener in New York and Diamond in Boston, and by an
Englishman, Dr. Robert Race, in London, hundreds of researchers
conducted thousands of wide-ranging investigations. Already, in
Wiener and Levine's fruitful efforts, a major theme of all future Rh
research had been disharmoniously struck: When any important
discovery was made, it would be made twice, at about the same
time, by two separate individuals or groups who henceforward
would war over credit for its discovery. As a corollary to this
theme, more often than not one co-discoverer and warring con-
tender for credit would be Alexander Wiener or one of his disciples.

The Rh discoveries would prove to be Levine's and Wiener's
most significant work. They perhaps sensed this at the time. Levine
then was forty years old; Wiener was approaching thirty-five. Rh
would shape the reminder of their lives. Wiener, the more creative
of the two, brilliantly attacked a host of problems in the diagnosis,
treatment, and prevention of Rh disease. His restless mind probed
many new pathways—whose definitive exploration he often left to
others.

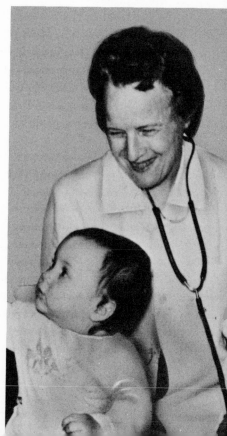

Dr. Darrow was photographed with young
patient for family snapshot collection.
(*Circa 1945, Courtesy Mrs. Chester Darrow and the American Medical Women's
Association.*)

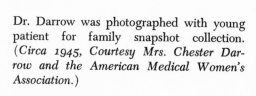

Wiener never left his job in the blood laboratory of the New York City Medical Examiner. He provided key evidence in several sensational criminal cases, testifying as to whose red cells could—and whose could not—be present in bloodstains left at the scene of a crime. Wiener maintained a private serologic practice—one of the few of its kind—at an office near his home in Brooklyn, and did transfusions and blood research at hospitals nearby. He maintained his academic affiliation at New York University, where he eventually became a professor in the department of forensic medicine.

Levine took a wholly different route, one which, in terms of making the Rh discoveries widely available, may well have been the more productive. The rest of his active career would be devoted to research in industry. The company for which he went to work was Ortho Products, Inc.—now Ortho Pharmaceutical Corporation—a subsidiary of the giant Johnson and Johnson medical supply company. Ortho was set up by J.&J. in 1940 to make and market its vaginal contraceptive jelly, *Ortho-Gynol*; the company was named for the product.[4] With the popularization of "The Pill" and other forms of contraceptives in the 1960s, Ortho would become a major pharmaceutical manufacturer. By 1970, its domestic sales accounted for 6 percent of J.&J.'s annual gross sales of over one billion dollars, e.g., about sixty millon dollars.[5]

Levine joined Ortho at the invitation of the company president, who earlier had given him a grant to support his Rh research. Ortho Products formed an Ortho Research Foundation with a mission to invent better contraceptives; Levine went on its payroll in 1944.

Once aboard, Levine stimulated Ortho to make and market diagnostic serums for Rh and other blood tests. In the mid-1960s, a special division, Ortho Diagnostics, was set up to market the three dozen or so blood lab products he and his associates had developed.

While Ortho was well-known in the birth control field and among blood-workers, it cultivated a stiff and withdrawn public image. In part this expressed J.&J.'s policy of maintaining a low public profile. According to *The New York Times*, the parent company traditionally balked at any substantial probing into its internal affairs.[6] This reticence was probably reinforced by the considerations of Ortho's odd product mix. As an ad agency copywriter for the Ortho account later would explain, the company wanted to sell a lot of its contraceptives without jeopardizing its sale of blood products to Catholic hospital blood banks.[7] When Levine first went to Ortho, it was located in Linden, New Jersey, near Newark. It later moved to Raritan, New Jersey.

As scientific and public awareness of Rh increased, so did the rivalry and enmity between Levine and Wiener. They fixated on the question of who deserved credit for making the key discoveries.

Levine had clear title to having demonstrated Rh's role in erythroblastosis. Wiener clearly had been first to point to the hazard Rh incompatibility posed to routine blood transfusions. He also had claim to having named the Rh factor—a claim later devalued by others who advanced allegedly simpler ways to denote the discovery.

The ultimate focus of contention was a simple-seeming problem: Who discovered the Rh factor? While this was clinically less important than the consequences of the discovery, for these two scientists, treading in the footsteps of the discoverer of the ABO blood groups, the question of who discovered the Rh factor could, and did, become a cruelly sharp bone of contention. They tore at each other with it—to the detriment of both, and the honor of neither.[8]

The battle grew more bitter—beyond the ability of colleagues and friends to calm it. Wiener, competitive and assertive, and Levine, angry and defensive, would fight on for years. Neither was innocent of animosity, and years later, a long-time colleague of Levine's would recount being drawn to audit their volatile exchanges: "Levine would get me on the other extension," he said, "and they would shout back and forth at each other."[9]

Fortunately, competition was not incompatible with progress.

A first major step was development of diagnostic anti-Rh antibody preparations, or *reagents*. If a reagent clumped a person's red cells, they were Rh-positive, and could not safely be given to an Rh-negative person.

It was a problem finding enough potent anti-Rh antibody for routine blood typing. Wiener at first used diagnostic serums made by injecting rabbits and guinea pigs with rhesus monkey red cells. Levine used serums from Rh-negative mothers who had delivered erythroblastic babies, and hence had high levels, or *titers*, of anti-Rh antibody. Rapid introduction of Rh blood-typing during World War II forestalled many thousands of potentially fatal transfusion reactions in multiply-transfused fighting men and civilians.

Wiener and Diamond found that they could make large amounts

of anti-Rh serum by deliberately injecting Rh-positive red cells into Rh-negative men. These men could not then be transfused with Rh-positive blood, for fear of transfusion reaction, but they suffered no other ill effect, since they could not get pregnant, and hence were not threatened by erythroblastosis. This deliberate immunization of Rh-negative men—a situation parallel to the erythroblastosis-inducing sensitization of women by their Rh-positive fetuses—later would prove to be an excellent human model in which the disease could be studied.

By about 1950, all blood banks used Rh reagents to insure the Rh compatibility of all transfused blood.*

Rh blood-typing lowered the incidence of erythroblastosis, for many Rh-negative mothers had initially been sensitized to the Rh factor by blood transfusions. Blood had been given liberally in the late 1930s and early 1940s—many practitioners gave blood injections as tonic. Wiener was to estimate later that the incidence of erythroblastosis was cut in half when doctors were stopped from giving Rh-incompatible injections and transfusions.

Identification of the Rh factor yielded almost immediate benefit for erythroblastic babies. Blood transfusions were a standard treatment. But now it was possible to choose between donor blood that

* The *plus* or *minus* after an individual's ABO blood group, as in A+ or O−, indicates the Rh blood type and means A, Rh+ or O, Rh−.

Dr. Diamond developed effective ways to diagnose and treat erythroblastosis. (*Circa 1940, Courtesy of Children's Hospital, Boston.*)

would make matters worse and donor blood guaranteed to help. These babies still carried anti-Rh antibody brought with them from the womb. Hence, any Rh-positive blood they were given would also be attacked, complicating their symptoms. Two New York blood bankers, Dr. Peter Vogel and Dr. Eugene Katzin, co-workers with Levine, realized that they could prevent this added damage and preserve the transfused blood by giving these babies only donor blood that was Rh-negative. Vogel first, then Katzin, and soon most blood bankers began to give the babies only Rh-negative blood, Vogel later would recall. This blood was impervious to attack by the anti-Rh antibodies the babies still harbored in their bodies. It was in no way injurious to them, and by the time it was replaced by a baby's normal production of Rh-positive cells, the dangerous maternal antibody was long gone—and the threat to the baby's life had passed.

Rh-negative blood transfusions saved some babies. Others failed to rally. Wiener, first, and then a New York transfusionist, Dr. Harry Wallerstein, decided that more definitive blood therapy was needed. Both devised methods to slowly remove *all* of the baby's jeopardized blood through a cut down to one blood vessel, while simultaneously replacing it by infusing Rh-negative blood into another. Wiener took blood out of a wrist artery, replacing it through an ankle vein. Wallerstein took the Rh-positive blood out of a vessel inside the skull.

Wiener's first attempt, in 1944, to save an erythroblastic baby failed. The name he coined to describe the technique, *exchange transfusion*, won acceptance. Wallerstein then succeeded in saving an erythroblastic baby by exchange transfusion in 1945.

Both men's methods were difficult, and Wallerstein's, Wiener and Diamond charged, was dangerous as well. Diamond, in Boston, now developed a simpler method, which would be widely accepted all over the world: He undid the baby's newly tied umbilical cord, inserted a tube into the umbilical vein, and alternately took out old blood and put in new, a few teaspoonsful at a time, until most of the blood had been exchanged. Repeated changes might be done in this way until the baby rallied. When skillfully done, the risk was nil.

A soft-spoken young Yankee pediatrician, Dr. Fred Allen, Jr., who worked with Diamond at Boston's Children's Hospital, now made the important discovery that exchange transfusion did indeed save lives—but for reasons wholly different than had been believed! Others had focused on the destruction of the baby's red cells and the added strain this imposed on the baby's blood-forming tissues, heart, liver, and other organs. The yellow pigment, or *bilirubin*, which the liver makes from the remains of the ruined red cells, was felt to be relatively unimportant; similar bilirubin, and the resultant jaundice, occurred in other diseases, and seemed harmless.

In fact, Allen showed, fatal brain damage almost always occurred in babies who were deeply jaundiced.[10] This implied, he said, that erythroblastic bilirubin was a deadly poison. Babies were perhaps being killed or crippled by bilirubin's action on their brains, not by blood loss or its consequences.

Bilirubin will bind to *albumin*, the major protein in blood serum. When it is so bound, Allen suggested, it is harmless. Other investigators confirmed this, and confirmed that in mild erythroblastosis the babies usually have adequate amounts of albumin to safely bind the bilirubin they make, and so recover. But when there was severe blood damage, bilirubin production outstripped the available albumin reserves; brain damage and death quickly followed.

Exchange transfusions prevented this by providing albumin to bind loose bilirubin so that it could be harmlessly excreted. Albumin supplements were added to make the exchanges more effective. Exchange transfusions also helped because the Rh-negative donor cells were impervious to anti-Rh antibody remaining in the baby. Hence, production of bilirubin was limited.

Methods were developed in the early 1950s to monitor babies' bilirubin levels. Exchange transfusions thus usually could be given before their brains became damaged.

Exchange transfusions proved enormously successful, and later would be estimated to have saved more than 200,000 lives in the first two decades in which they were used. Their relative contribution to life salvage of erythroblastic babies is quite as dramatic. Before exchange transfusions, about 25 percent of all erythroblastic babies admitted to Boston's Children's Hospital died of bilirubin-induced brain damage. By 1950, this toll had dropped to under 5 percent.

Even so, salvage of babies with late symptoms did not help those who died early. As before the advent of exchanges, fully a third of all babies born to Rh-sensitized mothers in obstetric hospitals affiliated with Children's died before birth or soon after. Thus, in Boston, at a leading Rh research center, the Rh death toll still stood at about 33 percent in sensitized pregnancies; elsewhere the toll undoubtedly was higher.

The Rh discoveries seemed at first to offer the obstetrician new tools. He could test a woman's blood. If she was Rh-negative, he could test the husband to see if he was Rh-incompatible. If so, this was a pregnancy to watch closely. The obstetrician could order a woman's blood tested periodically in pregnancy. When her serum first reacted with Rh-positive cells in a test tube she had become sensitized, and was making antibody injurious to her fetus. If her antibody titer rose precipitously, as it often did approaching term, her fetus was probably quite ill or dying. It seemed to make sense then to remove it as quickly as possible from its toxic environment by early induction of labor or even cesarean delivery.

It made sense, except that the antibody tests were not always a reliable index of the fetus' illness. A mother with a high anti-Rh antibody level might deliver a baby that was only moderately ill. A mother with a moderately high antibody titer could deliver a stillborn.

Obstetricians—Vince Freda would be one of them—did sometimes do early deliveries in cases they had carefully followed. But whether more lives were being lost to prematurity than were being saved by early delivery was difficult to decide. In the early 1950s Diamond and his colleagues in Boston and an equally eminent team of pediatric hematologists in Britain concluded that routine early induction of labor not only was useless, but was also extremely dangerous, since more babies would die early from the effects of prematurity than would die later from erythroblastosis.[11, 12] These conclusions were widely accepted. Only if a precise and specific measure of the fetus' health could be developed would early induction be reasonable—and no such tests existed.

The obstetrician was left in the lurch. With Rh-incompatible pregnancies he could only stand by, helplessly, waiting to see what would happen. If the baby survived to birth, then the pediatrician in the newborn nursery was the hero who usually could save it. But if it died before birth, it was the obstetrician's failure; the pregnancy was his responsibility, not the pediatrician's.

In two short decades enormous progress had been made against erythroblastosis. But with the obstetrician still a helpless bystander through most of the critical weeks of the disease, much still needed to be done. At his own institution, the Columbia-Presbyterian Medical Center in New York City, Vince Freda would find that during the 1950s, about 20 percent of erythroblastic babies died in the womb and that an additional 10 percent were so sick by the time they were born that despite exchange transfusions they died too.[13]

# 5

## Clues in Passing

As MORE WAS LEARNED about Rh hemolytic disease, a few puzzling facts emerged that later would spur attempts to deal more definitively with it.

Foremost was the fact that virtually all Rh-incompatible first pregnancies produced wholly unaffected babies.* Why? Wiener, in 1945, offered a suggestion: "There is some indirect evidence," he said, "that the maximum amount of fetal blood escapes into the maternal circulation at the time of labor and delivery, possibly due to the disturbances at the placental site. This would explain why the chance of the firstborn child of an Rh-negative mother having hemolytic disease is practically nil."[1]

Wiener failed to pursue this lead. Levine, if aware of it, probably doubted its relevance. Levine had calculated that as little as .06 ml of Rh-positive fetal blood—a single drop, no more—was enough to immunize a mother to the Rh factor. Though there was then no way to count fetal blood cells in the mother's circulation, it seemed evident that at least this amount of blood must leak through the thin placental barrier in almost every pregnancy. So the damage was done before delivery.

Why then did this not occur in first pregnancies? Levine provided no answer.

A second contradiction, which also remained unsolved, was implicit in Levine's analysis. Only a small percentage of second and

* Unless the mother had had an Rh-incompatible blood transfusion, in which case the first pregnancy was often affected.

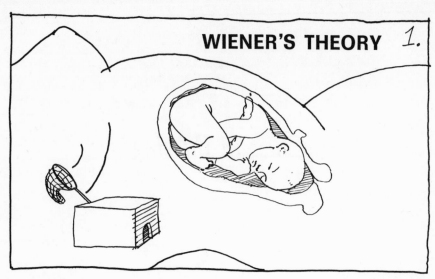

# WIENER'S THEORY

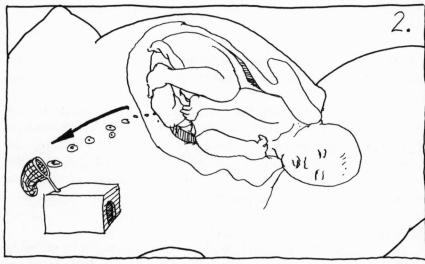

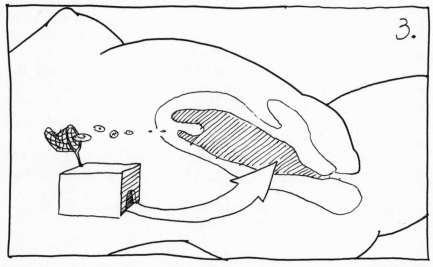

subsequent pregnancies that began with the mother unsensitized to the Rh factor ended in the birth of a sick baby. In fact, the sensitization risk in each successive pregnancy was about 10 percent.* Thus, given a cohort of 100 newly-wed Rh-negative women, all with incompatible Rh-positive husbands, if all became pregnant, all would have well babies. If all became pregnant again, this time 10 would deliver sick or dead babies. In their third pregnancies, the 10 percent already sensitized would have sick babies, as would 10 percent of the remaining 90; a morbidity rate of 19 percent. By baby three, a quarter of the 100 women would be delivering sick or dead babies, and by the fourth pregnancies more than a third would be affected.[2]

An occasional Rh-negative woman would deliver a dozen normal Rh-positive babies. But that was rare. Once a woman did become sensitized, whether in her second pregnancy or her twelfth, she was irrevocably sensitized for life. All her subsequent babies would be sick, and all usually were sicker than the first had been.**

Another lead, not recognized at the time, developed early on. The details of it are unimportant in this account. The key concept —while very likely inaccurate—would prove of paramount importance. It created an enormous conflict between Wiener and its authors.

The nub of the matter was that there quickly were found to be several variants of the Rh factor. Wiener said that all were the expression of a single gene, and hence were inherited together because the gene occupied a single point, or *locus*, on one of the human chromosomes. He identified this single gene's variant traits with symbols like $R^0$, $r$, $R^1$, $r'$, $R^2$, $r''$, etc.—none of which, as such, is significant to this account.

An alternative theory of the Rh genes was advanced by British biostatistician Sir Ronald Fisher, a friend and colleague of Britain's leading Rh expert, Robert Race.[3] He started with the established

---

* Estimates ranged from 5 percent to 20 percent per pregnancy; for convenience, 10 percent will be used here.

** Though not germane to this account, there was one surcease: the Rh factor is always expressed when the gene that determines it is present. This means that an Rh-negative mother lacks this gene. An Rh-positive father carries either one gene for the Rh factor, or two, i.e., he is either *homozygous* or *heterozygous* for it. If homozygous, then whichever of his two paired genes goes to an offspring, it will be Rh-positive. But if he is heterozygous, he may contribute either the Rh gene *or* the paired gene that does not confer the Rh factor—in which case the fetus will be Rh-negative, like its mother, and hence wholly unthreatened by Rh disease.

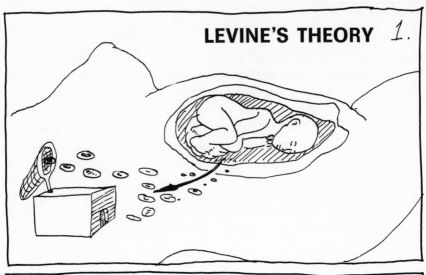

**LEVINE'S THEORY** *1.*

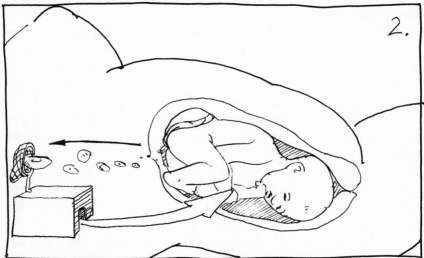

*2.*

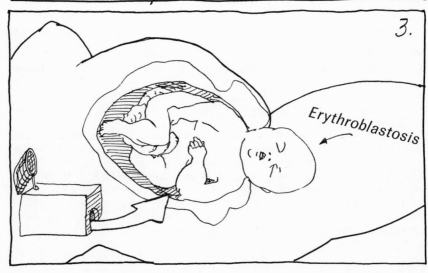

*3.*

*Erythroblastosis*

notion that each gene determines one, and only one trait. Only a few variants of the Rh factor had then been discovered, and Fisher said that they were determined by three pairs of genes on one of the human chromosomes. To explain how these separate and individual genes were passed on as a single heritable unit from one generation to the next, Fisher postulated that they were controlled and kept together by what he called a *supergene*.[4] It is this supergene concept that at one critical moment would direct to Rh hemolytic disease a creative inquiry that otherwise would have been spent far less fruitfully elsewhere.

Fisher felt that Wiener's Rh nomenclature was too confusing and in line with his own theory proposed an allegedly simpler notation in which the Rh gene pairs would be designated by the letters *C-c*, *D-d* and *E-e*, following Landsteiner's A and B. As an example, what for Wiener would be $R°$ would for Fisher be *D*. Fisher's notations were widely adopted in Europe, over Wiener's objections that they were genetically, serologically, and logically nonsense. The United States government decided, indecisively, that blood products would be labeled with Wiener's notation, followed by Fisher's in parenthesis—for example, "$Rh_o(D)$."

Wiener's priority claim was inseparable from the battle for the name "Rh," and he waged war on *C*, *D*, and *E* with malice and with mirth. The artistic highpoint of this battle came in the 1950s when a song appeared under the nom de plume—or, more appropriately, nom de guerre—of *I. M. Jaundiced*, a fifteen-stanza song ridiculing Fisher's theory. The thrust of this attack was that a blood factor called *d*, or "small d," whose existence Fisher had predicted on the basis of his theory, could not be found, although Diamond, Levine, and others had believed, erroneously, that they had discovered patients who carried it. The song, "Little d—Or, For Goodness Sake, Don't Make a Mistake," is sung to the tune of "The Man on the Flying Trapeze." Several of its choruses and two closing verses convey its tenor:

CHORUS
Again little d had turned out an illusion;
Like Fisher, so had Diamond been in confusion. . . .

CHORUS
In Science, there's only one thing to do:
Don't work in an armchair; in the lab find what's true.

VERSE XIII

To Fisher and Race it seems a disgrace

That of anti-small d there's nary a trace.
But it seems to me, and I'm sure you'll agree
That we must get rid of small c, d, e. . . .

VERSE XIV

If you want to find what really is true,
Since C, D and E no longer will do,
It's really quite simple, so why don't you look?
The facts can be found in Wiener's new book.[5]

Far more important than the differences between Rh factor variants, and far simpler to grasp, was the discovery—made independently and simultaneously by Wiener and Race—that there are two forms of anti-Rh antibody. Differences between them would loom large in later attempts to eliminate Rh hemolytic disease.

Antibodies are found in a part of the blood serum called *gamma globulins*. There are several gamma globulins, which differ chemically. The anti-Rh antibody that Wiener and Race had now identified occurred in one fraction, while the anti-Rh antibody previously studied belonged to another.

The two gamma globulins, in which these two antibodies exist, are differentiated in several ways, the most convenient of which is with the simple designations *7S gamma globulin* and *19S gamma globulin*. The antibodies themselves are designated, simply, *7S anti-Rh antibody* and *19S anti-Rh antibody*.*

Exactly how the two forms of anti-Rh antibody destroyed red cells was not known, nor is it known today. It appeared that 7S damaged a cell differently from 19S. The question of how each destroys would loom large later in attempts to control Rh disease. Anti-Rh antibodies were believed to act somewhat as do anti-A and anti-B, and either eat holes in incompatible red cells, clump them so that they stuck together, and/or coat them so that they would be recognized and removed from the blood as it passed through the liver and spleen.

A key difference between 7S and 19S anti-Rh antibody is that the 19S will not cross the placenta from the mother, who makes it, into the fetus. Thus, even if a woman has a high level of 19S anti-Rh

---

* S, for *Svedberg unit*, a determinant of a substance's molecular weight. Such properties have no bearing on the present account, and the designations 7S and 19S are used here only for their convenience.

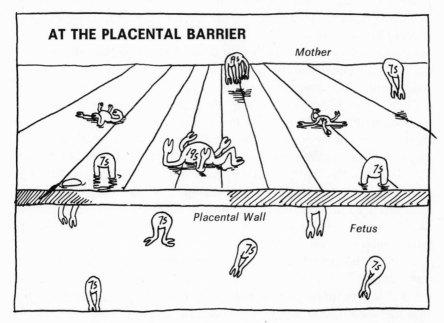

**AT THE PLACENTAL BARRIER**

Mother

Placental Wall

Fetus

antibody in her serum, it will not harm her fetus. The 7S antibody, on the contrary, does cross the placenta into the fetus, causing harm.

Diamond, in 1946, found out a fact about the two forms of anti-Rh antibody that years later would be a tantalizing clue to a youthful co-worker with Vince Freda: the essentially harmless—because contained in the mother—form of anti-Rh antibody, the 19S, tended to be the first to appear once a woman became sensitized to the Rh factor. Later, as the level of 19S in her serum dropped, there was a concomitant rise in the deadlier, placenta-penetrating 7S anti-Rh.[6]

The ultimate goal in the treatment of any disease is to prevent it. Levine's co-worker, Peter Vogel, would recall later that they had agreed, as early as 1941, that the most effective way to prevent Rh hemolytic disease would be to manipulate or suppress the immune reaction of an Rh-negative mother against her Rh-positive fetus' red cells. They agreed further that the chance that this would be achieved in their lifetime was, at best, remote.

Ironically, Levine himself would discover one door-opening clue in 1942; it would be almost his last great creative contribution. Irony of ironies: He failed to see that it was a clue, pregnant with possibility, and so left it for Wiener to see and exploit—although Wiener, too, in the end, failed to pursue it to the ultimate goal—the prevention of Rh disease.

Levine observed, in families he studied in 1942, that among parents of children with Rh hemolytic disease the husband was unlikely to be ABO-compatible with the wife.[7]

Having already demonstrated, starting with Mrs. Seno, that Rh incompatibility leads to fetal death through erythroblastosis, Levine had set out to examine the question of whether a father's—and hence a fetus'—ABO incompatibility with the mother might not also decrease the fetus' chance for survival. His data suggested that it would. A group A fetus, for example, whose blood would be attacked by normally occurring anti-A antibody from its group O mother stood a greater risk of dying in utero than did a group O fetus which was compatible with her.

If ABO incompatibility and Rh incompatibility each individually diminished a fetus' survival chances, what would happen to a fetus that was incompatible in *both* systems? Suppose, for example, that the fetus' blood was group A and Rh-positive, and the mother's was group O and Rh-negative.

Having observed, in his group of families, that among children with Rh hemolytic disease unusually many had parents who were ABO-compatible, and unusually few had parents who were ABO-incompatible, Levine suggested that the latter group was underrepresented because many babies who might have belonged to it had been killed off by their double incompatibility while still in utero. "Selective fetal death is a characteristic manifestation of immunization by the blood factors Rh and A and B," he speculated.

In other words, there are fewer than normal doubly incompatible babies born alive because more of them died in the uterus—as spontaneous abortions and miscarriages—too early to be counted.

Levine only implies this interpretation, which others would make explicit. This allowed Wiener to chide Levine for making "no attempt . . . to explain" his data.[8] Wiener, at that moment, was using Levine's data, and similar data that he and others had gathered, to offer a diametrically opposite interpretation.

Wiener said that the lower-than-normal percentage of ABO-incompatible matings in families of Rh erythroblastic babies—and the concomitant higher percentage of ABO-compatible matings—occurred not because double incompatibility created double jeopardy. Quite the contrary. He shrewdly deduced that the double

# LEVINE'S INTERPRETATION: DOUBLE INCOMPATIBILITY IS DOUBLE JEOPARDY

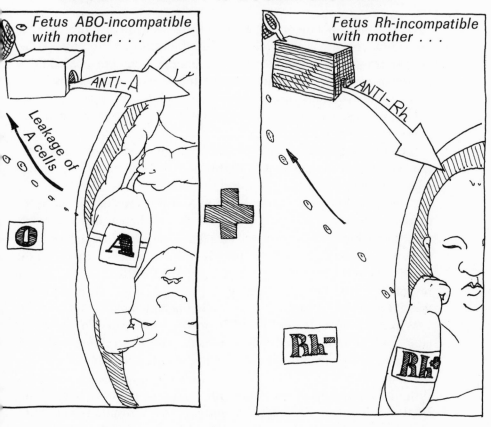

Fetus ABO-incompatible with mother . . .

Fetus Rh-incompatible with mother . . .

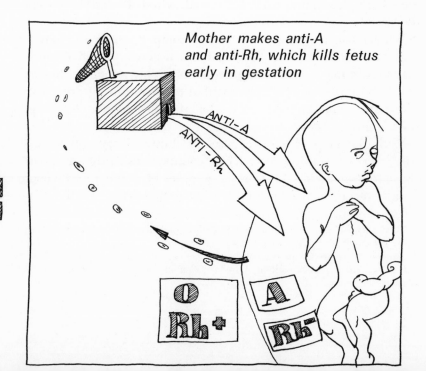

Mother makes anti-A and anti-Rh, which kills fetus early in gestation

incompatibility between mother and fetus—incompatibility in both the ABO and Rh blood systems—in fact served to *protect* the fetuses from illness and death. If a *smaller* percentage of doubly incompatible fetuses became sick, it followed—as the statistics of Levine, Wiener, and others in fact indicated—that more erythroblastic infants would be ABO-compatible than is the norm in the population at large.

Incompatibility for two red blood antigens conferred a *protection*, compared to incompatibility for one of them, Rh, alone. It was a brilliant deduction.*

Wiener had an explanation besides. A and B are "better" antigens than Rh. They are stronger, more potent, and hence more provocative to a woman's immune system. Thus, suppose a fetal red cell carrying the A antigen and the Rh antigen reaches the immune mechanism of a mother who is, say, group O, Rh-negative. It will respond to the stronger A antigen by producing anti-A, but will leave the weaker Rh antigen essentially unchallenged.

Why? It was a general physiologic phenomenon, Wiener would later explain, that a strong stimulus will tend to suppress a weaker one. Thus, it is difficult to see candlelight in the daytime, or to hear a whisper in a boiler factory. So it is difficult for a woman's immune system to respond to the weak Rh factor when it is busy doing battle with the more potent A antigen. As a result, fewer ABO-incompatible women become sensitized to the Rh factor, and when they do, presumably, they produce less anti-Rh antibody against their fetuses.

Wiener had a scheme to put this "competition of antigens" concept to work to prevent Rh sensitization and erythroblastosis. The plan was to inject enormous amounts of highly antigenic, but harmless, substances into Rh-incompatible mothers during pregnancy to divert their immune systems so that they would completely ignore the Rh antigen they were receiving from their fetuses.

With the help of a colleague, Dr. Lester Unger of New York City, Wiener set to work. The "counter-sensitizing" antigens he chose to overshadow Rh were large doses of typhoid and whooping cough vaccine, injected on weekly schedules throughout preg-

---

* This incident demonstrates a basis in reality for Wiener's perennial complaint that others get credit for his achievements. Levine was to be widely credited with providing the correct interpretation of the data, namely, that ABO-incompatibility affords "protection" against Rh incompatibility.[9] In fact, that key interpretation was provided by Wiener.

# WIENER'S INTERPRETATION: DOUBLE INCOMPATIBILITY PROTECTS

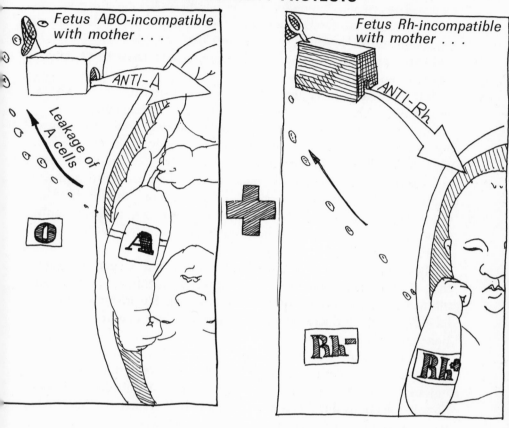

*Mother is too busy making anti-A to make anti-Rh, so fetus does not get sick*

nancy. The women responded to the harmless vaccine antigens by manufacturing enormous amounts of anti-typhoid and anti-whooping cough antibody—and very little anti-Rh.

When Unger reported their still-ongoing field trials to an international blood meeting in England in 1950, he already had followed, through delivery, 121 previously unsensitized women whom he and Wiener had given "counter-sensitization" treatments.[10]

None of 40 first-time pregnant women had delivered sick babies, but that was anticipated, since the disease rarely strikes first pregnancies. Much more important—and impressive—of the 81 women in second or subsequent pregnancies, only 2 had produced anti-Rh antibody—and in these 2 cases the babies were only mildly ill. The sensitization rate in the 81 women thus was 2.5 percent—only about one-fourth the rate that might be expected without the "counter-sensitizing" injections.

These, obviously, were successful results, and Unger proposed that many other clinicians try counter-sensitization, so that its ultimate value could be quickly determined. Surprisingly, only a handful of other doctors would bother to—and counter-sensitization was quickly forgotten.

Wiener himself soon lost interest in it, and later would explain that while "the method is quite sound, and works, it's a damned nuisance." Besides the pain for the women of getting 40 hypodermic injections during each pregnancy, he felt that the injections were too time-consuming for their doctors: "I myself wasn't too enthused," he later would say, "because I figured that if I had to keep doing the injections all of the time, I'd have no time for myself." His colleagues apparently shared his view. So a fairly promising, albeit difficult, method for preventing erythroblastosis was stillborn.

A second, more widely publicized Rh prophylaxis proved even more abortive. Wiener and others had tried to split the Rh factor into two, so that they could discard the antigenic, protein part, which stimulated the mother's immune system, while retaining a non-immunogenic Rh substance that would combine with anti-Rh antibody. The latter antigen fragment was called *Rh hapten*. Presumably, if injected into a pregnant Rh-negative woman, the Rh hapten would grab, nullify, and bind the mother's anti-Rh antibody like a blotter, so that it could not cross the placenta and harm the fetus. A pathology researcher from Pittsburgh, Mrs. Bettina Carter, announced that she had extracted a white substance from red cells that was Rh hapten.[11] When she injected it into women, and even when she gave it to them orally, she claimed, it inhibited anti-Rh antibody, protecting the fetus.

This brought great hope and excitement among Rh experts, including Ruth Darrow. Finally, a cure was at hand. Mrs. Carter's promising reports were published by some of the best immunologic journals.

Three years later, a verdict was rendered. Blood banker Dr. Tibor Greenwalt of Milwaukee made up a supply of "Rh hapten" from Mrs. Carter's recipe and treated 46 women with it during Rh-sensitized pregnancies. He concluded: "There can be no dispute with the evident fact . . . that 'hapten' accomplished nothing of value."[12] The Rh hapten was dead, and in dying it had sensitized many respectable blood men, like Greenwalt, to the notion that an immunologic solution could be found for the Rh problem. They now were conditioned to respond negatively whenever some other unknown investigator claimed to have found one. "Remember Bettina Carter!" they would say knowingly. "Remember Rh hapten!"

Dozens of other ideas were advanced, including eugenic plans. Wiener heaped ridicule on a bill proposed in the Illinois legislature requiring that blood tests be done and warnings issued to all Rh-incompatible couples who planned to wed. True love, he ventured, would not be deterred by blood tests and statistical risks.[13]

A less definitive method which was tried—and which worked— was to artificially inseminate a badly sensitized Rh-negative woman with Rh-negative donor sperm in lieu of her husband's. Darrow, acutely sensitive to the pain of parenthood denied, objected that "resort to such a procedure deprives two married people of a mutually produced child and an innocent man of fatherhood of a child by his own wife."[14] Better methods were needed.

Medically, attempts were made to toughen the placental barrier against fetal blood leaks by giving the mothers vitamin C and other medicaments.[15] These attempts failed. The "wonder drugs" cortisone and ACTH also were tried in mothers. They failed to curtail anti-Rh antibody production. The anticancer drug mercaptopurine, a veritable sledgehammer in the pharmacologic armamentarium, was briefly considered as a means to inactivate the mother's antibody-producing mechanism. Apparently, no one had the temerity to try it. Since it destroys rapidly dividing cells, its accidental passage through the placenta might have killed the fast-growing fetus. Large doses of aspirin also were proposed, to squelch the mother's immune mechanism; here too, prudence won out.

"Heroic"—for mother and doctor—attempts were made to take anti-Rh antibody out of the mother's blood by removing several pints of it each day, processing it, and then returning the red cells. This failed.

A curious experiment was reported by an Rh-positive physician whose wife was in jeopardy of delivering a sick baby. Instead of trying to *remove* her antibody, he tried to "desensitize" her with repeated doses of his own Rh-positive blood—which he injected into her veins. Predictably, her antibody level rose in face of this antigen challenge, and then, mysteriously, fell. What is more, the antibody seemed to change its character so that it now was less harmful. The baby lived.

These results seemed "remarkable" enough to pediatrician Fred Allen, who learned of the case, to try a similar treatment on several Boston women. He gave them his own Rh-positive blood rather than the fathers', since it was easier to obtain when needed. The women's antibody titers climbed rapidly, then leveled off, as the doctor's wife's had done—but their babies all died. Allen abandoned the project. The experiment had failed, like so many others. By the 1950s, a way to prevent erythroblastosis seemed no closer than it had the day the Rh factor first was discovered.

The first great generation of Rh research had ended. Ruth Darrow died in 1956. Levine was approaching sixty. Wiener published no new Rh-prevention schemes. "It is probable," the *British Medical Journal* had said, in the early 1950s, "that the diagnosis and treatment of hemolytic disease of the newborn in the larger towns of Great Britain and many other countries are now as efficient as present knowledge permits. . . . Any dramatic improvement in treatment must await some further fundamental discovery such as might lead to effective antenatal prophylaxis or treatment."[16] Echoing this prophetic assessment, Diamond and Allen conceded several years later, in 1957, that "history in the future will be made by those who . . . see more clearly than we what the basic problems are."[17]

It was in 1958 that Vince Freda arranged, through his chief in obstetrics at Columbia, Dr. Howard Taylor, Jr., to spend an academic year, the fourth of his five residency training years, working with Wiener at New York University. They embarked together on two complicated blood research problems in obstetrics: a study of the changing antibody profile of women who deliver ABO-incompatible erythroblastic babies, and a charting, in detail, of which antibodies in a mother pass through the placenta to enter the fetus, and which do not. When the time came to write an article on some of their findings, Vince would go on an evening to Wiener's home in Brooklyn.

"Vincent, are you ready?" Wiener would ask. "Then," Vince recalls, "he'd start to dictate, and I'd write what he said. That would be it—one draft—no matter how abstruse the subject. 'Don't simplify. Don't talk down to people!' he'd tell me. 'Let them come up and meet you. That's how people really learn!' "

Vince, too, clearly learned much in this way from his mentor, who later would remark upon his enjoyment of the younger man for his devotion to his work and "his alert and very open mind. He didn't have the idea that he knew everything ahead of time."

In exchange, Wiener provided Vince with structure—"scientific discipline" he would call it—the same boon Landsteiner had granted to him a generation before. Wiener, less selfish than Landsteiner, depicts this inspirational endowment in concrete terms: An older man serves a younger man, not by foisting his own ideas upon him, but by providing a disinterested critique of the younger man's plans. The younger man truly saves himself time and labor in the laboratory and avoids the humiliation of publishing half-cocked ideas and faulty findings. The older man also provides a haven that the younger man may seek when he is depressed because his experiments are not going well.

"Vincent knew," Wiener would say, "that if I found any fault with his work I wouldn't hesitate to tell him. And he knew I had no ax to grind. Landsteiner served much the same function for me. When I'd write something, I'd show it to him, and if it didn't pass muster, I wouldn't publish it. Landsteiner couldn't stand sloppy thinking and neither can I, which saved me from a lot of mistakes. Vincent would show me his experimental protocols. He knew that if he left something important out of an experiment, he'd have lost a year's work, or more." Vince also knew Wiener's proclivity to pounce mercilessly upon "foolish" theories that others might mistakenly choose to publish. Wiener expressed himself skillfully, and his rhetoric conveyed a rancor that is rarely revealed in scientific publications. "Vincent," Wiener would say, "did not want to be included in *that*."

Vince's growth from protégé toward co-equal colleague in Wiener's esteem is indicated in the salutations of the memos and letters that Wiener directed to him on the progress of their research endeavors. In 1957, one of these missives might begin "Dear Dr. Freda." A year or so later, the opening had become "Dear Vincent" —which perhaps somewhat frightened Vince, in whose awed feelings his mentor would always be "Dr. Wiener."[18]

Wiener could hardly have known, and Vince himself may not have been consciously aware of the fact, that there grew up in him, during their year together, a powerful resolution to conquer the clinical consequences of the blood incompatibility that his mentor had helped discover, but had failed to resolve. "Wiener taught me Rh serologic techniques," Vince later would say. "I applied them in obstetrics, which is where the problem really is."

The baton had been passed from the first to the second—and perhaps last—great generation of Rh disease researchers.

# 6

## Youthful Alliance

By the time Vince finished his year's apprenticeship with Wiener and moved his base of operations from NYU-Bellevue, on the East River, back to Columbia-Presbyterian, high over the Hudson, he had acquired considerable competence in blood research techniques. He had also gained the will to conquer Rh hemolytic disease.

Awareness of what he planned may have dawned on Vince only gradually. Not only was it a grand and ambitious aim, it was a unique one—to which he brought surprisingly unique qualifications. A lot had been said—and a lot more has since been said—about the fascination and challenge of erythroblastosis. It violated a fairly universal Law of Nature: A mother does not mount an immune attack against her unborn child. It was uniquely implacable: Once it struck in a family, all subsequent offspring usually would suffer. Frustratingly, it could be easily diagnosed before the patient was born by testing the mother's anti-Rh antibody levels. But doctors standing by only could watch her baby die—unable to come to its aid.

These are attractive ironies, but they fail to explain Rh's attraction for the generation of researchers who defined and made the first clinical inroads against erythroblastosis for the simple reason that none of them had set out to solve the Rh problem. Most, in fact, like Wiener and Levine, had stumbled upon it while coming from or going to someplace else. They then had had the excellence of judgment to stay with it and probe what they had found.

Vince was different. He conceived his primary task, as he became aware of it, to be an all-out attack on Rh disease.

Vince was also one of the few obstetricians in the world with enough immunologic knowledge to think seriously about doing something about it. Few obstetricians were spared the need to tell a mother that her baby had died, and that her subsequent babies probably were similarly doomed. Yet few obstetricians seem to have been adequately motivated by this unhappy fact to declare war against the responsible disease. In fact, none of the important names in Rh research, up until that time, was an obstetrician. On the other hand, the serologists, blood bankers, and pathologists—who tested and selected bloods for exchange transfusions and autopsied those fetuses the obstetricians failed to save—all lacked the quite human stimulus that might be expected to move a clinician to action: the need to bring dire news to a new mother.

Vince had put himself in the middle. He delivered the babies and dealt with their mothers. He also knew something about the disease, and had resolved to learn—and do—more.

Strategically, once back at Columbia-Presbyterian, his first task was to build himself a study population of patients and case records similar to those which Wiener had been carefully accumulating in Brooklyn ever since 1940. For an obstetrician, this was not easy to do. While more than 4,000 babies were delivered each year at Columbia-Presbyterian, only about 40 to 50 would have erythroblastosis, and this represented the combined deliveries of dozens of obstetricians working with private as well as clinic patients. One man, delivering several hundred babies annually, might see only a couple of cases of erythroblastosis—far too few for study purposes. Moreover, at Columbia-Presbyterian, as elsewhere, records on Rh-incompatible deliveries were not kept and collated in the obstetrics department, but in the blood bank. Thus, while a blood banker might collect as many Rh cases as he wished, an obstetrician, given the accepted hospital division of labor, could not.

Vince took a first, unusual step in bringing Rh under obstetrical purview by setting up a serology laboratory on the OB floor of the Columbia Medical College building, near the delivery suites. This provided him leverage for seeing and studying Rh cases being delivered by colleagues. He could give them tentative Rh antibody readings on their patients without waiting for samples to be sent up for definitive analysis in the blood bank. He also went after the hospital's records of Rh-incompatible deliveries—a delicate matter in terms of professional jurisdictions since Rh-typing was a major, jealously guarded activity of the blood bank, whose chief, Dr. John Scudder, was himself expert and quite interested in problems of Rh.

At first, Vince sent a research technician to copy data from the blood bank records. Later, after his interest in Rh files had been remarked, he came himself on several occasions. Vince then got a useful boost from the obstetrics department. The Columbia-Presbyterian blood bank was supervised by a committee of representatives from each hospital department. An obstetrics committeeman had been taken ill, and an interim appointee was needed to finish his term. Obstetrics chief Howard Taylor chose Vince because of his special interest in blood. This was a departure from custom, for hospital committee posts customarily were held by senior men, rarely, if ever, by residents.

At blood bank chief Scudder's invitation another resident, a pathologist who worked in the blood bank, was also tendered the unusual privilege of attending the committee's meetings. His name was Dr. John Grant Gorman.

John, like Vince, was unusual in that—unlike most pathology residents, who consider blood banking a bore—he had been attracted to blood and blood research. He had enjoyed his obligatory service in the blood bank and had stayed on there, informally, after it was over, using the blood bank as his home base in the hospital. Scudder, delighted to find a younger man with an interest in blood banking, had encouraged him to stay and, perhaps for the same reason, had stretched protocol to permit John to attend blood bank committee meetings. It was at one of these meetings in the spring of 1960 that he first met Vince, who was introduced to him, probably by Scudder, as "the obstetrician who's interested in our Rh records."

It would prove to be a critical encounter.

John, who was twenty-eight years old, was nearing the end of his pathology training. He was a slight, polite, bashfully attractive young man, with curly hair and grey, deep-set eyes.

John was a native of Australia and had grown up in Bendigo, a town not far from Melbourne. His forebears on his father's side, Irishmen, had come to Australia from the countryside near Liverpool, England. His parents both were physicians—Dr. John S. Gorman and Dr. Jean Grant Gorman. To them, it must have seemed a matter of course that their first son, whom they named John Grant Gorman, would one day be a doctor too.

John, however, had felt differently. He had not been keen on a medical career. His father later would concede that "a little push" by his parents had been needed to get John to go on to medical school.[1] Nonetheless, after premedical work at Xavier College in Melbourne, he earned his Bachelor of Medicine degree (M.B., B.S.)—the equivalent of the American M.D.—at the University of Melbourne. Then he did a year's internship. Still lacking enthusiasm for medicine as a vocation, he came to the United States in 1955. John tried pediatrics for a year, and did not like it. Then he switched over to pathology at Columbia-Presbyterian. Like Vince, he was now in the last year of his specialty training.

One reason blood bank work was of interest to John was that he had decided that he had no taste for clinical medicine; he disliked dealing with patients, perhaps because he was shy. Blood banking promised a secure professional base from which he could pursue his true bent: the fruitful expression of an extremely quick, idealistic, and inventive mind. Already he had conceived of a machine that would perform, automatically, one of the more tedious of the routine blood tests, the prothrombin time, which measures the amount of clotting factor in a patient's blood.

Immunology and genetics were the areas that held the greatest fascination for John. In the 1950s Melbourne had become one of the world's leading centers of immunologic research because of the presence there of immunologist Sir F. Macfarlane Burnet. In 1960 Burnet would become the first Australian to win the Nobel Prize for Medicine.

John sorely regretted that his move to the United States had deprived him of direct contact with Burnet and Australian immunology. He had also come to regret that he lacked training and experience with the experimental techniques of contemporary immunologic research. But he had begun to realize that his growing knowledge of blood—a body organ intimately bound up in immunologic issues—might give him a model system in which he could develop and test his own ideas. Already, with the help of a surgical colleague at Columbia-Presbyterian, Dr. James Chandler, John had originated a concept of his own, a cute wrinkle on the theories of Burnet, and he was looking for ways he might prove it.

Rethinking Burnet's theories would lead John to the Rh factor.

Burnet's problem—the central, unresolved problem of immunology—had been to forge a sound theory to describe how the body detects and identifies an antigen and produces a specific antibody that will selectively search out and destroy it. Burnet theorized that in embryonic life, without ever having come in contact with them, each animal or human *host* manufactures cells precoded to make antibody against each and every possible antigen. Each antibody-containing cell, or *lymphocyte*, might contain antibody against only one of the tens of thousands of antigens a host would later encounter. But each of us has millions of lymphocytes so that all possible antigen threats might be covered.

After birth, when the individual did begin to encounter antigens, each one that intruded upon its body would be noticed and recognized only by the lymphocytes carrying specific instructions against it. Contact with their specific enemy would cause these lymphocytes to reproduce themselves, rapidly, forming a population, or *clone*, of antibody-containing lymphocytes, each carrying identical immunologic instructions. All cells in this clone—an immunologic phalanx—would attack and destroy the invading antigen against which they had been specifically coded.

There was a corollary to the question of how specific antibodies are formed to meet specific antigen intrusions. It was: How, and why, does a host sometimes tolerate rather than attack an intruding antigen? Why does a pregnant mother, for example, not reject her fetus? Why, also, does a host's immune system tolerate the protein chemicals of its own body, or *self*, and not attack them?

As a partial answer, Burnet believed that before birth immunologic activity remains in abeyance. In that period, the host's "self" antigens, its body proteins, find and overwhelm the antibody-producing cells that might later form clones against them.

Similarly, tolerance to a specific antigen, such as a cancer, might occur if an antigen was potent enough to quickly destroy all of the corresponding antibody-producing cells before they had a chance to mount an effective defense against it. In this and other theories, immunologic *tolerance* occurs because a host lacks antibody-producing cells primed against an antigen. It was here that John had developed a different view.

His was a bit of immunologic sleight-of-hand. He proposed that tolerance toward an antigen was not the opposite of immunity to it. Rather, he said, tolerance was a specific form of immune response. Instead of producing antibody-containing cells to meet and destroy an antigen, a host might instead produce cells that would permit it to live with, or tolerate, the intruding substance.

How might this occur? In explanation, John noted that antibody-producing cells that respond by attacking an antigen are called *immunocompetent.* The population of these cells, made quickly in response to antigenic attack, is a *clone* of immunocompetent cells. His innovation was to postulate the existence of another kind of cell, which responded specifically to an antigen's presence and multiplied, but did not attack its antigen. These hypothetical disarmed lymphocytes he called immuno*in*competent cells. When one of them proliferated in response to antigenic challenge, it produced an immuno*in*competent clone.

A given antigen, John reasoned, might stimulate growth of an

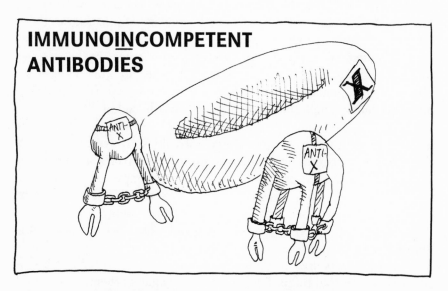

immunologically competent clone, an *in*competent clone, or both. But, he postulated further, a control mechanism must limit the total number of lymphocytes produced in response to any specific antigen. Otherwise they would multiply wildly, preempting body space from other needed cells.

How would immunologically competent and *in*competent lymphocyte populations affect each other? Competitively, but indirectly. Beginning with Charles Darwin, theories on competition between biologic populations had stated that two populations with similar origins, structures, or functions will compete for space within the same ecologic niche. While these theories described

# THE FITTEST SURVIVE

*Immuno_incompetent Antibodies*

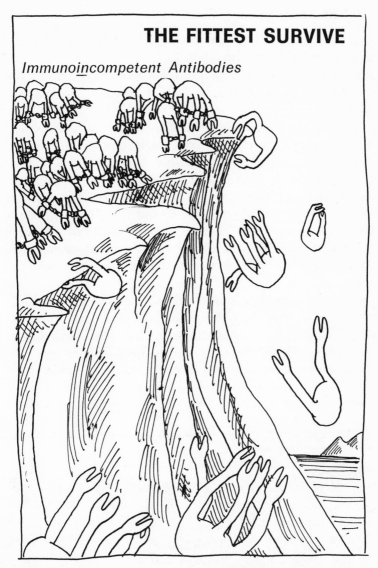

competition between free-living organisms—animals, plants, bac-
teria, etc.—John believed Darwinian "natural selection" and "survival of the fittest" might also apply to lymphocyte cell populations
in a host.

If both the immunocompetent and immuno*incompetent* lymphocytes multiplied in response to an antigen and struggled to maintain
their place in an ecologic niche large enough for only one of them,
then a slight survival advantage in one would allow it to fill the
entire niche, excluding the other. If the immunocompetent cells
predominated, the host would produce antibody that would de-

stroy an antigen. If the *in*competent cells prevailed, the host instead would tolerate the antigen.

John's wish to test this hypothesis was frustrated both by his lack of immunologic training and his lack of access to an immunologic lab. But there was at least one observation from the blood lab that seemed to support his theory! An Rh-negative woman challenged by the Rh antigen on fetal red cells might produce 19S or 7S anti-Rh antibody to combat it. Presumably, the two forms of the antibody were made by cells from two separate clones. Moreover, as Diamond had suggested over a decade earlier, the 19S anti-Rh tended to appear first, when a woman was initially sensitized to the Rh factor (see page 63).[2] Then, as the 19S level fell off, the levels of 7S antibody rose, suggesting that the 7S cell clone now had the advantage and was filling the available ecologic niche in the mother.

The 19S antibody, because it did not pass the placenta, did not harm the baby. The 7S, which appeared later, did cross the placental membrane and caused illness in the baby. Though logically unsound, this undoubtedly suggested to John that the 19S was produced by an immuno*in*competent clone, while the clone that was making the 7S was—destructively—immunocompetent.

More important, here was a way to test at least part of his hy-

**JOHN'S PLAN**

pothesis! If 7S and 19S antibody were produced by competing cell clones sharing a limited niche then the conferring of a slight survival advantage on one of them might indefinitely keep out the other. The clinical consequence could be enormous. The harmless 19S antibody usually appeared first. If it were boosted, even a little, perhaps the mother would never produce 7S antibody—and as a result would never injure her baby. It dawned on John that injections of pure 19S anti-Rh antibody might forestall growth of the clone that would produce 7S anti-Rh. How much better to fight fire with fire than to use one form of the anti-Rh antibody to combat another!

By early March 1960, John's interest was fired up, and he started a notebook which he entitled "Review of Literature: Saline [19S] vs. Blocking [7S] Antibody."[3] In it he jotted down abstracts of papers he found on the differential relationship between the two antibody forms and noted those which suggested ways they might be obtained in a pure state.

John also read the blood bank records of some 400 Rh-sensitized mothers to find out if, as Diamond had suggested, pregnancies characterized by 19S anti-Rh antibody production remained free of 7S anti-Rh. Some in fact did. More important, the patients' charts which John had thumbed through to find this out were the same ones sought by Vince—who also was searching for clues in Rh cases. This common interest led to their being introduced to each other at the blood bank committee meeting. Afterward, aware of their shared interest in the Rh factor, they talked, and later talked again.

# 7

## Dialogue

JOHN WAS ATTRACTED by Vince's enthusiastic belief that—somehow —something more could be done to save erythroblastic babies. Vince was delighted to find a congenial contemporary in the blood bank who had begun to think creatively about Rh and might go further.

Both Vince and John were shy. Both tended to be anxious, even indecisive, in social conversation. John stammered when excited. Vince, who projected a cordial and agreeable image, was often over-rushed with work and overwrought. He sometimes found himself tongue-tied—caught in confusion between embarrassment for a supposed slight and a deep-felt desire to please.

In sharp contrast to their social intercourse, the two men's conceptual colloquy, a dialogue of ideas, grew to be determined and decisive. They were both well-read, conversant, and cognitively agile and adept in a wide and unusual range of subjects, including clinical obstetrics, blood banking, hematology, and immunology.

Their talks together became frequent and long. The setting shifted from the blood bank to Vince's closet-width laboratory on the medical college obstetrical floor. A long, thin room, two yards wide by five long, it was equipped with a sink, cabinet, and counter top which might have been new before World War II. The most important piece of equipment, for their purposes, was a small slate blackboard screwed onto one wall. On it they diagrammed, erased, and then schematically redrew their problem: a pregnant Rh-negative mother. Inside her, an Rh-positive fetus. Between them, the womb and placenta—represented by a rough-drawn chalk circle. One arrow, outbound, indicated fetal blood passing through the placenta into the mother, where it would trigger an immune reaction. A second, inbound arrow stood for anti-Rh antibody passing across the placenta to the fetus, whose blood it would destroy. Could one of the arrows be broken? Could one of these fateful passages be forestalled?

Each tentatively sketched solution was committed to memory and quickly erased from the blackboard. Vince and John failed to commit any of their early work notes to paper or print—an oversight they later would come to regret. The ideas they judged most useful would appear, many months later, on grant applications and, ultimately, in journals. But a decade later, the sequence and progression of their plans to defeat Rh disease could be re-created only from memory.

Both men would recall, long after the fact, that once they had pitted their minds to the problem—Can we prevent erythroblastosis?—in the spring of 1960, their key thinking was accomplished quite quickly. John believes it was completed in a couple of weeks. For Vince, the passage of time has compressed all memories into the recollection of a single, sparklingly productive day.

"The disease exists," Vince declared, "only because the mother's anti-Rh antibodies get through the placenta to the fetus, but the red cells can't. If the fetus could only get some of mother's Rh-negative red cells, to counteract the anemia, it probably wouldn't die."

Vince wondered if it would be possible to operate on the mother and breach the thin placental barrier with a shunt, or tube, that led from one of her blood vessels into one of the fetus'. Like a conduit between two pools, the shunt would permit revivifying blood from the mother to seep or flow into her dying fetus.

John raised an objection: even if it proved surgically feasible, the result would be destructive to the fetus' few remaining Rh-positive cells, since the mother's blood carried anti-Rh antibody that would destroy them. It was logical to suppose, he said, that the placenta acted partially as a dam, keeping at least some of the antibody away from the fetus.

Vince disagreed, on the basis of some new knowledge that he just then was beginning to collect for publication. In a sensitized mother, the anti-Rh antibody circulates in the bloodstream. Vince was comparing antibody levels in maternal blood and in samples from the babies' umbilical cords at delivery. He was finding, contrary to what might have been expected, that the concentration of 7S anti-Rh antibody invariably was the same in the baby as it was in the mother.[1] So, Vince told John, the placenta was not a dam. A transfusion of maternal blood would not materially raise the concentration of destructive antibody in the fetus, since it already was as high as in the mother's blood.

Besides, it didn't really matter what happened to the fetus' few remaining Rh-positive cells. Even if they were completely destroyed by maternal antibody, it could better survive to birth on mother's wholly Rh-negative red cells. Then, when no longer exposed to her anti-Rh antibody, the infant's blood-forming tissues could leisurely replace the transfused Rh-negative cells with Rh-positive cells of its own making.

Vince's shunt scheme, in essence, was an attempt to overcome the incompatibility of maternal and fetal blood types by actually changing the fetus' blood from Rh-positive to Rh-negative during the critical last weeks of gestation—a continuous exchange transfusion in utero. There was one overriding problem—and Vince lacked the data to solve it: Blood pressure in the mother's circulation might be different from that in the fetus. Opening a tube between the two naturally separate systems would tend to bring their blood pressures into equilibrium—at a level closer to that of the mother. What would be the consequence for the fine vessels and tissue structures in the fetal organs? Neither Vince nor John knew.*

Vince had been mulling over John's competing-clones proposal. It certainly was ingenious, he felt. It might also be very dangerous. No one knew for sure that 19S antibody-containing cells—with which John wished to fill the mother's anti-Rh ecologic niche in order to preempt production of cells carrying placenta-penetrating 7S antibody—did not sometimes get across. If so, this 19S antibody could kill the fetus. Few obstetricians, or mothers, would wish to take such a risk.

"Why use anti-Rh antibody of any kind?" Vince asked. "Maybe it isn't necessary."

He said that it was a common physiologic observation that the body normally responds to an excess of any natural substance by

---

* No one as yet knows today.

turning off the gland or organ that makes it—or by activating an antagonist. An adrenalin injection, for example, will cause the healthy body to turn off the adrenal glands. Thyroid extract injections will suppress the thyroid gland because the healthy body

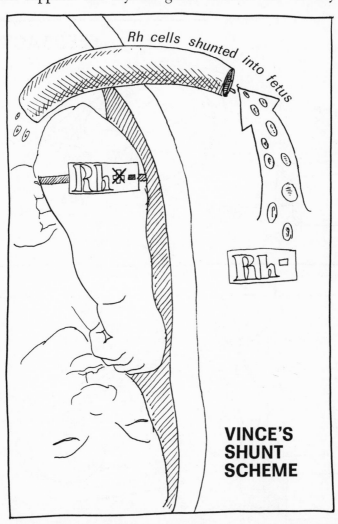

knows when it has enough thyroid hormones. Blood transfusions, similarly, depress blood-forming activity in the bone marrow. The body, in short, is kept in balance by feedback mechanisms.

To exploit these mechanisms to keep an Rh-sensitive woman from producing anti-Rh antibody, perhaps it would not be necessary to give another form of anti-Rh antibody as such, as John had suggested. Perhaps some other harmless antibody would do the job as well. Perhaps, even, just flooding her circulation with large amounts of gamma globulin would turn off her immune system. By giving gamma globulin, perhaps they could stop the mother's im-

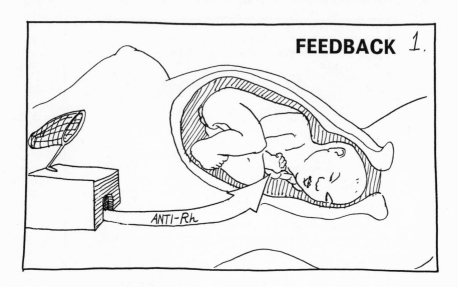

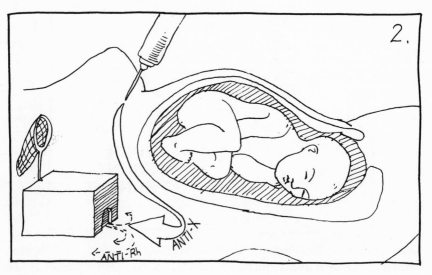

munocompetent cells from making gamma globulin and the antibodies it would contain, including anti-Rh.

"Maybe, John, we could inject enough harmless antibody, in the form of gamma globulin *without* anti-Rh, that her body will decide not to produce its own dangerous gamma globulin *with* anti-Rh. Or, maybe we could give an antibody that the mother *recognized* as anti-Rh, but wasn't—something that would keep her body from making anti-Rh of her own. This something would make her immune system say, in effect, I've got enough anti-Rh antibody. I don't need to make any more!"*

Vince had sounded out several established Rh experts on the feedback scheme. None had been very excited by it. The overriding problem, they reminded him, was the danger of severe allergic reaction from intravenous injection of gamma globulin, which his plan required. Customarily, to avoid this danger, gamma globulin was injected into muscle.

John was more receptive than the experts, but agreed that enormous doses would have to be given. Many separate and painful intramuscular injections would be needed to swamp a woman's antibody-producing mechanism. John predicted that this "pincushion" approach would render it unacceptable as therapy.

He had read, he added, that an attempt was being made in Switzerland to produce gamma globulin suitable for intravenous injection, but it had not been perfected. Perhaps it would be worth waiting for, or worth trying to find from another source. "Feedback" seemed to him promising enough to try.

John's excursions into immunologic theory had led him to a new idea. Immunology's hottest topic at the moment was organ transplantation, and the unresolved problem of transplant rejection. Work by Burnet, and by his soon-to-be-cosharer of the 1960 Nobel Prize, Dr. Peter Medawar of London, had served to elucidate the graft rejection dilemma: a host, the recipient, becomes sensitized to antigens in the tissues of another individual, the donor, and so rejects the donor's organ.

John recognized Rh disease as a comparable occurrence. A host, the mother, becomes sensitized to antigens in another individual's tissues—the Rh factor on red cells of her fetus—and so mounts an immunologic attack against it.

* Wiener, it will be recalled, already had tried, with some success, a somewhat similar "competition of antigens" plan. He gave large amounts of a harmless antigen, such as typhoid vaccine, to overwhelm the woman's immune system so that it would be too busy to make anti-Rh.

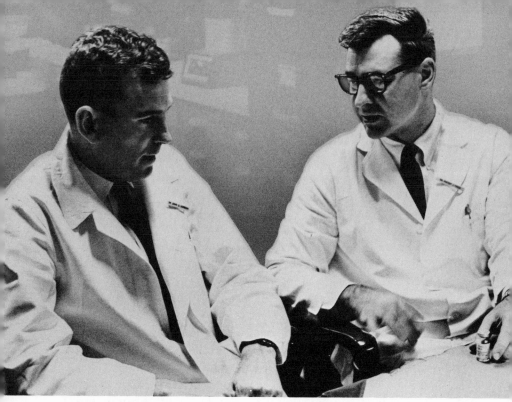

Drs. Gorman (left) and Freda talk in Freda's lab. (*Elizabeth Wilcox, 1963.*)

An experiment in transplant immunology suggested to John a solution to the Rh problem. It was a path that, in itself, would prove to be obstacle-ridden, but one which would also lead John to other, more promising points of departure.

Medawar had taken a white mouse and had transplanted onto it a piece of skin and fur from a black mouse. Naturally, the white mouse's immune system quickly reacted, produced anti-black mouse antibodies, and rejected the graft.

Medawar had found how to prevent this reaction. He had discovered that newborn mice pass through a short *immunologic null period*, during which their immune systems would accept rather than attack skin transplants. What was more striking, even after it became immunologically competent, on its second or third day of life, a white mouse would continue to tolerate a black patch that had been grafted on in its first, immunologically null, day.[2]

Most striking of all, once a white mouse had accepted antigens in black mouse skin in its null period, the black mouse was now immunologically part of itself. Thus, if Medawar injected a newborn white mouse with ground-up black mouse skin, he then could transplant skin patches, kidneys, or other organs from the black mouse to the white one throughout its lifetime. These grafts would not be rejected. Medawar's findings suggested that, as a general rule, higher animals may pass through a short immunologic null period during which a fetus or newborn will accept foreign antigens as part of itself.

Pondering these experiments, John's mind bridged the enormous gap between neonatal mice and Rh-negative women. Why not render all Rh-negative human females tolerant to the Rh factor? Why not give them tolerance-inducing injections of Rh-positive cells?

It would not do to wait until an Rh-negative woman grew up, married an Rh-positive man, and then became pregnant with his Rh-positive child. By then, she would treat the Rh factor like any other antigen—and react against it. Rather, the injection would have to be given in the *first days of her life*—in her "null period" —if, in fact, she possessed one.

In John's cosmic proposal, all Rh-negative girl babies would be inoculated, at birth, to protect the Rh-positive babies that they might conceive years later as wives of Rh-positive men. Presumably, they then would be tolerant of Rh-positive red cells that leaked through the placenta into their circulation—just as the white mice inoculated at birth with black mouse antigen would later tolerate black mouse skin grafts. Seen in its most dramatic light, what John proposed was to eliminate Rh incompatibility by rendering all Rh-negative females tolerant to the Rh factor from birth.

Vince was impressed. His collaborator had come up with something entirely new in their talks: a specific plan to prevent Rh sensitization. But Vince doubted that the plan would work. Medawar's null period concept *did* seem to find support in one fact well-known to pediatricians: It is unwise to try to immunize a newborn baby against an infectious disease because the baby may fail to respond to the tamed antigen in a vaccine; it may fail to produce antibodies and remain unimmunized. This might be due to the fact that the baby was in the null period and therefore incapable of immunologic response.

Recently, however, it had begun to be believed that a baby failed to respond to a specific vaccine if—and only if—its mother had had the disease in question, or had herself been immunized against it. In either case, the fetus had received preformed, or *passive*, antibody through the placenta from its mother. The passive antibody protected it, temporarily, from the corresponding antigen and disease, but also kept it from mounting its own immune response to an antigenic challenge in the form of a vaccine.

"The *real* reason you don't inoculate infants," Vince said to John, "is not that they are immunologically null and *incapable* of forming antibody! Rather, it's because they have maternal antibody in their blood, which protects them temporarily and acts as a barrier between the vaccine and their immune systems."

Vince could see one other important reason to doubt that an immunologic null period was a developmental stage in humans. He pointed out to John that he, like any other obstetrician, often was called upon to deliver infants very prematurely, by cesarean section or by induction of labor. But no matter how many weeks or months early he delivered them, he said, they showed an ability to develop antibodies as soon after birth as normal 9½-month babies.

John conceded that, even in mice, the immunologic null period apparently sometimes ended before birth, and sometimes after. But the possibility that it continued for even a few hours, or a day, after delivery and so might be beneficially exploited, seemed to him to be worth exploring.

Vince reluctantly agreed to try John's scheme. "If you succeed," John said, encouragingly, "you'll be able to say you're first to induce useful tolerance to a specific antigen in humans, as in Medawar's mice!"

"But if I fail, and we've used Rh antigen from Rh-positive blood, instead of giving an infant girl *tolerance* to Rh-positive babies she might later carry, we could get just the opposite. We might inject a newborn Rh-negative female with the Rh-positive material and *sensitize* her to it so severely that she would always be highly reactive to Rh-positive blood. She then would inevitably cause erythroblastosis *even* in her first Rh-positive baby, as well as in all that might come after!"

A safe way to test John's proposal, the two men decided, would be to inject another, essentially harmless antigen into an infant in place of Rh. Success in inducing tolerance to *any* antigen might establish the existence of a null period in humans, and would lend considerable weight to John's hypothesis that tolerance to the Rh antigen could be similarly achieved.

It would never do, of course, to render an infant tolerant to an antigen that might later reappear and cause harm, a disease germ for example; this would be an invitation to the disease—and would be both unethical and medically unwise. The trick would be to find and use an antigen that a baby was going to become tolerant to anyway.

Vince had a bright idea where to find one. Babies born to have group A or group B blood do not possess the characteristic anti-body against the other blood type at the moment they are born. A group A baby is genetically primed to react against B blood, for example. But before having actually encountered the B antigen he or she will not have manufactured antibody against it.

The B antigen, however, is present not only in B blood but in milk, sweat, urine, and skin secretions of group B persons, as well as in dust, dander, and a wide variety of animal and vegetable stuffs. Hence, before too many days have passed, every newborn group A baby has encountered, reacted to, and become resistant to B antigen; group B babies have become similarly resistant to A. Group O's are resistant to both. Thus, Vince reasoned, no great harm would be done if, right at birth, an A baby were given an injection of B antigen, since in the normal course of events it would soon be exposed to it anyway.

If the experiment failed, and the youngster immediately became sensitized to B, this would only mean advancing, by several days or a week, its "natural" immunity to B blood and other substances. On the other hand, if John's extrapolation of Medawar's experiment was correct—and there was a day or so null period during which tolerance could be induced—the experimental injection would end up being beneficial, since the group A baby would be rendered tolerant to the B antigen and hence might be protected for life against a serious transfusion reaction should it inadvertently be given a mismatched pint of group B blood. And success in inducing tolerance to the A or B blood factor would argue strongly that Rh tolerance could be induced as well.*

---

* Retrospective analysis, based on hindsight and the need for clear exposition, impose a clarity and logical structure on ideas that in their formative stage were less precisely and certainly less clearly perceived. "You don't pursue a thought through to its conclusion," John would say later. "You stop and rest. It's rather a sloppy situation!"

# 8

## Fight Fire with Fire

FATE, IN THE GUISE of a book salesman, here lent a hand. The salesman represented W. B. Saunders, a medical publishing company in
Philadelphia. One day on his rounds through Presbyterian Hospital
he had stopped in the pathology department to give John a com-
plimentary copy of a new edition of Saunders' textbook, *General
Pathology*, edited by English Nobelist Sir Howard Florey.

The gift was not entirely gratuitous. One of John's responsibilities as a senior resident in pathology was to begin to pass on to
others some of the special knowledge he himself had only recently
acquired: He had been assigned to teach tissue pathology to a class
of Columbia medical students. Since his own expertise in this area
was not much advanced over theirs, he accepted with genuine
thanks the textbook the salesman handed to him in the hope that he
would have it assigned—and hence ordered—for his entire class.

Thumbing the thick red volume, John's eye had fallen on a fateful sentence, written by two Oxford University pathologists in a
chapter on immunology: "The presence of circulating antibody,
whether produced actively or received passively, depresses and
may completely inhibit the immune response to the relevant antigen, although not to other antigens."[1]

In other words, if a person for some reason had a particular
antibody circulating in his blood when he became exposed to the
corresponding antigen, this so-called *passive antibody* would block

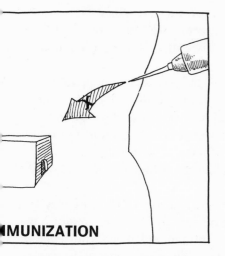

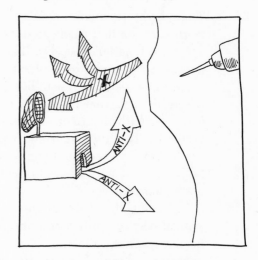

**IMMUNIZATION**

or "blanket" the antigen so that it would not provoke an active immune response. The *way* in which the passively introduced antibody would prevent an immune reaction was unknown to the textbook authors, Drs. Gareth Gladstone and Edward Abraham—and it remains unknown. But, they declared: "There is little doubt that, by uniting with the antigen, antibody blocks its capacity to stimulate the immune response. . . . In addition to this 'blanketing' action, antibody hastens the elimination of antigen from the body, and thus shortens the period during which antigen can stimulate the immune reaction."

The phenomenon of *passive antibody protection* against immunization had been well documented by a number of researchers.

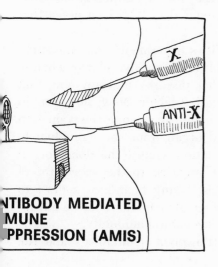

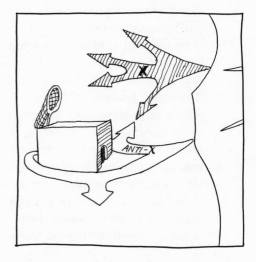

**ANTIBODY MEDIATED**
**IMMUNE**
**SUPPRESSION (AMIS)**

Though the textbook failed to say so, John and Vince later would learn that the first to observe it and formulate the theory had been a Harvard pathologist, Dr. Theobald Smith. He regarded it as a nuisance that was to be avoided.

Smith, a pioneer researcher in diphtheria prevention, had proposed, in 1908, that the best form of prophylaxis would be to inject a person with a mixture of diphtheria antigen and antidiphtheria antibody. The antigen would provoke an active immunity, providing lifetime protection against diphtheria. The antidiphtheria antibody injected with it would neutralize the antigen so that it would not be harmful.

Balancing the doses of the two antagonistic substances was the critical part of Smith's proposal for he found, ". . . what might have been expected," that an excess of antigen *enhanced* the level of immunity obtained, compared to that obtained from a balanced, "neutral mixture." Conversely—and it was this concept, restated in the Florey textbook, that had caught John's eye and mind—"an excess of antibody reduces the possibility of producing an active immunity, and may extinguish it altogether."[2]

For clinicians, passive antibody's ability to prevent an individual's active immune response to antigen had remained a little-known nuisance—a curiosity at best. No practical use had ever been found for it. For immunologists, who occasionally re-explored it, passive antibody protection was perhaps of conceptual interest. It was a complicated phenomenon, cumbersome to describe and easy to forget. No snappy catchword captured the sense of it, although later the descriptive phrase for it, *antibody-mediated immunosuppression*, would be abbreviated as *AMIS*—a usage that will be adopted here.

In the half century following Smith's experiments, *immunization* had been regarded as a wholly helpful and positive phenomenon— protection against diphtheria or other disease—and anything that *prevented* immunization was a negative factor. Now, however, in John's day, transplant surgery had begun to change this valuation of immunity: in transferring a vital organ from one individual to another, the recipient's immune reaction against the donor organ was an *undesirable* phenomenon. Compared to the vaccinator of children, the transplant immunologist trying to induce a graft to "take" faced a diametrically opposite challenge: It would be advantageous for him to *inhibit* the recipient's natural immunity.

John, deeply intrigued by both transplant immunology and Rh, now came up with a chess master's dialectical inversion of moves. As he reread the eye-catching sentence in Florey, the idea struck him that if an Rh-negative mother killed her fetus because she had become immunized to its Rh-positive blood, then why not inject her with *passive* anti-Rh antibody. The passive antibody should prevent her becoming *actively* sensitized to the Rh factor!

Expressed in terms used in the Florey textbook before him, John's formulation provided that "the presence [in the mother's blood] of circulating [anti-Rh] antibody . . . received passively depresses and may completely inhibit the immune response to the [Rh] antigen [from the baby's blood]."

That, John realized, with growing excitement, should keep the mother from producing anti-Rh antibody of her own, which, in turn, would save the baby!

What made this formulation the more enticing to John was its concurrence with two of the theories he and Vince had already considered. To inject the mother with anti-Rh followed both from his immuno*in*competent cell plan and from Vince's theory of feedback. The use of anti-Rh antibody to suppress anti-Rh antibody had become the central, productive theme in their dialogue: anti-Rh against anti-Rh; a negation of a negation; fire fighting fire.

Expounding the theory to Vince and explaining that a small but ample literature, cited in Florey, attested to its general applicability—and hence possible extension to the Rh system—John declared:

"If you give the mother anti-Rh antibody, you're giving passive antibody. That should keep her from producing her own antibody against her baby's Rh-positive cells."

"When would you give it?" Vince asked.

"During pregnancy."

"But you can't. There's nothing to stop injected antibody from crossing the placenta, just as the mother's own antibody would do. It's precisely anti-Rh antibody that causes the disease; you'd be inducing erythroblastosis fetalis!"

"Well, you can't give something that contains both 7S and 19S anti-Rh antibodies," John said, backing off momentarily. "The 7S *would* pass through the placenta. You're right. That might be dangerous.

"But what about the 19S antibody all by itself. It apparently doesn't cross through to the baby. If we had it purified and concentrated, it might keep the mother from being sensitized by the fetus'

Rh-positive red cells; the fetus itself, protected by the placental barrier, would not be injured."

Vince liked the idea, John later would recall. Vince later was to live so intimately with this idea, for years, that he himself would

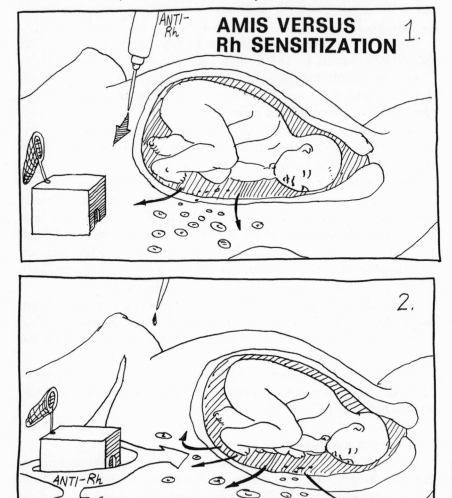

lose track of those specific features that at first rendered it attractive. Its problems, which long were to prey on his mind, he would remember better: It was well and good to talk about injecting pure 19S antibody, he told John. But there was no such stuff available. The scientific task of separating out the various naturally occurring parts of gamma globulin was still in progress; no commercial process for producing the 19S fraction had been patented, let alone a 19S that had a high anti-Rh titer.

True, they did have on record, in the blood bank, the names of dozens of women with demonstrable titers of 19S anti-Rh antibody, due to sensitization by Rh-positive fetuses. These women might be asked—and paid—to contribute their blood, rich in 19S antibody, for injection into pregnant Rh-negative women who had not yet become sensitized to the Rh factor.

"How dangerous would it be," Vince asked, "to give the mothers raw plasma containing 19S anti-Rh antibody?"

"Too dangerous! Because raw plasma may transmit hepatitis. Gamma globulin doesn't. So gamma globulin would be safer."

"Even so, giving the antibody during pregnancy is taking too great a chance," Vince protested. "What if, even only once in a while, it gets through to the baby!"

Vince felt torn. John's passive antibody proposal in many ways complemented his own thinking on Rh prevention. If they *could* prove that 19S antibody *never* passes the placenta, it might be useful in women already sensitized to the Rh antigen as well as in those in whom sensitization was just occurring. Giving an already-sensitized woman 19S passive antibody would be the ultimate refinement of his feedback proposal: He would be giving her one Rh antibody, a harmless one, to keep her from making a dangerous form of the same antibody. But the problem of safety plagued his mind. Putting antibody that might be deadly to the baby into its mother's blood, separated from it by just the two cell layers of the placenta, seemed to him too dangerous, and he resisted it. Was there some other way to apply the passive antibody theory, some other time to give the anti-Rh injection to the mother so that it could not endanger her baby? Vince did not know. Neither did John. But the passive-antibody plan, like other proposals formulated during their long conversational probing of the Rh problem, seemed enticingly attractive.

# 9

## "Ego-Peddling"

Spinning fine schemes to solve the Rh problem was one thing. Doing something about them was an altogether different—and more difficult—matter. While their conversations continued, weeks and even months went by and Vince and John did nothing to put their prevention plans into practice.

The road blocks were external and internal. Albeit eager, both were new, relatively untried men at Columbia-Presbyterian. Both were just then completing their long residency training. They worked close to the bottom, and in John's case far outside the mainstream of an extremely rigid and set medical hierarchy. New ideas were not sought for among the junior men.

Vince and John used occasional encounters with Rh experts, at Columbia and elsewhere, to broach their prevention schemes. They felt that their best hope for moving their ideas forward would be to gain support from the established men—Fred Allen in Boston, Wiener, and Levine, with whom Vince attempted to make contact. John would later look back with disdain on these attempts—most of which met prompt rebuff—as immature "ego-peddling."

"We talked to these guys to see if they thought our ideas were worthwhile. What did we want? Some form of approval, or encouragement. We had a mental block against applying for our own grant and running our own research effort."*

There was a reality to their reticence: the need for research

* This "ego-peddling," it subsequently would turn out, was not without value. Two years later, when Vince applied for a costly research grant to advance their work, one

funds, departmental sponsorship, and administrative approval. "To start something around here takes major effort, to get the needed approval and get started," John would say. "Anyone without strong will would be defeated by the inertia."

It was inappropriate for a young man, a resident, or young instructor to apply, by himself, for funds for a major research project that would involve hospital and medical school personnel, and even patients. Experiments involving a few animals and the corner of a laboratory bench might be sanctioned. But the proper route for a bright young researcher with an idea to launch was to get signed aboard by an older, firmly established man—as Vince had already been by Wiener—and then, by dint of hard labor on the chief's pet project, earn the right to conduct some small and nonpresumptuous piece of clinical research of his own. "It would have been groundbreaking for us, as junior men, to apply by ourselves for a grant," John would say subsequently. "We didn't have the self-confidence."

Neither had they reached the point of directly challenging established views. John visited Rh pioneer Philip Levine at Ortho that spring, on blood bank business, and would later recall that there was little Levine might say that he was not prepared to accept as *writ*. John did not raise the Rh prevention hopes with Levine because they were incompletely formulated at the time they talked. But shortly thereafter he visited Boston, also on blood bank business, and made a point of discussing the plan with Fred Allen. John would later recall being surprised when Allen remarked that he himself had thought of just such a plan to use anti-Rh antibody injections to prevent Rh immunization—and had dropped it because it seemed doomed to fail. Others, who could not even claim to have thought about the idea, were equally quick to condemn it. Even Wiener, for all his personal regard for Vince, was not especially encouraging. In the older generation, there seemed few buyers for Vince and John's ideas.

Then, on July 1, 1960, the day John and Vince completed their residencies, ending their long years of medical training, a shake-up in the pathology department fortuitously advanced their plans. The chief of pathology left Columbia, followed by many of his junior men. His successor was a Boston-trained pathologist, Dr. Donald McKay. He asked John to stay on at Columbia and offered the

---

of his preceptors at Columbia would write in his behalf: "Dr. Freda [is a] capable and imaginative investigator . . . [and is] *willing to seek advice from experts in those areas in which he feels less well qualified.*" (Emphasis added.)

young Australian his first faculty appointment as teaching associate in the pathology department. Concurrently, John was appointed assistant director of the Presbyterian Hospital blood bank.

McKay was deeply committed to research. His aim was to make his mark by sharply increasing the pathology department's scientific yield. To spur members in this direction, he summoned them to his office, one at a time, to ask if they had research projects planned or underway. John told McKay about his incompetent cell theory, his work with Vince on Rh, and several other projects. McKay, whose own research interests lay far afield, nonetheless listened carefully and said, encouragingly, that he would support John if he wanted to ask for research money for some of his schemes.

John set to work. By August he could report in a letter to his family in Australia: "[We have] completed the 'competition theory' [paper] and submitted it to *Science* [the weekly publication of the American Association for the Advancement of Science]. I don't know whether they will accept it or not. We could be lucky if it turned out to have any basis in truth. I fear we may be just boys in a man's world, but there is no penalty for trying. I am at present filling in forms for various grants for research. We will ask for about $40-50,000. . . . There is no penalty for thinking big."[1]

Vince, meanwhile, had begun to make progress on the clinical front in his war on erythroblastosis fetalis. From the time Wiener had first taught him Rh immunologic theory and blood-testing techniques, he had begun to single out, and ponder, each case of Rh incompatibility he encountered in the prenatal clinic or in the delivery room. A woman at risk—Rh-negative, with an Rh-positive husband and an Rh-positive fetus—delivered an unaffected first child. The first pregnancy rarely yielded an ill baby; this was one of the engimas of the disease. At the time a woman delivered her first child, moreover, it was rarely possible to find anti-Rh antibody in her blood. She *seemed* wholly unaffected by the disease. Yet if she was tested again, early in her next pregnancy, antibody might be found; her fetus would be erythroblastic. How could it be that she became sensitized and delivered a sick baby, apparently wholly within her second pregnancy, yet had not become sensitized and delivered an ill baby the first time she became pregnant? The matter was puzzling. The literature was unclear.

With John's help, Vince had begun to keep track of blood bank records on some of these women—but these results were always posted after the fact. Looking at a patient's chart, he could learn that she had had no anti-Rh antibody in her blood when she delivered her first child. She did have antibodies, and delivered a sick baby, the next time she was pregnant. That could be seen. But the record gave no clue as to *when* sensitization had first occurred, or why. Neither did the study of charts provide any way to select and follow unsensitized women from the very start to find out the precise time and circumstances of their initial, irrevocable sensitization to the Rh factor. It seemed obvious to Vince that the way to carefully study a large number of Rh cases would be to pick them out when the women first appeared for prenatal care and treat them separately all the way through to delivery. About 250 women at risk were delivered at Presbyterian each year. If he could be the obstetrician for many or all of them, he could quickly amass much valuable data. But Vince knew that this would require administrative restructuring of the entire obstetrical service—more work, and an entirely new hospital practice which Presbyterian Hospital could not be expected to undertake lightly.

On the side of efficiency, Vince explained to his chief, Howard Taylor, his establishment of a blood-typing lab in the OB department had already proved a time-saver. Further efficiency could result if all Rh cases were put under one obstetrician's supervision.

Threatened fetuses—those whose mothers developed high anti-Rh antibody titers—often were delivered by induced labor, so that they would be born between 9 A.M. and 5 P.M. This scheduling allowed the blood bank to have on hand adequate blood for exchange transfusion, if needed, and it ensured full daytime coverage by the pediatric staff to do the exchanges. By funneling all cases to one obstetrician, rather than having them distributed among the more than a dozen men who delivered clinic patients, workaday communication with the blood bank and the pediatrics department could be improved.

Vince's proposal still was very much in the talking stage when, fortuitously, Taylor left, about Labor Day, for a trip to Australia. His tour included visits to several obstetric hospitals.

Erythroblastosis fetalis was an especially severe problem in Australia for genetic reasons; it is especially common among families of Scottish, Irish, and English descent who make up the majority of Australia's population. One of the world's first clinics for prenatal care and delivery of Rh-sensitized women had been set up at the Royal Women's Hospital in Melbourne. Taylor stopped in to visit its chief, Dr. S. Lance Townsend. In a letter mailed from Australia, he told Vince: "In many places where I have stopped, there has been much more active interest in erythroblastosis than it seems to me we have shown at home."[2]

The boss had been won to the idea. When Taylor returned to New York in mid-October, he told Vince, "You really ought to get going on your Rh clinic." Plans now moved forward quickly. In a prospectus that he presented to Taylor and the obstetric staff, Vince recommended that a Presbyterian Hospital Rh clinic "collect into one group *all* pregnant women who are predisposed to producing a child affected with hemolytic disease of the newborn."

"You're even going to study *non*sensitized women?" a colleague asked at a staff conference.

"*Especially* the nonsensitized ones," Vince answered. "Nobody before has bothered to study healthy Rh mothers. It's in them that we may find an important clue."

Besides a better understanding of the pathogenesis of the disease, Vince added, "the purpose of this clinic" is to "improve our ability to prognosticate, and, by careful individualization in the antepartum management, attempt to improve the overall outcome" in Rh-sensitized pregnancies. "As new ideas and modes of therapy appear in the literature—as some already have—we will then be in a position to quickly apply and evaluate them in a systematic manner." And, Vince added, in the first written clue of his talks and plans with John, the clinic would provide a place "to attempt new methods of [Rh] prevention proposed by our own staff."[3, 4]

The first session of the Presbyterian Hospital Erythroblastosis Fetalis Antepartum Clinic convened one Tuesday afternoon early in 1961. It would continue to meet, on successive Tuesdays, for more than a decade. Vince was Rh clinic chief.

He now had women whom he could study and in whom he could test new methods to limit Rh disease. He also had a mark to shoot for: His review, with John, of Rh cases in the blood bank files showed that in the previous decade, 1950–1960, the fatality rate at Presbyterian Hospital for fetuses and newborn babies of Rh-sensitized women had been 30 percent. Could he reduce this toll?

Money to fund the special studies which Vince proposed was still a problem. Neither Columbia University nor Presbyterian Hospital had much to offer. Late in November, having talked the matter over with Wiener, Vince had written to Philip Levine requesting an appointment. Levine wrote back early in December saying that year's end was a busy time at Ortho. He proposed they meet early in the New Year.[5] John, meanwhile, had been led in the path of good fortune by his chief, McKay.

Early in the autumn, his ambition had suffered a setback when his incompetent cell paper was rejected by *Science*. "This is quite a disappointment for me," John wrote home to say, "but I suppose we are just too much of unknowns in the field to launch such a speculative idea from a conservative platform. We shall have to earn our right to have a platform by doing some work in the field and attempting to get some proof of the theory. . . . If the idea has any truth, time is on our side, and if it is not true, it is just as well we did not get our names associated with it."[6]

To support the work that needed to be done, John had half-heartedly begun writing a research grant application to the U.S. Public Health Service's National Institutes of Health (NIH). Like *Science*, NIH was part and parcel of the medical research establishment, and he had little hope that it would be any more eager to buy his odd and untested plans. Then, in October, McKay had called him in to say that a new source of research money had just opened up; he would help John tap it. That source was the municipal government of New York City.

The potential funding agency, McKay explained, was called the Health Research Council (HRC), an arm of the City's Department of Health. The HRC had been founded in the mid-1950s to subsidize scientific activities in the city hospitals. New York had thus made itself unique among American cities by being the first and only one to provide municipal tax funds for medical research.

The goal had been set of appropriating through HRC one dollar annually for each New York City resident, and 1961 would be the first year that the full amount—$8 million—would be available. Since word of this largesse had not yet spread through the research community, those who did know about it had reason to believe that, at the outset at least, any reasonable request would be funded. McKay, who had close connections among HRC advisors, told John he would sponsor an application grant for Rh and other work that might validate the theory of the immuno*in*competent cell. The deadline for submitting the application, he added, was February 15.

John completed the application late in January, just before his departure for a month-long visit to Australia during February; it was posted for him in his absence. He asked $77,646 for research that would extend over a five-year period. John's grant request, with a covering letter from Columbia Medical College Dean Dr. H. Houston Merritt, dated February 14, 1961, is the first dateable documentation of John and Vince's plans.[7, 8]

John's research proposal is heavily theoretical. It begins with an exposition of the immuno*in*competent cell theory, which he hopes to prove. While this theory and the passive antibody protection theory that John had found in Florey's textbook may be separate and distinct ideas, both lead to the same course of action: the injection of one, apparently benign, form of an antibody into an organism to prevent it from producing another, dangerous, form of the same antibody in response to antigen. In John's mind, and in the grant application, the ideas become essentially fused as one.

He proposes first to find out, using antigen-antibody systems in animals, if the protective phenomenon can be quantified. In other words, will a certain amount of antibody given to an animal along with a certain amount of the corresponding antigen consistently affect the animal's immune system in the same way? Can standard doses of *passive* antibody be found which always will prevent antigen from provoking *active* antibody production?

If so, "these experiments will be extended to human volunteers, using the [Rh] antigen-antibody combination. Rh-negative male volunteers will be preinoculated with anti-Rh serum [passive antibody] in varying quantities, then challenged with small doses (2 ml) of Rh-positive cells.* Experiments will be planned to detect whether the subjects who have been passively equipped with a circulating [anti-Rh] antibody will be less likely to become sensitized [to the Rh factor] than [unprotected] controls. Further tests will be done on subjects who are already sensitized to Rh to determine whether passive inoculation with antibody will prevent the expected boosting of titers that follows challenge with small doses of Rh-positive cells." This proposal reflected Vince's "feedback plan." Next, John wrote, "it is planned to process anti-Rh [serum] into gamma globulin . . . and to further separate. . . . 19S . . . from . . . 7S anti-Rh so that the effects of these two components can be investigated separately."

The next step would be to resolve Vince's fears that 19S anti-Rh

---

* John recognized that the hepatitis risk interdicted the use of serum in large groups of patients. They would have to be given antibody in a hepatitis-free form of gamma globulin. For limited, experimental purposes, however, whole serum from a few carefully watched donors would be safe, John felt. This serum could be obtained, he noted in his grant, from some of the several hundred Rh-sensitized women whose records were on file in the blood bank.

antibody might cross the placenta and harm the fetus. John proposed to inject Rh-negative mothers whose fetuses were known to be Rh-negative—and hence not in jeopardy from the Rh factor—with 19S anti-Rh antibody late in pregnancy. Then, when the babies were born, their bloods would be examined to see if they contained the antibody injected into the mothers. If not, it would be proved that 19S does not cross the placenta and hence could safely be given to Rh-negative mothers carrying Rh-positive fetuses.

"If all . . . tests have favorable results," John said, "a relatively large trial will be undertaken in which a series of Rh-negative mothers will be covered *during their entire pregnancies* with passively administered 19S anti-Rh [antibody] and the incidence of active sensitization to [the] Rh [factor] recorded and compared with a control series of mothers." ( Emphasis added. )

Having completed the application and turned it over to McKay for approval and submission, John departed on February 1 for Melbourne. He arrived at an exciting moment for Australian immunology. John's intellectual idol, Macfarlane Burnet, had just returned home from Stockholm with the Nobel Prize. He was the first Australian to win it. He shared it with English immunologist Peter Medawar.

When John visited his old medical school, the University of Melbourne, Burnet's triumph was being celebrated with great éclat. John felt nostalgia for the familiar medical community he had left. He had recently listened, perhaps not without envy, to a brilliantly expressive immunologic discourse by Burnet's protégé, an Austrian-born Australian, Dr. Gustav Nossal. Though just John's age, "Gus" Nossal, who had stayed at home, already was looked upon as Burnet's intellectual heir apparent, and it was widely felt that one day he might become Australia's second Nobel achiever. John, who had forsaken Australia, had no such comfortable patrimony of prospects in view.

One morning, John went to the university's immunologic institute, where Burnet was chief, to hear a lecture. Afterwards, at tea, he broached his immuno*in*competent cell theory and Rh passive antibody protection plan to some of his former medical school classmates. He also chatted with several visiting immunologists who had come from abroad to work with Burnet. John's theories were politely received.

It was hot summer in Australia, and John and his father, John S. Gorman, golfed and relaxed in the sun. At the seashore for a week, they discussed together the merits of the *in*competent cell theory and the possibility that the work with Vince—in addition to providing an effective Rh prophylaxis—might yield facts to confirm it.

John was back in New York early in March. A letter came from the Health Research Council's scientific director, internist Dr. George Mirick, acknowledging receipt of his grant application.[9] John, meanwhile, focused his attention on another of his projects— which now was about to feed fruitfully into the Rh work. The eager agility of his thinking had always stood in inverse proportion to his enthusiasm and patience with repetitive, routine handwork in the blood laboratory—which work he abhorred.

On his first tour through the blood bank, in 1959, John had been especially frustrated with one of the standard tests, the prothrombin time, which indicates the status of a patient's blood clotting mechanism. To do the test, a technician adds the clot-forming substance *thromboplastin* to a specially-prepared sample of the patient's blood, then determines with a stopwatch the time required for the first bit of clot to form. Each prothrombin time test was a painstaking, mindless chore, John felt. He had hit on the idea that labor might be saved, and ennui avoided, if the test could be automated, and had designed a prothrombin machine to do it. The week of his return from Australia, he had the prototype model set up and operating in the pathology department.[10] He now lacked only materials to test it.

Fate again came to his assistance in the guise of a salesman. This time, the sales representative, John Nerres, was from Ortho. He stopped in at the blood bank with samples of a new Ortho thromboplastin for prothrombin time testing called *Acuplastin*.

When Nerres handed him a sample vial of *Acuplastin*, John's eyes lit up with inspiration. "Hey, that's great!" John exclaimed. "I'd like to work with some of this," he said—and led the salesman into his lab to show him his prothrombin machine. He switched it on and prepared several tubes of blood for analysis using the Ortho thromboplastin.

While the machine was running, John's mind skipped from blood clotting disorders to blood wasting disorders. He blurted out to the blood products salesman at his side: "Can you get me some gamma globulin with high titers of anti-Rh antibody—for another experiment I'm doing?"

Delighted with John's show of interest, Nerres said he would try.

He walked out of the lab to a phone booth to call a scientist at Ortho whom he knew to be deeply involved in gamma globulin production. The man he reached was an immunologist, William Pollack.

Recollections later would vary on exactly how—and when—they first met. Apparently, a short time later, Bill Pollack gave a talk at Francis Delafield Hospital, a municipal cancer hospital that is part of the Columbia-Presbyterian Medical Center, and staffed largely by its doctors. John Gorman later would recall going to the talk with John Nerres. Then, when it broke up, they joined Bill Pollack and his host at Delafield, pathologist Dr. John Ultmann, for lunch. There, apparently, John Nerres introduced John Gorman to Bill Pollack.

The conversation quickly came around to John's interest in potent anti-Rh antibody and the reasons for which it was needed. Bill was no stranger to problems of blood incompatibility and Rh disease. A hard-eyed, blunt-spoken Englishman of thirty-five, he had trained and worked as a blood-bank technician. In Britain, unlike the United States, blood banks are run by specially trained administrative technicians, not by doctors. Since these technicians are responsible for life-and-death decisions—the cross-matching of blood for transfusions—they attend medical classes. But their orientation is more toward chemistry and the other exact sciences than it is toward patient care.

Bill had earned a bachelor's degree in chemistry and physics at the Imperial College of Science and Technology of London University. He then had won his master's degree in biochemistry and physiology at St. George's Hospital Medical School, also in London, and was soon to get his Ph.D. in immunochemistry and immunology from Rutgers University in New Jersey. His bent had been toward theoretical science—a purer, cleaner, more exacting discipline, he thought, than clinical medicine—and at first he had felt that the most rewarding pathway in science was the classical progression from pure ideas to hypotheses to the establishment, with the aid of data, of Natural Laws. As he had matured, he had shifted, to find paramount importance in data—exact, measurable, scientifically sound—as the ultimate touchstone, without which ideas are mostly idle speculation. Bill would grow to regard with increasing contempt the scientific claims of medical scientists—M.D.s—whose work he regarded as unimaginative and almost always sloppy.

Like John Gorman, Bill had conceived of his blood-banking ability as the basis upon which he might pursue his interest in scientific research—especially immunology. Reciprocally, his immunologic expertise inspired his blood-banking—and that is how he had gotten to Ortho.

Bill emigrated to Canada in the mid-1950s, where he got a job as chief of the clinical laboratories at a hospital in Vancouver, British Columbia. There, he produced several remarkably potent diagnostic serums for use in blood testing. This feat came to Ortho's attention, and the company's bold Director of Diagnostic Research, Glen Hill—a former Air Force pilot, self-taught serologist, and super-salesman of blood products—was sent to recruit Bill.

Ortho's offer—full-time work on research, at higher pay—brought Bill to New Jersey in 1956. Hill was his immediate boss. Philip Levine worked in a nearby lab. Bill's primary task, growing out of his early triumph at Vancouver, was research and development on yet-more-potent and effective reagents for the diagnosis of Rh and other blood group incompatibilities. His agreement with Ortho also provided time, equipment, bench space, and official encouragement for some research of his own choosing. On the day John Gorman first met him at Delafield Hospital, Bill already had launched an investigation into the immunochemistry of the Rh antigen-antibody response, including the differences in activity between the 7S and 19S antibody forms.

Bill's interest therefore was quickly provoked by John's description of his plans, with Vince, to provide an immunologic solution to the Rh problem. With John Nerres, they adjourned after lunch to Vince's lab for a long, late afternoon of exploratory discussion. Nerres went home to dinner about six, but the others—John, Vince, and Bill—stayed later. It would prove to be a key encounter.

Bill thought less of Vince's feedback plan for burning out the immune response in women already sensitized to Rh factor than he did of *AMIS*—the passive antibody protection phenomenon John had first found in the Florey textbook. John listened, with growing excitement, as Bill said that yes, he was quite familiar with the fact that passive antibody injected along with antigen would dampen the immune reaction.

Bill explained, perhaps cryptically—for the matter then was a trade secret—that *AMIS* figured in the manufacture of diagnostic reagents at Ortho. In this process an antigen was injected into a rabbit. The antibody that it made was then removed, purified, and bottled. It had been confirmed that tiny amounts of preformed, or passive, antibody, injected into an animal along with the antigen, would significantly increase, or *enhance*, its immune response. The animal would produce more, or more potent, antibody—a benefit for Ortho.

This enhancing ability of passive antibody was exactly the oppo-

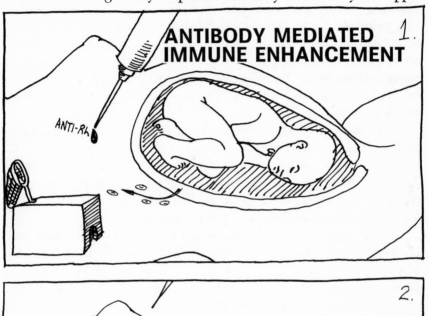

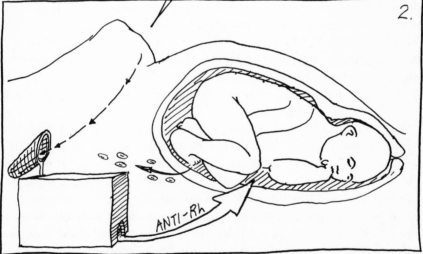

site of the *AMIS* effect, suppression of the immune response, that John and Vince hoped to exploit. But, Bill hastened to assure them, he had encountered immune *suppression* as well as *enhancement*, when antibody was injected with an antigen. The same passive antibody, in fact, would either suppress *or* enchance an immune response to antigen depending on how much passive antibody was given.

In experimenting with various amounts of antigen and antibody, Bill said, he had found that enhancement occurred when far more antigen was given than antibody. But when the antibody overwhelmed the antigen, then the opposite effect—*AMIS*—occurred. This principle might well be used to prevent immunization to the Rh factor, Bill declared. But one would have to be extremely careful to give potent doses of passive antibody in order to be sure to avoid enhancement. To enhance a woman's probability of becoming sensitized to the Rh factor would be to create the disease one hoped to prevent.

As familiar as he was with antibody-induced immune enhancement and suppression, and as steeped as he was in Rh, Bill would say, later, "I had never thought of applying the *AMIS* principle to the Rh system." No one had ever before attempted to manipulate the human immune mechanism in this way. But the idea, when once he heard it from John and Vince, seemed plausible.

"It was fortunate that the three of us came together," he would say later in retrospect. "I was one of the few people in the country who could suppress antibody production with antibody—as I could do the opposite: enhance it. What was remarkable was that here we were, three people interested in eradicating a disease that struck thousands. Vince was closest to the heart-wrenching aspect of it because he took care of the mothers. John and I had vicarious interests. John was concerned more with ideas than with facts—he was a tremendously good theoretical immunologist, despite his lack of formal immunological training."

Bill, the professional immunologist, had both training and the wherewithal needed. He said that he could make 7S anti-Rh fairly easily. The 19S would be more of a challenge. It could be isolated, but little was known as to whether it could be purified, and, if so, whether it would remain stable and potent.

Despite the spectre of *enhancement* which he had raised—for the first time for John and Vince—Bill did agree with John that the optimal time to inject the passive anti-Rh antibody would be during pregnancy. It was then, according to the classical accounts of Levine and others, that the fetus' red cells were crossing over into the mother's circulation, immunizing her against its Rh factor.

Bill's familiarity with the *AMIS* principle from his work at Ortho led him to see a real possibility in its application to Rh that the more established experts to whom Vince and John had tried to "peddle" their ideas had missed. Driving home to New Jersey that evening over the George Washington Bridge, Bill made a decision. "I decided we'd collaborate," he would recall later. "But I wasn't yet sure of the extent of our collaboration."

# 10

## *Stern*

AMID GENERAL SKEPTICISM there was one chain of research inquiry that could be interpreted as confirming John and Vince's hope that *AMIS* would prevent erythroblastosis. John and Vince were aware of this thinking.

What, by fluke, they were not aware of was a key experiment, recently completed, that appeared to *prove* that anti-Rh antibody, if injected into unsensitized Rh-negative individuals along with Rh-positive red cells, would nullify completely the cells' Rh factor; none of the recipients of these injections had become Rh-sensitized.

Had John and Vince known of this experiment when it first was described, the previous summer (1960), it might well have changed their plans, for its author would have seemed to them to have already largely demonstrated that which they, even now, only had hopes of proving. Strangely, the author of the experiment—a Chicago immunologist, Dr. Kurt Stern—had had no inkling at all of what he himself had proved! Neither, clearly, had Bill Pollack or Philip Levine, both of whom had attended the scientific gathering at which Stern first described what he had done.

Thus, in the spring of 1961, John and Vince were unaware of this most recent experiment in a line of inquiry that supported their hopes. The Ortho scientists were ignorant of the experiment's importance, as was the author of the experiment himself. And all were completely unaware that the same thread of inquiry had been picked up elsewhere by others who, even then, encouraged in their own work by what they knew of Stern's, were preparing an announcement that would strike like a lightning bolt from the blue.

This key line of thought had begun with Levine—with his observation, in 1942, pointing to the fact that children with Rh hemolytic disease were unusually likely to be ABO-compatible with their mothers (see Chapter 5). Wiener had supplied the interpretation that it was not that a dual incompatibility—ABO and Rh— was more dangerous to these babies, so that they tended to die in the womb, and hence did not survive to be counted as erythroblastic newborns. Rather, to the contrary, he said, ABO incompatibility *protected* fetuses from the consequences of their Rh incompatibility with their mothers, so they tended not to become ill and hence were underrepresented in statistics on babies with Rh hemolytic disease. Thus, a relatively small percentage of babies with Rh hemolytic disease were ABO-incompatible with their mothers, while a relatively larger percentage were ABO-compatible with them.

Wiener attributed this protection to "competition of antigens": the mother's immune system was too busy making anti-A and/or anti-B to bother about making the more deadly anti-Rh. But matters did not rest with this interpretation. Wiener's British archenemy, Robert Race—the champion of Fisher's CDE nomenclature and theory—concurred with Wiener that ABO incompatibility protected against Rh incompatibility. But he had come up with an alternative explanation *why*.

He had chanced upon it—"casually," he would later recall—in the late 1940s. Race then was in his early forties, and already had become Britain's leading expert on blood groups. He was a bright, easygoing scientist with an even temper and a good sense of humor; his most distinguishing physical characteristic was his shock of brilliant orange hair.

Race had as a postgraduate student an attractive, raven-haired Australian, Ruth Sanger, who would eventually become his wife. He had assigned her a thesis project on blood groups. When the thesis was completed, they had revised it for publication as a book under their joint authorship—*Blood Groups in Man*. It won them world renown. Its first edition appeared in 1950, and it was in the course of preparing it from Ruth Sanger's thesis that Race, pencil in hand, thought deeply for a moment about double incompatibility and Wiener's explanation that ABO incompatibility protects against Rh disease by preoccupying the mother's immune system. He doubted it.

Thinking, he wrote an alternative explanation: "If Rh sensitization is due to fetal cells entering the maternal circulation, it seems possible that if they carry, for example, the A-antigen, and the maternal serum contains anti-A, then *these invading cells may be eliminated before they have time to act as an Rh antigen.*"[1] (Emphasis added.)

The fetus' Rh-positive cells, if they happen to be ABO-incompatible with its mother, are for that reason destroyed and removed from her body before they can provoke an anti-Rh immune reaction —and so the fetus is spared! It was a brilliant deduction, casually arrived at; and once Race had recorded it for publication, he gave it no further attention. Beyond the single sentence, quoted above, he would never write one word more about it. Nor would he ever, according to his own testimony years later, attempt to pursue his idea experimentally in any way.

That was left for others to do.

One of these others was Chicagoan Kurt Stern, a short, round,

Dr. Race and his wife, Dr. Sanger, wrote blood banking bible. (*Al Giese, 1965.*)

bespectacled immunologist who would pursue Race's interpretation of Levine's observation until he had achieved the most excruciatingly close near-miss to success—and glory—in the entire hotly contested history of Rh. In failing, for himself, he would twice

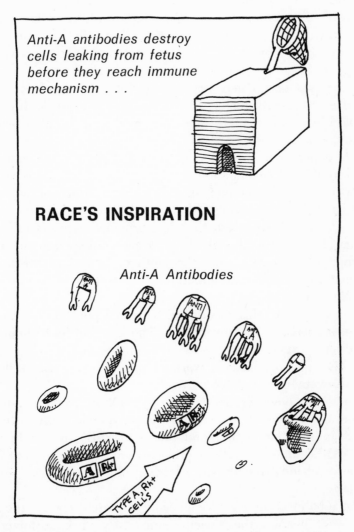

Anti-A antibodies destroy cells leaking from fetus before they reach immune mechanism . . .

**RACE'S INSPIRATION**

Anti-A Antibodies

TYPE A, Rh+ CELLS

provide critically needed clues that would advance others' quests for success.

Stern had long been an admirer and disciple of Philip Levine, whose photo hung over his lab bench in the Mt. Sinai Hospital, where Stern was blood bank chief. Shortly after Race and Sanger's book appeared, Stern designed an experiment to study the interaction between Rh and ABO. With a colleague, pathologist Dr. Israel Davidsohn, Stern visited the Illinois State Penitentiary at Joliet, forty miles from Chicago, and elicited the help of 39 Rh-negative men incarcerated there. He injected them repeatedly with Rh-positive blood, thus mimicking the sensitizing fetus-to-mother bleeds of Rh-incompatible pregnancies. Seventeen of the men were given blood that was Rh-incompatible, but ABO-compatible with their own. The other 22 were given blood that was both Rh-incompatible and ABO-incompatible with their own.

In the first group, more than half the men, 10 of 17, became sensitized to the Rh factor. But in the group given doubly incompatible blood, less than 10 percent, 2 out of 22, became sensitized to the Rh factor.

This experiment proved conclusively that the protection provided by double incompatibility had nothing at all to do with early miscarriages, as Levine had suggested, since the use of male volunteers ruled out miscarriage, along with all other aspects of pregnancy, as a variable. Stern thus had provided experimental confirmation for Race's thought that rapid elimination of doubly incompatible red cells from the mother's body was the probable explanation for ABO incompatibility's protection against Rh sensitization.

Stern's report of this experiment had been published in 1956 and was well known to Rh researchers.[2] The fact that he had continued his prisoner experiments was less well known in the spring of 1961, since his report on this later work had yet to be published; it would appear several months later, in August.[3]

Stern had, however, *read* his report to his blood-banking colleagues the previous summer, 1960, at the annual conference of the American Association of Blood Banks (AABB) in San Francisco. The AABB's annual meetings provided an important forum for the exchange of ideas on Rh, since leading blood researchers attended regularly.

The 1960 meeting was an especially important one for the AABB because it marked the sixtieth anniversary of Landsteiner's discovery of the ABO blood groups. Special guests, including some from abroad, had been invited. Who came, who heard Stern, and who responded to what he or she heard would turn out to have an important bearing on all subsequent Rh research.

Ruth Sanger came, heard Stern's talk, talked to him about it, and carried home to London the meeting program which contains an abstract of his report.[4] Levine came and gave the keynote address, honoring Landsteiner. If he heard Stern's paper—and he well may have—he apparently failed to grasp the important clue to Rh prevention that it contained. Bill Pollack delivered a paper in San Francisco that he, Glen Hill, and a young co-worker at Ortho, Hans Hager, had written. Even if he heard Stern's paper, he would not have appreciated its specific value for Rh prevention plans because he had not yet met Vince and John, had no inkling of their plans, and brooded none like them of his own.

Vince, an obstetrician, normally would not attend a blood meeting, and did not go to this one. John, who normally would have been present, had had to cancel his plans because at the last minute Columbia had run short of travel money, and he, as low man on the totem pole, had been bumped from the blood bank contingent. Had he been there, however, and had he heard Stern, he might well have remarked a stunning similarity between one of Stern's experiments and his own developing plans with Vince to prevent Rh sensitization. In the "ego-peddling" frame of mind that he and Vince shared that summer, he might, with good reason, have approached Stern to share with him their plans, for Stern might have seemed to John to have anticipated their own hopes with action. Alternatively, it is possible that by August John's thinking had not reached the stage where he would have recognized a similarity between Stern's thinking and his own, though he certainly would have done so a month or two later.

As it was, John was not present and no one who was, including Stern himself, saw that in what he said there was a pregnant clue to Rh disease prevention. Only the sharp eye and prepared mind might have picked it out of his talk, the abstract of which said, in part:

It was shown previously that experimenal Rh sensitization in man . . . [is] inhibited in hosts possessing preformed antibody for another antigen of the sensitizing red cells. Additional studies were carried out in order to obtain more insight into the mechanisms. . . .

[E]xperimental designs and their results were: (1) Injection of Rh-positive ABO-compatible cells, coated *in vitro* with anti-A antibody, into Rh-negative recipients: this procedure did not interfere with the development of [anti-]Rh antibodies. (2) Injection of Rh-negative recipients with Rh-positive ABO-compatible red cells previously coated *in vitro* with [anti-]Rh antibody: this failed to produce Rh sensitization even after repeated exposure to the antigen. . . .[5]

Stern's aim had been to study ABO's effect on Rh, which he accomplished, in part, in experiment No. 1, which later would prove to be of little interest. The second, potentially epoch-making, experiment he intended only as a control on the first, with another variable substituted for ABO incompatibility.

His control experiment thus called for injecting Rh-positive cells into Rh-negative prisoners. To eliminate ABO as a factor, recipients and donors were of the same ABO blood group—group O.

To create a perfect analogue with the ABO experiment, however, Stern would have to "coat" the red cells with an antibody. In the main experiment, he had used anti-A antibody to coat group A red cells. For the control experiment, then, he needed to coat Rh-positive red cells with an antibody other than anti-A or anti-B. The only one that invariably would bind to all Rh-positive cells was anti-Rh. So Stern had carefully mixed Rh-positive red cells with anti-Rh antibody in a test tube. Then he had injected the antigen-antibody mixtures into Rh-negative prisoners.

The men's immunologic situations thus somewhat resembled pregnancies that are Rh-incompatible but ABO-compatible— pregnancies that commonly end in Rh sensitization. Stern expected that some, perhaps all, the men would be sensitized to the Rh factor by the injection of anti-Rh antibody-coated Rh-positive cells. Sixteen prisoners were given two to five shots each over a several-month period. The results astonished Stern: "None of the men developed Rh sensitization."[*][6]

These results would also astound John and Vince, when finally they saw them, for Stern clearly seemed to have shown that *AMIS* will prevent sensitization to the Rh factor! He had injected Rh-positive red cells, the equivalent of a fetal bleed, into Rh-negative men. With the red cells, he had injected anti-Rh antibody— precisely the antibody John proposed to use—and no one had become sensitized. True, in Stern's experiment, unlike anything John and Vince could hope to do, the antibody had been bound, in advance, to the Rh-positive red cells. In mothers, the antibody would have to seek out the antigen on its own, as they were rushed and tumbled together through the mother's bloodstream. Nevertheless, what Stern had done was a strong indication that if the injected antibody could find the fetal red cells, Rh sensitization would be prevented, according to the *AMIS* principle.

[*] "In striking contrast" to this, when he injected 10 other men with plain, uncoated Rh-positive red cells, 5 became sensitized to the Rh factor, as expected.

Stern, however, failed to perceive that *AMIS*, an immunologic phenomenon which he was aware of, had been operative in his experiment. Neither had he sought another explanation for the men's failure to become immunized. Nor did he see that in injecting them with anti-Rh antibody he had bared a potent tool to prevent Rh sensitization.

By the following spring, John and Vince still had not learned of Stern's more recent experiment. But Vince could see some support for their own endeavor even in Stern's earlier work. If anti-A or anti-B antibody would destroy Rh-positive fetal cells before they could cause sensitization—as Race had suggested, and as Stern had proved—then would not passively administered anti-Rh antibody provide equivalent protection in those pregnancies not otherwise protected by incompatibility for ABO? To Vince, if not to John, there seemed a strong similarity between the proven protection of ABO incompatibility and *AMIS*—and the fact that the former clearly worked augured well for the latter.

# 11

## Needle in the Womb

OBSTETRICS IS A SURGICAL SPECIALTY; an obstetrician cuts, rips, pulls, and pushes. Vince, whose passion was to swarm over and defeat erythroblastosis, was not fully satisfied by immunologic innovations. He avidly sought other, more active methods to advance his campaign.

Paramount in his mind was a more accurate means to determine precisely how near death a pregnant mother's fetus might be. Since the fetus of an Rh-sensitized mother becomes sicker as term approaches, as its uterine environment is progressively poisoned by antibody, it made surgical sense to remove it, prematurely, as soon as it was developed enough to survive. In the early 1940s, obstetricians began to induce labor prematurely in mothers with rapidly rising anti-Rh antibody levels who had already had one or more severely ill infants. Some babies were saved.

Then the success of exchange transfusions, and the ascendance of the pediatricians who did them, started an opposite trend in Rh management. Now, even severely ill liveborn babies delivered at term often could be brought through with one, two, or more full exchange transfusions. The pediatricians and hematologists with whom they worked felt that obstetrical meddling—meaning early induction—served only to complicate their jobs. A few infants might be gotten out alive that way who would have died by term. But this doubtful salvage, they believed, was more than offset by the loss of life and added prematurity due to too early delivery.

Diamond, at first an exponent of early induction, tended to discourage it as survival odds soared for full-term Rh babies to whom he gave full exchange transfusions.[1] The dean of British blood bankers, Dr. Patrick Mollison of the government's Medical Research Council, set out to see if early induction was worthwhile. Seventeen hospitals participated in his complicated and difficult investigation—which Mollison himself conceded was not without flaws.[*]

Mollison's conclusion, however, was clear-cut: "The practice of inducing labor 3 to 5 weeks before the expected day of delivery, as a routine . . . was associated with a *lower* incidence of surviving infants than was the practice of allowing labor to occur spontaneously."[2] (Emphasis added.) He reiterated later that "it is unlikely that premature induction of labor increases the chance of the survival of an infant with hemolytic disease. . . . On the contrary, such a practice may diminish the survival rate."[3] This condemnation, carrying the Medical Research Council's cachet, seemed to doom routine early induction of Rh babies.

Mollison's decision against early induction might benefit those fetuses destined to survive in the womb until delivery at term. But one in every five or ten failed to survive that long, and when they died, they—and their mothers—were the obstetricians' responsibility.

In rare, specific instances, an obstetrician might *still* deliver early —Mollison's attack invalidated only "routine" use of induction—if he could determine how close the fetus was to dying. The maternal anti-Rh antibody levels, while not always an accurate guide, sometimes could be quite helpful.

Rapidly rising titers in a first affected pregnancy, for example, were an especially ominous sign that might prompt even a careful and conservative obstetrician to induce labor at 36 weeks or possibly earlier. But to do so, he absolutely needed to know the maternal Rh antibody levels on a week-to-week, or even a day-to-day, basis. Without them, he would be totally lost.

It was just this predicament that had suddenly faced a young

---

[*] Whether a woman would be induced early or allowed to carry her ill baby to term was determined arbitrarily on a random basis, instead of being decided on the basis of changes in her clinical picture and anti-Rh antibody levels. All liveborn babies, moreover, whether delivered prematurely or at term, were arbitrarily limited to a single exchange transfusion. Thus, for example, the question of whether early induction plus two or three exchanges conferred better survival odds than term delivery and a single exchange could not be settled.

English obstetrician, Dr. Douglas Bevis, a hospital-based practitioner at St. Mary's Hospitals in the Midlands city of Manchester; his colleagues called him "Tiger." For Bevis, who had been trying to improve methods of fetal diagnosis and infant salvage, Mollison's quasi-official condemnation of early induction had come as a tremendous blow. A second severe blow now came from inside Manchester: The chief of the regional transfusion center, Dr. Fred Stratton, ruled the Rh antibody titers on pregnant women's blood were clinically worthless—and took his technicians' valuable lab time as well. So no more would be done.

Bevis would have to sail blind. For all that was now known about Rh and erythroblastosis, he had no more data upon which to intervene in his patients' behalf than obstetricians had had before Levine and Wiener made their great discoveries. He could help only if he could find out, in some other way, how sick a fetus was at any specific moment.

"It occurred to me to do a biopsy on the baby, grab off a bit of tissue that might show the severity of its illness," Bevis would later recall. "The easiest way to get it was in the liquor"—the *liquor amnii*, or amniotic fluid, in which the baby floats inside the womb. Cells and other substances shed or excreted by the fetus collect in the fluid.

Bevis already had studied amniotic fluids which he had collected via the vagina during labor, and he knew that in erythroblastosis the fluid characteristically was yellow instead of clear, as is normal. Could fluid be drawn from the uterus earlier, in the sixth, seventh, or eighth month? Would it provide clues to the viability of the fetus?

These were shocking, revolutionary questions. The womb and its contents were sacred territory, a privileged sanctuary that for better or for worse was safe from prying medical hands and tools. Besides delivery and abortion, there was only one precedent for penetrating a pregnant womb: In *hydramniosis*, the condition in which there is an excess of amniotic fluid, obstetricians might insert a drain to relieve the pressure. Usually they entered vaginally, although some English and European obstetricians took a shortcut: They pushed a thin, pointed tube straight down into the skin of a woman's belly, through the layers of subcutaneous fat and muscle, and then through the uterine wall into the fluid-filled uterus. Americans had had little success with this transabdominal entry, and the dean of American obstetricians, Dr. Nicholson Eastman of Johns

Hopkins, reported untimely induction of labor in four of five instances his group had attempted the procedure—which, he added,
"cannot be recommended."[4]

Bevis' boss also believed the transabdominal route risky. But
Bevis, a thin, serious man with smiling, dark eyes, intrepidly broke
medical precedent. He poked a needle into a woman's belly, and
through it to the womb, for reasons wholly without therapeutic
rationale for her. The sole purpose was to do a test that *might* be
diagnostically helpful for the fetus.

Most women on whom he did these transabdominal punctures
were Rh-incompatible, and expected erythroblastic babies. He needled them as early as the twenty-second week of gestation—the
middle of the sixth month—and in some he repeated the procedure
twice monthly a half-dozen times. Since early induction was taboo,
his stated rationale was that amniotic fluid assay would permit an
accurate prediction of how sick the baby would be when it finally
was born, and what kind of care it would need.

Bevis' needling technique apparently was expert, for none of his
first one hundred patients went into premature labor. Neither was
there any evidence, once the babies were born, that the needle
point had touched them—or, if it had, that they had been harmed.
Bevis stuck in the needle at a point midway between a woman's
navel and pubic bone; he inserted it quickly, under local anesthesia; took only a teaspoonful or so of fluid; sealed the puncture
wound with plastic after withdrawing the needle—and reported
that the women felt no more than mild discomfort, which lasted at
most a few hours.

If the fluid samples were stained yellow by the constituents of
the fetal red cells broken down by the mother's anti-Rh antibody,
the baby was in jeopardy. But, Bevis found, the visible color of the
fluid was not diagnostically adequate. He analyzed a dozen chemical
constituents of normal and abnormal amniotic fluid and settled on
iron, which is released when red cells are destroyed, as the best
indicator of erythroblastosis.

What seemed sensible experimental medicine at St. Mary's in
Manchester seemed menacing to the medical press in London.
When Bevis submitted a report to the *Lancet*, it created considerable editorial consternation.[5] Publication was held up, temporarily;
the feeling was, Bevis would recall, that this was "human vivisec-
tion."

Four years later, in 1956, when Bevis wrote his final report on amniotic fluid analysis—he was leaving his St. Mary's appointment for a clinical practice—he had considerably refined his "predictive" technique. He now measured not iron, but the concentration in the fluid of the bile pigment bilirubin, which is also released when fetal red cells are destroyed. He did this by measuring the fluid's opacity with a light-analyzing instrument, the *spectrophotometer*.

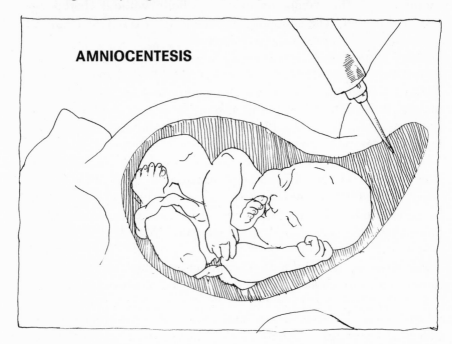

**AMNIOCENTESIS**

Bevis now felt he could tell when erythroblastosis threatened a fetus. This allowed him to issue a sharp, if deferential, challenge to Mollison: "There is a definite place in treatment for premature delivery in cases where . . . sudden hemolysis occurs, but the risks of prematurity must obviously be considered . . . [and] clinical judgment must be the final arbiter."[6]

Diagnostic *amniocentesis* might then have died a-borning, for outside of Manchester, interest was nil. But Bevis' successor at St. Mary's, to whom he gave his spectrophotometer, decided to pursue the fluid studies. Dr. A. Harold Walker, who had been a student of Mollison's, nevertheless had kept his own counsel on Rh management. Early induction had seemed to him to be a remarkably useful technique, and he had been "shattered" by Mollison's recommendations, which he felt amounted to a ban.

Could the ban be broken? Walker, a pink-faced, prosperous-appearing practitioner, with suave manner and an eye for organizational detail, decided to shape Bevis' essentially experimental method into a diagnostic indicator for early induction. He did the diagnostic punctures on a series of his patients, and in a year succeeded in simplifying and refining the fluid assay: Performed only once, in the thirty-second or thirty-third week, Walker found, the fluid would show on the basis of a single key "bulge" on the optical density curve if the baby would be severely affected. His predictions were right over 90 percent of the time.

Using the test, and delivering early in appropriate cases, Walker eventually was able to *halve*, from 36 percent to 16 percent, the stillborn and newborn death rate among erythroblastic deliveries at St. Mary's. He also cut the incidence of brain damage, *kernicterus*, from 14 percent to 1 percent of cases, and significantly reduced the demand for exchange transfusions.[7]

"The increased accuracy of the early liquor test makes it highly desirable that [it] be offered to all patients at risk," Walker ventured in 1957. "There have been no accidents . . . and the patients are not distressed. Indeed, when a patient is given a good prognosis concerning her baby, considerable peace of mind is derived from such news."[8]

The time, nevertheless, was not yet ripe for openly advocating amniocentesis as the key to managing Rh-threatened pregnancies. One of Walker's young assistants in the late 1950s, a carrot-haired, pleasant-faced Scottish obstetrician, Dr. John Robertson, would later recall that while they performed the diagnostic "taps" at St. Mary's, officially they still did not do much in the way of early induction: "I, as the under-man, simply induced the woman when the line showed a bulge on the graph."

The medical establishment, in fact, was not yet ready for amniotic fluid assay. The *Lancet* ran two long editorials in 1958 and 1959 on managing Rh-threatened pregnancies. The first mentioned Walker's work, which, while requiring "confirmation and elaboration," may prove of "real practical value."[9] The second editorial, a year later, swamped in the fine points of antibody tests, ignored amniocentesis entirely.[10] Seven years had already gone by since Bevis published his first paper, and in all of Britain only Bevis, Walker, and Robertson thought the method worth pursuing.

It was thus left for a clinician at the far end of the globe, a doughty, cheerful New Zealander, Dr. A. William Liley, to bring amniocentesis out from the underground and transform it into a sensitive, qualitatively accurate tool for fetal diagnosis. In major papers published in New Zealand in 1960 and in the United States the following year, pediatrician "Bill" Liley—about whom much will be heard later—set forth precise guidelines for finding the optimal delivery time for each Rh baby: Certain specific bulges in the optical density curve of bilirubin called for immediate intervention if the baby was to be saved.[11, 12]

New Zealand, as a part of the British Commonwealth, lay under the influence of Mollison and the English medical establishment, but Liley felt he had enough data to raise a challenge: "Liquor analysis is a test for anemia, which, if severe, might warrant premature delivery," Liley declared. "In the controlled trial of unselected premature induction reported by Mollison [in 1952], it was found that the severity of the affliction as judged by anemia was the same in liveborn infants whether or not labor had been induced. No such criticism can be leveled at the [New Zealand] results."[13]

Liley's test of the liquor made it possible to select for early de-

Dr. Freda draws amniotic fluid from pregnant woman's womb. (*Arthur Leipzig, 1964, Courtesy Medical World News.*)

livery those infants who were most in jeopardy, so that the worst afflicted were the first delivered—and many lived who would otherwise have died. No longer could it be said, as Bevis had, that "clinical judgment," an intuitive decision, took precedence over objective laboratory determinants in managing Rh pregnancies. Liley said: "The extension of amniocentesis to all patients with [anti-Rh] antibodies, irrespective of past history, has provided . . . and can provide . . . many more opportunities for careful judgment to influence favorably the baby's chance of survival."[14]

After New Zealand, there were reports from France and other countries on amniocentesis. But even by 1961 there were none from the United States—because American Rh experts were not interested in the procedure, or considered it barbaric. Vince Freda, as yet unfamiliar with Liley's work, was not in a position to propose amniocentesis as the key to early induction. Rather, when drawing up plans for his Rh clinic in late 1960, he proposed to correlate fluid density determinations with fetal deaths over a five-year period to see if the method had merit.

No one in the United States could show him how to perform amniocentesis on pregnant obstetrical patients. Fortunately—and ironically—a colleague at Columbia was conducting experiments on pregnant rhesus monkeys. By needling their bellies, Vince became adept at taking out fluid without provoking delivery. When he began doing amniotic diagnoses on patients with their namesake disease late in 1960 or early in 1961, he very likely was the first American obstetrician to do them.

# 12

## Timing

FROM THE TIME they first discussed applying *AMIS* to the prevention of Rh disease, Vince had felt himself locked on the horns of a difficult dilemma vis-à-vis John. The idea that passively administered Rh antibody would prevent sensitization to the Rh factor enticed and excited him. Morever, of all their plans, this seemed the least likely to jeopardize the health of the mother. Her blood type need not be changed. She need undergo no complicated operation to run a shunt from her circulation to her baby's. Huge amounts of extraneous antibody need not be given, as in his "feedback" plan. The fact that no one had ever demonstrated an adverse effect on the health of a *mother* who had been sensitized to the Rh factor all but guaranteed that injecting a woman with these antibodies, which she well might have produced herself, could hardly harm her.*

But what about the safety of the fetus? Injecting anti-Rh antibody into a mother meant injecting her with the one substance in the world that would act specifically against the Rh factor on fetal red blood cells. Vince was appalled at the thought of what might happen to a fetus whose mother got the antibody injection while she was carrying it in her womb. Resolution of the problem of the fetus' safety seemed to him a priority item of business upon which the success of the entire venture might hinge.

---

* Unless, of course, she was then given a transfusion of mismatched Rh-positive blood.

John held other priorities. It would do, at first, he thought, to demonstrate that *AMIS* did indeed suppress adults' sensitization to the Rh factor. This could be decided, without fetal risk, in experiments performed in males. If it worked, there then would be time enough—and added incentive—to find ways to safely apply the principle to pregnant women. He believed that 19S anti-Rh antibodies, which probably could not cross the placenta into the fetus, would be safe in most cases. Moreover, given some initial success in testing the principle in Rh-negative males, ways might be found to bind the antibody molecule to a larger, inert carrier substance that would permit it to act protectively in the mother but keep it from passing the placenta.

Besides, the issue of risk was less of an overpowering consideration for John than it was for Vince—not because the young Australian was careless, but because, as a blood banker, he knew and accepted the fact that risk was an unavoidable, if unwelcome, part of each day's transactions; in every 100 pints of blood he signed out, for example, John knew that one or two carried hepatitis. There was not then, nor would there be even much later, any way to avoid this risk completely. However careful one might be, an irreducible hazard remained, and learning to live with it was part of John's professional training.

Vince, on the other hand, dealt not with impersonal pints of blood, but with individual flesh-and-blood patients, women whom he would follow and feel responsible for for months or even years. While he might be extraordinarily bold about what he would do to a mother in order to give her a chance to deliver a living baby, his was a clinical rather than a statistical approach to the danger involved. Unless he personally, as a practitioner, could grapple with each happening, he wanted as little as possible to do with the procedure. This feeling had influenced his original response to John's *AMIS* proposal, no matter that it seemed immunologically attractive. He was very wary of 19S antibody injections during pregnancy: What if a mother-to-fetus bleed occurred, carrying the deadly antibody along with it? And he was doubly wary of 7S antibody, which he knew would quickly traverse the placenta.

"We don't want to take *any* chances," Vince later would recall saying to John, right at the start. "If we want money from a government research grant, and we do, we want to be as safe as possible. Why take a chance on harming even a hair on the baby's head?" His fear would be reinforced, in the months ahead, by the sudden wave of reports of horribly deformed babies being born to mothers who had been medicated, *during pregnancy*, with a presumably safe sleeping pill, thalidomide.

Locked on the horns of his own dilemma—the attractiveness of *AMIS* as a way of preventing Rh disease *versus* the danger to the fetus of injecting anti-Rh antibody into its mother—Vince was intensely motivated to try to find a *time* when it would be truly safe to give the anti-Rh antibody injection. The safest moment, of course, would be one in which there was no baby inside the mother for it to harm. But that *seemed* impossible, for to be useful the anti-Rh antibody would have to be injected before or during the time a mother was becoming sensitized to the Rh factor on her fetus' red cells.

When *does* a mother become sensitized to the Rh factor? Little consistent thinking had been done on this problem, for, as Allen and Diamond had only recently pointed out: "Discussion about the *way* in which a woman becomes sensitized to Rh is, to date, only of academic interest, since presumably nothing can be done to prevent red cell transfer from fetus to mother in the normal case, and *one cannot yet interfere with the fundamental process of antibody production with ease or safety*."[1] (Emphasis added.)

Because Vince, with John, presumed that the "fundamental process of antibody production" might safely, if not easily, be interfered with in order to prevent maternal sensitization to the Rh factor he, more than any earlier worker, now was motivated to plumb to its depths the question of when and how sensitization occurred. In so doing, he would find the need and resolution to challenge the classical doctrine of Levine and others whose views he and John had heretofore accepted without question.

Production of anti-Rh antibody in the mother was triggered by fetal Rh-positive cells. That much no one doubted. It seemed reasonable therefore that sensitization occurred when these cells first entered the mother's circulation.

When did they?

This was a matter about which there long had been much speculation but little evidence; only now were data starting to appear. To the naked eye, and even on an ordinary microscope slide, a fetus' red cells are visually indistinguishable from its mother's. As far as Vince was aware, the fetal cells' presence could be demonstrated only in the rare case in which a fetus became ill or injured and hemorrhaged, so that large amounts of its blood seeped or spilled into its mother. Delicate antibody tests then could detect the fetal cells in the maternal circulation.

Big bleeds were the exceptional situation, however, and had little to do with the ordinary events of pregnancy during which passage of even a single drop of fetal blood might, according to Levine, cause Rh sensitization. Vince knew no way to measure bleeds of this magnitude directly, and hence could not determine when they first occurred.

At the level of theory, there were two principal views as to when these sensitizing bleeds from fetus to mother took place: Either during the long months of pregnancy. Or, at delivery.

The former view was the more popular. It came from Levine. The latter had been suggested by Wiener (see page 57).

Good arguments could be marshalled to support Levine's hypothesis that the sensitizing bleed could occur at any time after the gestating fetus first had its own circulating blood. As Allen and Diamond pointed out, the placental membrane, which had been calculated to have an area of some 70 square feet, is no thicker than the membranes of the kidneys—which up to two million red cells cross daily to pass from the bloodstream to the urine. A comparable number of fetal red cells, crossing the placenta, might well suffice to trigger Rh sensitization. Two other well-established facts, Allen and Diamond said, tended to support Levine's hypothesis that small blood leaks *during* gestation caused maternal sensitization. The first stemmed from the fact that ABO incompatibility appeared to protect mothers from Rh sensitization (see page 64). If sensitization was forestalled because fetal cells were *destroyed* in the mother's body during pregnancy, they must have *entered* her body during pregnancy—a clear indication that Levine was correct, and that it was during pregnancy that Rh cells got into and sensitized the mother.

The second argument raised by Allen and Diamond to support Levine's view was simpler: The level of anti-Rh antibody could be seen to rise in a mother during a pregnancy in which she would deliver an ill baby. This rise seemed clearly to reflect penetration of the mother's body by antigen-bearing fetal red cells. "These facts," they asserted, "suggest that slow leakage of small quantities of blood is the usual way in which fetal red cells reach the maternal circulation in the causation of maternal sensitization [to the Rh factor]."[2]

The contrary view had been raised by Wiener. He had asserted, far back in 1945, that "there is some indirect evidence"—which he did not describe—"to suggest that the maximum amount of fetal blood escapes into the maternal circulation at the time of labor and delivery, possibly due to the disturbances at the placental site."

In other words, only *after* a pregnancy, as it were, on the delivery table, did the most dangerous bleed occur. Wiener's theory had one huge logical advantage over Levine's: It explained why erythroblastosis rarely occurs in a woman's first pregnancy. "This would explain," said Wiener, "why the chance of the firstborn child of an Rh-negative mother having hemolytic disease is practically nil."[3] If the sensitizing bleed comes only when the pregnancy is ending, then the disease could not appear until the second time the mother became pregnant.

Wiener, as erratic as he was brilliant, abandoned this line of inquiry almost as soon as he had proposed it. Rather, in pursuing his "competition of antigens" plan, in which antigens to compete with the Rh factor were injected into women *through the course of pregnancy*, he implicitly acceded to Levine's view that sensitization first occurred *during* the pregnancy that produced the first sick baby. If the sensitizing bleeds occurred only at delivery, as he once had asserted, then the competing antigens would need to be injected into the mother *only* then—not throughout pregnancy, as Wiener had, in fact, done.

Wiener's original insight that the bleed at the end of a first pregnancy produced sensitization that compromised the second was not wholly abandoned. Chicago pathologist Edith Potter in 1948 reiterated it as a general rule: "While the reason for the rarity of the disease in the first pregnancy is not definitely known," she said, "it seems evident . . . that immunization must be initiated prior to the pregnancy during which the fetus becomes affected."[4] She conceded however that there was no way to decide between the logical explanation that sensitization occurred only at the end of a given pregnancy, and the more problematic alternative that two pregnancies somehow were needed. Subsequently, the first hypothesis faded from sight—Vince later would say that Wiener never once mentioned it to him—while the latter was ingeniously elaborated by others.

It was postulated that not one, but *two* stimuli of antigenic red blood cells were required to cause the disease. The first, or *sensitizing*, stimulus, which might occur in a first pregnancy, failed, for mysterious and unexplained reasons, to produce detectable antibody levels in the mother and did not harm the baby. But the next fetus-to-mother bleed, in the next pregnancy, provoked the mother's immune system to a powerful anamnestic, or *recalled,* antibody response that produced both rapid rise in antibody level and illness in the fetus. In short, an immunologic epicycle—an initial, invisible, intrinsically harmless sensitizing stimulus—had been invented to explain the contradictory observations that women seemed jeopardized by their first Rh-incompatible pregnancies but failed to show effects of that jeopardy until later ones.

The resolution thus raised more contradictions than the contradiction it was designed to resolve. Not the least of these was a new form of immune response that did not result in antibody production. The old heads had grown tired. Since none of them, except Allen, any longer thought very forcefully about preventing Rh sensitization, none was really moved to plumb the problem of when and how it occurred.

Vince was urgently so moved. For if Levine were right, and Rh sensitization would have to be stopped while a woman was pregnant, then John's intriguing *AMIS* proposal might be stillborn. Vince felt sure he could never inject anti-Rh antibody into a woman who was with child. From the ferment in his mind to reconcile John's plan and his own fears, there grew a new resolution: Perhaps—hopefully—the sensitizing bleed did not occur in a first pregnancy until it was ending, on the delivery table. No one had ever demonstrated the existence of a priming sensitization, and, besides, even if two stimuli were needed, there was plenty of time in the long months of a pregnancy for two to occur. Yet in first pregnancies that virtually never happened.

"Why postulate a hidden priming stimulus which you can't stamp out!" Vince declared to John. "Why isn't Rh sensitization an all or nothing event. Either a woman's sensitized, or she's not. Either the right number of cells get across to produce an immune response, and antibody, or they don't get across—and there's no response.

"Maybe Levine's reasonable theory is all wrong. Maybe the key bleed comes at delivery!"

If frequent, perhaps continuous tiny bleeds could in fact cause Rh sensitization, as Levine asserted, then why did only 10 percent of Rh-incompatible pregnancies cause sensitization? "The fact that

# VINCE'S HOPE

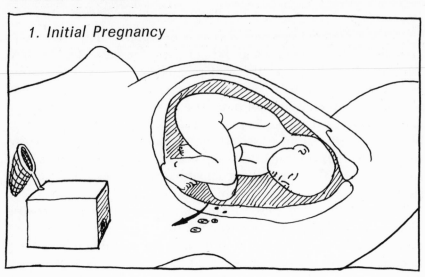

1. Initial Pregnancy

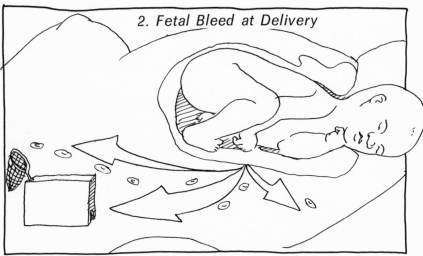

2. Fetal Bleed at Delivery

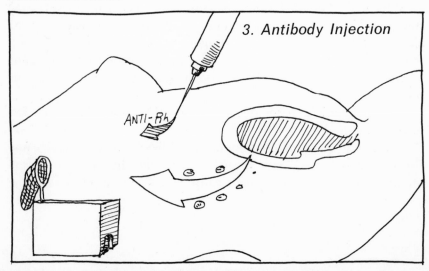

3. Antibody Injection

ANTI-Rh

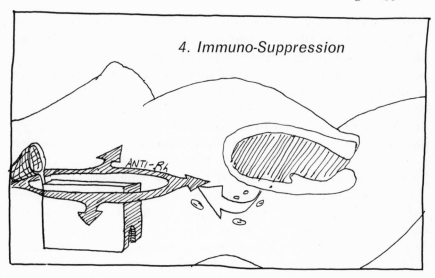

4. Immuno-Suppression

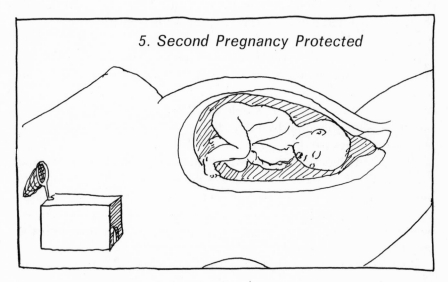

5. Second Pregnancy Protected

so few do," Vince declared, "argues strongly that more is involved than passage of a few red cells from fetus to mother. *That* happens in every pregnancy."

If not in pregnancy, where else but at delivery. Vince, unlike the immunologists who doubted this view, had daily experience at the delivery table. He could see, each time he turned, twisted, and pulled forth an infant the very real sprays, spurts, and gushes of fetal blood which came from the cord and the placenta as well as from the baby itself. This blood fell upon open uterine and vaginal tears and rips and seeped into severed vessels of the mother.

These were big bleeds. Watching the intermingling of fetal and maternal blood in the operative field in which he worked, Vince became more and more convinced that what he was seeing was the sensitizing bleed. *This* was the key moment when a mother first got enough fetal blood to cause immunization to the Rh factor. Later, a tiny bleed that occurred even early in her next pregnancy might provoke a more sensitive, anamnestic immune response—the first that would actually harm a fetus. But it was here, during the delivery of the previous child, that the damage was really being done.

If only he could prove it, and persuade John! For if Vince were right, there might still be time, in the moments after the baby had been safely delivered—but before the placenta was pulled loose and more fetal blood spilt—for the anti-Rh antibody to be effectively used. Perhaps, Vince allowed himself to imagine, I might deliver the baby, *then* give the anti-Rh injection, *and then* deliver the placenta—and *still* be in time to prevent Rh sensitization.

How could this be proven?

All his speculation would become real, Vince realized, if he could prove that mothers who had no antibody when they went into labor did have it in the weeks or months that followed. If his hypothesis were correct, it would be those women who had antibody titers in the months after delivery—and *only* they—whose next pregnancies would produce erythroblastic babies.

"We postulated that there would be some women who showed no antibody at delivery in whom we nevertheless would be able to find antibody in the postpartum period, six weeks to six months later," Vince would later say. "If the postulate were correct, it would be precisely these women who would have trouble with the next Rh-incompatible baby."

The delay of six weeks, to the time of the standard postpartum obstetrical visit, would allow the Rh-positive cells that had entered the mother at delivery to begin to die off and be sequestered for removal in the spleen, which is one of the body's most immunologically active organs. Fetal red cells may survive up to six months in the maternal blood. So only by testing at the end of that interval could Vince be sure whether cells that entered at delivery had—or had not—caused Rh immunization.

Was there any way to anticipate what he would find? John asked. Astonishingly, there was not. Thousands of doctors had written tens of thousands of research papers on Rh and erythroblastosis, and Wiener, among others, had stated clearly that the rational way to find a preventive was "to ascertain . . . the factors underlying the development of sensitization."[5] Yet no one, apparently, had ever done so, no one had ever followed women's antibody levels from the start of their obstetric careers, when they first became pregnant, through delivery, into the period between pregnancies, and then to subsequent confinements.

Specifically, no one that Vince knew of had ever studied the between-pregnancies period when, he believed, the key to the riddle would be found. True, such a study would be highly troublesome and inconvenient to do. Pregnant women were patients of their obstetricians, not of the consultant blood men or immunologists. Once a patient had been sent home with her first baby, there seemed little ground to recall her, except for her one routine six-week checkup, for anything as alien to her own immediate needs as a blood test for research purposes only. If Vince wanted these data, clearly he would have to find them himself.

Which he now was equipped to do—in his Rh clinic—if he could find the required money. In the clinic, he would see women coming for prenatal care in their first pregnancies, and he could do periodic antibody tests on their blood to see when and if Rh sensitization occurred. With adequate nursing, technical, and record-keeping support, these women could be kept track of after delivery.

# 13

## Forward Motion

WHEN BILL POLLACK WENT IN TO WORK at Ortho the day after his talk with Vince and John, he did not sit down to write a memo to his chiefs. In the cool light of morning, the *AMIS* phenomenon still seemed a promising possibility for preventing Rh disease, one well worth his effort to pursue. But Bill mentioned this intention neither to his immediate chief, Glen Hill, nor to Philip Levine, who was at work in his own laboratory just down the hall. In fact, for several months, the only confidant at Ortho with whom he would share his plans—and his labors—was a young assistant in his laboratory, Hans Hager.

Bill's rationale for silence was simple. Ortho, as he knew it, was a bold company, willing to spend money developing new ideas—provided there were hard scientific data to back them. Vince and John had no such data at all for what was at best an "iffy" proposal—an Rh prophylaxis. They had only airy speculation and a theoretical position based on antigen-antibody systems that perhaps behaved quite differently from Rh.

On the positive side, Bill realized, an Rh preventive *would* wonderfully complement Ortho's commercial position as a primary supplier of Rh diagnostic serums. It could be an important money-maker, and the fact of Levine's long association with Ortho could not help but enhance its commercial appeal.

Phil Levine, on the other hand, might be the last to buy the idea, for it flew fully in the face of his belief—which Bill himself had never until now thought to question—that sensitization to the Rh factor occurred during and probably throughout pregnancy, and could not be prevented. True, documentation for this doctrine was weak. But it would need to be specifically refuted, with unimpeachable data, before anyone at Ortho would give it serious credence.

A preventive against Rh disease was not a wholly new idea; Bill knew of several such schemes. All certainly had been presented to Levine at one time or another for his approbation. All ultimately had been shown to lack scientific merit, and Levine could be counted on to have, at best, little tolerance for yet another like them. Bill would recall, with a shudder, that the name of one hapless author of a worthless Rh cure was a standing joke when blood men gathered to swap stories.

Bill, at the age of thirty-five, was a highly trained and self-exacting scientist. He was remarkable for the enormous driving power of his mind. He was shrewd in company politics. He was ambitious. And he was cocky. In the eyes of his co-worker and admirer, Hager: "Bill was one of those persons to whom everything seemed possible—including the impossible."

Hager, an open-faced, agreeable man with wide, expressive eyebrows, had been born in Germany, reared in Holland, educated in England, and professionally trained—as an agricultural researcher —in New Jersey, at Rutgers. After college, while waiting for travel documents that would allow him to pursue his career in Africa, he had taken a temporary job at Ortho, where he first was assigned to Levine. Hager became caught up in immunochemistry, stayed, and was reassigned to Bill's lab.

Even in his wildest dreams, Hager had not foreseen that there might be a role for him in a life-or-death drama of medical research, and he was thrilled when Bill explained to him the captivating idea that erythroblastosis might be prevented by injections of anti-Rh gamma globulin. When Bill asked if he would like to help make the prophylactic material, Hager readily agreed.

Several factors in Bill's situation at Ortho favored him in their task. His contract permitted him to conduct some research of his own choosing. He was advantageously situated regarding access to the needed raw material: One of his jobs was to examine, from time to time, the potent anti-Rh human serums that Ortho bought to process into Rh testing reagents with an eye to finding ways to increase their potency. This supply source Bill and Hager would raid for the serum they needed.

Bill was equally well situated with respect to equipment. The method he would employ to obtain potent anti-Rh gamma globulin was *fractionation*. This process, developed during World War II, separates serum into its component elements.

Fractionation was a new technique in the pharmaceutical industry; Ortho owned one of the first commercial fractionation plants. Bill had been assigned to find new and improved ways to use it. Available fractionation techniques would permit him to isolate the gamma globulin fraction that contained 7S anti-Rh antibody. Fractionation of pure 19S anti-Rh was a much more dicey matter. If it could be done at all, Bill would have to develop the method to do it.

For both the 7S and 19S fractions, purification, standardization, and sterilization techniques would be required to ensure that they could be safely injected into humans. These tasks all lay ahead. No one had ever prepared an isolated anti-Rh gamma globulin fraction for pharmaceutical use, and there were no guidelines on how to sustain stability and potency once one was in the bottle.

More than the experimental material's uniqueness contributed to this problem. Ortho's diagnostics division was not what is known in the pharmaceutical trade as a "parenteral house"—one whose

Dr. Pollack attacks research problem in his Ortho lab. (*Circa 1960, Courtesy Dr. Hager.*)

products are intended for injection into humans. They were made for use in the test tube, in blood bank laboratories. As a result, Ortho diagnostics did not practice the extremely rigid sterile control techniques required in plants that made products "for use in humans." An Rh prophylaxis would be an exception. Hager later would say that, from the outset, he and Bill shared a "deathly fear" that the material they made would turn out to be contaminated and dangerous. "It was the first time our lab made anything for injection purposes," he would recall. "That hung over us like a big, black dragon."

Bill felt they should develop a model system, in laboratory animals, in which they could demonstrate and quantitate the ability of *AMIS* to forestall sensitization to blood factors; he assigned this task to Hager. But Bill did not want to wait for the animal studies before making an antibody preparation for testing in humans. "Bill wanted to do it 'Like that!' " Hager later would say. " 'Rush! Rush! Rush!' "

Hager himself had a reason to rush. He was scheduled to leave Raritan in mid-May for a long trip to Europe. Could they complete the first batch before his departure? In a refrigerator in their lab was a quart of potent anti-Rh serum. Bill and Hager set up a rudimentary fractionation system on a lab bench. They used salts of ammonium to precipitate the gamma globulin out of the serum—much as one may use vinegar to precipitate the curd out of milk.

Working evenings, and on time taken from other projects during the day, they soon had extracted from the quart of serum the tiny amount of gamma globulin which contains the anti-Rh antibodies. When they tested it, it was enormously potent—so potent, in fact, that they had difficulty quantitating its potency.

The batch was finished when Hager departed for Europe on May 15. Neither before nor in the wake of his departure did Bill breathe a word of their work to his superiors at Ortho. "We bootlegged it," Hager would say later. "We didn't dare tell anyone what we were doing—for fear they'd turn off our water!"

Meanwhile, an opportunity had arisen to test Levine's view of the venture. He had responded to Vince's letter, written the previous autumn, asking for an interview. Late in April, Levine wrote, would be an opportune time for them to talk.[1] He sent a road map and Vince, his wife Carol, and his lab technician drove to Raritan to keep the long-awaited appointment.

It was a nice day for a visit. Everyone was most cordial. Vince and the young women got a Cook's tour of Ortho's plant and polite welcomes from its officials. "We . . . were most pleased to have you come out and see us," the company president declared, "as we feel exchange of information is so important to our research endeavors."[2]

Vince's entourage did not bump into Bill during their tour of the plant, and Vince did not mention the fact of their collaboration to any Ortho official he met. With regard to the reasons that had prompted him to come, the day was disappointing as it was cordial. Vince, who was still ego-peddling, wanted approbation for the project. And he wanted money. He got neither.

Levine listened politely while Vince described the Rh clinic. He glanced through a draft of a research grant application to the federal government that Vince was completing. But, Vince would recall later, Levine offered little in response to his direct appeal for research support; Ortho's budget for out-of-house research projects was wholly committed for the year. Even more discouraging, Vince felt, was Levine's reaction to their plans to use anti-Rh antibody injections to prevent Rh sensitization. It would not work, Vince would later recall Levine as saying. It wouldn't work, as Vince hoped, if the injections were given after delivery, because sensitization had already occurred. And it couldn't work during pregnancy, as John proposed, because there was no way to keep the antibody from crossing the placenta and harming the fetus.

John's request for support had also run into a snag.

The scientific director of New York City's Health Research Council, George Mirick, had telephoned John's boss, McKay, to say that the grants review committee had discussed the application and had decided not to approve it. The problem, Mirick confided, was that John Gorman was a new and untried name in the research community; the project he proposed was costly. It would be far more satisfactory, given these circumstances, if the more established of the two investigators involved in the work were listed as project chief.

Mirick returned their application.

John had the title page retyped so that McKay now appeared as "principal investigator," with his own name second, as "co-investigator." Reflecting the rapid evolution of his thinking, he deleted all but passing reference to the immunologic clone theory—which had been the theoretical basis for the February submission. In May, John pegged his plans wholly on *AMIS*. He also used the occasion of rewriting the grant to double the monies requested for the first year, from $12,000 to $25,000.[3] Then he mailed the application back to Mirick.

On May 11, in a covering memo to members of the HRC grants committee, Mirick declared: "Enclosed is application No. U-1154 submitted by Dr. Donald McKay as suggested by the Committee at its last meeting. You will recall that Dr. Gorman's application for an investigatorship was declined without prejudice and it was voted to suggest that Dr. McKay submit an application . . . with himself as principal investigator and Dr. Gorman as co-investigator."[4]

Before finally rendering a decision, the panel decided it ought to interview the would-be grantee, and it was, of course, John whom they summoned for a conference. Mirick recalls that, for his part, he strongly doubted that John's plans for preventing erythroblastosis would work, and he would later reveal that most if not all of the reviewers shared this skepticism. Nevertheless the *AMIS* principle had never been studied in the Rh system, and so it was at least worth a try. The HRC would gamble the money. On May 19, HRC approved the grant request for the amount of $59,387, to be provided over three years. It would be three weeks later, after the award had been rubber-stamped up through the top of the city bureaucracy to the mayor, that John would receive word of his windfall—but by then the world picture in anti-Rh research would be strikingly and dramatically changed.

Vince, too, now completed his grant request, which he planned to submit to the federal government. Not to be outdone by John— and with more than a touch of bravado—he asked for $23,000 for the first year and for a total of over $100,000 for five years, to execute what can best be described as a master plan to defeat erythroblastosis. Everything was included: the *AMIS* experiments, studies on the induction of tolerance to the Rh factor in the null period, amniocentesis, a controlled study of the value of early induction of labor, the Rh clinic, and more. But his primary aim, Vince asserted, was "to determine whether it is possible to prevent the initial sensitization of Rh-negative mothers by the intravenous injection of Rh antiserum in the third stage of labor."[5] Vince's observation and speculation on the events of Rh sensitization are neatly summed up as theory:

The rationale for "protecting" the mother with [anti-]Rh antiserum immediately after the baby is born is based on the following premise: That most of the *initial* sensitizations to the Rh factor occur at the time of labor when the volume of fetal red cells escaping into the mother is large enough to do so. However, once the initial sensitization has occurred then the small amount that probably seeps through the placenta throughout pregnancy is usually sufficient to cause the secondary or *anamnestic* response. . . .

The presence of a circulating specific antibody appears to render the subsequently injected corresponding antigen relatively non-antigenic. This phenomenon, which has been noted by several workers using distinct antigen-antibody systems, appears to be a general one in immunology.

Vince concedes that John's preferred plan—to give the 19S anti-Rh antibody during pregnancy—"probably [is] a more effective method," but must await the availability of the 19S gamma globulin fraction and proof that it will not cross the placenta. Meanwhile, if injections after delivery of the baby prove protective, it would become worthwhile to pool serums carrying potent anti-Rh antibodies and extract them in the form of gamma globulin—as Bill was preparing to do.

One other plan that had arisen in their long talks the previous summer would be tried: the induction of tolerance to antigens during the "immunologic null period." Vince had already tested this by injecting A and B antigen into newborn babies of different blood types to try to render them tolerant to A and B. He had failed, completely. None became tolerant. The immunologic null period in humans, if there was one, ended before birth. To surmount this barrier, he now planned to inject A and B substances into mothers during pregnancies, on the premise that they would cross the placenta and reach the baby who, perhaps at this early stage, would accept them as part of itself. If the method worked with A and B substances, it then could be tried with Rh antigen.

Before retyping the application for the final time, Vince carried it to Brooklyn one evening to show to Wiener. His mentor was less negative than Levine had been. He told Vince that applying *AMIS* to the Rh system—an idea that had not occurred to him—seemed plausible. It might work, although Wiener doubted Vince's unusually boastful assertion that one day *all* physicians would have to give the antibody injections, on pain of being held negligent in the care of their patients. Wiener took a dim view of the other, nonimmunologic methods his protégé proposed to employ in his all-out attack on Rh disease. Amniocentesis, he felt, was largely useless and unsafe.

Wiener later would recall that he kept his doubts largely to himself. True to his role of unprejudiced elder adviser, scientific consultant, and personal confidant, he did not impose his own ideas on Vince: "I had no preconceived notion," he would say later. "Vincent brought me his experimental protocols to see if I could find anything wrong with them. My only concern was that he do a valid experiment, so that after he got through two or three years of work he'd not have to tear up the results because he'd forgotten one of the controls."

As Vince later recalled the conversation, Wiener concluded on a different note, saying: "It won't work, Vincent. But you have to try it!"

Vince proofread and signed the application form on May 15, then sent it on to the medical school dean, Houston Merritt, for official submission to the United States Public Health Service's National Institutes of Health. Merritt's signature is dated May 26, 1961. Five days later, on May 31, the application had reached NIH headquarters in Bethesda, Maryland, and had been logged in for evaluation.

It could not have been more than a day or so later that Vince received an urgent phone call. Wiener was on the line.

"Vincent! Vincent!" he exclaimed. "Some newspaper reporters just telephoned me. They say a group in Liverpool, England, just reported a method like yours to prevent Rh sensitization by giving injections of anti-Rh antibodies. They've tested it. It's in the May 27 *British Medical Journal*.

"The reporters wanted to know what I think about the idea. . . ."

Vince was stunned. So was John, whom he quickly reached in the blood bank.

From the sound of it, their thunder had been stolen.

When they went to the medical school library to find out, the librarian told them that the *British Medical Journal* (*BMJ*) was posted from London by surface mail—and would not arrive until three weeks after its date of publication. Ironically, while they were waiting for it to arrive, New York City finally sent word that it had approved John's grant.

John had another, more immediate cause for worry to divert his mind from the report that they had been scooped on the Rh project. He was deeply immersed in his textbooks, studying for the last—and ultimate—test of knowledge that would be required of him by the American medical qualifying system: his certification examinations for the American Board of Pathology. They were scheduled for the middle week of the month. It was a hot, humid June in New York. John crammed for his tests. He and Vince waited to see—worried about what would be in—the May 27 issue of the *BMJ*, in transit from England in a ship's hold.

Mid-month John took his tests. And the journal came.

# 14

## Butterflies and Blood

THERE IT WAS! A long, detailed, closely reasoned report presented, conspicuously, under the names of no fewer than seven investigators, the majority of whom were identified as members of the department of medicine at the University of Liverpool. Their paper was entitled "Experimental Studies on the Prevention of Rh Hemolytic Disease."[1]

In it, these authors first relate a series of preliminary studies that had led them to their central proposition that the "protection" against Rh sensitization afforded by ABO incompatibility between fetus and mother could perhaps be duplicated in ABO-compatible pregnancies. "It . . . seems obvious," they declared, "that a way to prevent sensitization in an ABO-compatible mother would be to destroy the fetal cells rapidly by some other means. Since the cells are by definition Rh-positive, the injection of anti-Rh would be the first thing to try."

And they had tried it. Not in women yet, to be sure. But in a small group of male volunteers, Liverpool policemen it would later turn out. Into each they had injected a simulated fetal bleed of one teaspoonful (5 ml) of Rh-positive blood. The injected cells had been marked with radioactive material so that their presence or absence in the men's bloods subsequently could be assessed. A half hour later three of the six men were injected with two teaspoonsful each of serum containing anti-Rh antibody.

The purpose of the anti-Rh antibody injections, as the Liverpudlians conceived it, was to seek out and destroy the Rh-positive cells before they could provoke the men into sensitivity to the Rh factor. As their primary measure of efficacy, they measured the speed with which the anti-Rh antibody removed the Rh-positive cells from the men's circulations. Anti-A antibody, they knew, would quickly remove group A cells from a group O individual. Their concern was to know how closely anti-Rh antibody would come to duplicating this feat by removing Rh-positive cells from an Rh-negative individual.

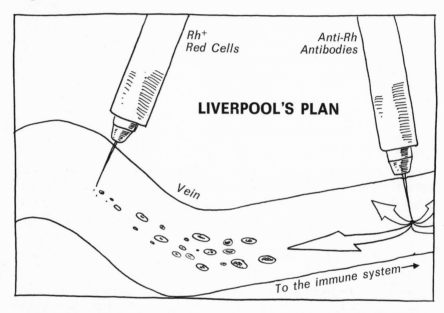

Two days after the injections, the three bobbies who had not been given the "protective" anti-Rh antibody still had close to 100 percent of the Rh-positive red cells remaining in their blood. But in the men who had received the antibody, the Rh-positive cell count had fallen by half, as measured by radiologic and immunochemical methods. Results of immunologic tests, which would show whether quick clearance of the alien cells in fact would prevent immunization to the Rh factor—the ultimate test of the anti-Rh injections' value—had been included in the design of the experiment, but were not included in the *BMJ* report; it had been submitted for publication before they could be completed. Nevertheless, on the basis of the Rh-positive cell clearances, the Liverpudlians felt able to conclude: "Our results suggest that it may be possible to prevent most cases of Rh sensitization, and thus in time eliminate Rh hemolytic disease." A leading editorial in the same issue of the *BMJ* concurred that this "ingenious method" might "successfully prevent active immunization" to the Rh factor.[2]

Objectively, Liverpool had made a stunning presentation. New proposals to "prevent" a mortal disease appear all too infrequently in the pages of reputable medical journals. The Liverpool group's achievement was the more stunning to Vince and John for their having arrived at, and tested, clearly ahead of them, a preventive method that seemed almost identical to their own. What would turn out to be even more remarkable, however, is the fact that Liverpool had pursued an entirely different route, based on entirely different logic, to arrive at the same treatment proposal: injections of anti-Rh antibody into mothers at risk, at delivery. The New Yorkers' route had been obstetrical, serologic, and immunologic. *Genetics* had been the spur in the Liverpool investigation, and the Rh prevention plan, as they put it forth, stemmed ultimately from an inquiry into evolutionary changes in the coloration of swallowtail butterflies' wings!

More even than the New York investigators were the Liverpool workers innocent of the specific knowledge and disciplines that traditionally had been involved in Rh research: Their original group included neither obstetricians, pediatricians, nor even serologists. Most of them were internists—specialists in the medical care of nonpregnant adults—who in their clinical careers might never be called upon to see, let alone treat, a case of Rh hemolytic disease. If the New York men were amateurs in Rh immunohematology, as their critics rightly complained, the Liverpool group could only be considered dilettantes, pure and simple—"lunch-time immunologists," one of them would later say.

The full story of their approach to the Rh problem would emerge only years afterwards, but in fact it had begun in 1952 when one of the men in the group—and its eventual chief and leader—answered an advertisement for "Butterflies Wanted" that had appeared in a classified ad sheet circulated by the Amateur Entomologists' Society of Great Britain. His name was Dr. Cyril A. Clarke. He was an internist, practicing in Liverpool—and he was quite a remarkable man. A former military surgeon, a skilled sailor and yachtsman, Clarke projected that born-to-command manner that characterizes the English ruling class—a swagger stick would have seemed, in his hands, a natural appurtenance. A suggestion of a foxy smile at the corners of his mouth suggested that "The Professor," as he would come to be called, while not a man to trifle with, was also not without his own, sly sense of humor.

Clarke, who would become Liverpool University's Professor of Medicine several years later, was an avid collector and amateur breeder of butterflies:

As a child I was fascinated by butterflies, particularly a yellow swallowtail butterfly that flies in a marshy area of the east coast of England known as the Norfolk Broads. After World War II, I wanted to breed these insects but found it easier said than done. Swallowtails usually will not mate in a cage, as they need an elaborate courtship flight to stimulate pairing. My interest in the insect did not wane, and by persevering I learned a simple trick to make captive swallowtails mate. Holding the female in the left hand and the male in the right, one brings the pair close together, pries open the male's claspers with the nail of the left hand middle finger and thereby induces the male to lock onto the female, after which mating follows naturally. . . .

In 1952, I happened to acquire a female butterfly of a black swallowtail species common in America (*Papilio asterias*), and in an idle moment one Sunday afternoon I hand-mated her to a male of the yellow British species (*Papilio machaon*). Since the two species are related, the mating was successful, and their first-generation offspring turned out to be like the American parent—showing that black and American were dominant to yellow and British![3]

Clarke now bred the American-looking black hybrid offspring with the British yellow parent species. This genetic "back cross" yielded offspring half of which were wholly black and half of which were wholly yellow. This was contrary to what Clarke might have anticipated, according to Mendelian laws of genetics, if several genes were involved in determining swallowtails' wing color. If two genes were involved, for example, one fourth of the offspring would have been black like the American parent, one fourth would have been yellow like the English parent, and half would have been a hybrid hue between the two extremes. "Clearly, then," Clarke concluded, "the ground color of the wings must be controlled by a single gene. A butterfly that inherited the dominant gene for black from either hybrid parent would have black wings, whereas only an offspring that received [the recessive] yellow genes from both parents . . . would be yellow.

"It was this experiment," Clarke later recounted, "that aroused my interest in genetics."[4] Shortly thereafter, he read the "Butterflies Wanted" ad, which had been placed by geneticist Dr. Philip Sheppard of Oxford. Sheppard, a young, tweedy, scholarly man who in his spare time had become a rifle shooter and an expert marksman as well as a butterfly hunter, was a true and proper geneticist—a doctor of philosophy, D.Phil., with wholly academic credentials, and neither training nor talent in clinical medicine. He had placed the ad to solicit eggs or breeding insects of a French butterfly for a comparative genetics-and-behavior study.

Clarke did not have the insect that Sheppard had specifically solicited but seized the opportunity to write to him to describe his hand-mating technique and the breeding experiments that it made possible. Sheppard was deeply intrigued and arranged to meet Clarke. They hit it off well together, and so joined forces to delve more deeply into the data that could be obtained by adding hand-mating to the techniques of genetic research. Assisting them in this effort was Clarke's wife, Féo, a high-strung, patrician woman who played an active participatory role in his various professional and recreational ventures.

Shortly thereafter, Sheppard journeyed abroad for a year of work in genetics at Columbia University, in New York City. Returning to England, he moved from Oxford to Liverpool to facilitate his collaborative researches with Clarke. His Oxford work had been fi-

Dr. Clarke hand mates yellow and black butterflies to create hybrid. (*D.R.Z.*, *1969*.)

nanced by the Nuffield Foundation, an English equivalent of the Ford Foundation, and when he moved to Liverpool, Nuffield agreed to transfer his support with him and extend it to cover his joint research with Clarke.

They decided to tackle the mystery of the inheritance of mimetic patterns, or *mimicry*, in swallowtails. In the tropics, certain tasty swallowtails escape predation by birds because they resemble insects of other species that taste bad to eat. The bad-tasting insects are designated *models*; their good-tasting look-alikes are *mimics*. "Models and mimics," Clarke said later, "usually fly together, and birds which have sampled the distasteful models tend to leave the mimics alone even though these are highly palatable."[5]

The puzzle that had stumped geneticists since Darwin was: How does a mimic evolve? How is it possible for one species to develop in such a way that it closely resembles another species?

The primary clue they would pursue is the fact that mimicry occurs only in female butterflies. This had been learned only after years of frustrating field work, in which it invariably turned out that all mimics caught in the net turned out to be ladies! Their gentlemen could not be found. Then, by careful observation of their choice of partners in the wild, lepodopterists discovered that all mimics' mates were ordinary-looking swallowtails.[*] It could then be assumed that it was from similarly ordinary-looking primitive female swallowtails that today's mimics had evolved. Sheppard, as a geneticist, was especially interested in swallowtail mimicry because it dramatically revealed the interaction of one set of genetic traits with another: Maleness clearly suppressed in a butterfly all of the dozens of changes—wing shape, window size, body color, etc. —that would invariably appear in females of the same subspecies.

Since the several traits that differentiate a mimetic female from her nonmimetic brother appear to be inherited as a unit, it seemed conceivable that all were controlled in some way by a single gene. But, classically in genetics, one gene, by definition, controls one, and only one, trait. To resolve this paradox, Sheppard suggested that mimicry represented the expression of what had been called a "supergene," a series of genes that were linked together, probably

---

[*] "The reason for the relative constancy of male pattern," Clarke and Sheppard explain, "may reside in the nature of butterfly courtship. It is known that color is important in butterfly mating behavior." It has been "suggested that this is particularly true in the male, and that a novel color-pattern fails to stimulate the female to copulate. Consequently, male color-pattern is particularly conservative."[6]

because of their close proximity on one of the butterfly chromosomes, and hence carried from generation to generation as a single unit. The supergene concept, it may be recalled, had been advanced by Robert Race's associate, Sir Ronald Fisher.

The supergene could explain why all mimic traits usually appear together, as a unit, and do not normally segregate in offspring so that some have one combination of traits while others have another. Obviously, it is the block inheritance of traits that keeps a mimic species looking like its model. Yet if the one gene, one trait rule were true, then the supergene must be made up of many single genes that each keeps an individual identity.

A mutant butterfly that Sheppard and Clarke received by mail from an African supplier seemed to confirm this hypothesis: While it displayed several of the typical mimetic traits, in one it differed from expectation. This suggested that a rearrangement of genetic material had occurred that affected only a single gene in the normally unified supergene package. Using Clarke's hand-mating technique, the two men subsequently were able to confirm this belief, for in interbreeding mimetic and nonmimetic forms of one swallowtail species, they produced a mutant that had the long tails and small white wing window of the mimic, but also the black body color of the nonmimetic mate.

It was at this obscure way point in their journey that Clarke and Sheppard's butterfly researches arrived at a crossroads with clinical medicine. The supergene and the puzzling problem of the inheritance of discrete but closely linked genetic traits were by no means restricted to the lower orders of being. In fact, it will be recalled, the concept of the supergene had been invoked by Fisher to explain how the several forms of the Rh antigen, presumably each determined by a single gene, could be inherited together as a unit. To geneticist Sheppard, the blood groups in man were in a way equivalent to butterfly wing color variations. Study of the inheritance of red cell antigens by Landsteiner, Levine, Wiener, Race, and others had produced the largest and most carefully worked out body of available data for humans on the transmission and interaction of specific genetic traits.

Butterfly wing colors had an advantage, for research purposes, in that the insects could be mated and genetically manipulated. But they had a disadvantage, too: Next to nothing was known about the chemistry of butterfly wing color control—how a gene creates color and what happens when several color-creating genes interact.

For human blood, on the other hand, there was a vast experimental and clinical literature, and even a situation inviting scrutiny in which a supergene's interaction with other genetic determinants might be assessed. That was the interaction of Rh and ABO, stemming from Levine's original observation on double incompatibility and Race's interpretation of it.

To Sheppard, the genetic situations in swallowtail mimicry and Rh seemed provocatively similar. In each case a closely related set of traits—the mimetic body changes of the insects, the various Rh factors in humans—seemed to be inherited as a unit because they were controlled by a supergene. Just as the supergene interacted with the butterfly's other genetic components in such a way that sex—maleness—canceled out its effect, so ABO incompatibility between fetus and mother interacted with and limited the effect of the Rh supergene by preventing Rh sensitization and erythroblastosis.

Sheppard thus saw in Rh-ABO interaction an opportunity to pursue his interest in the inheritance and interaction of closely linked genes and traits. "It is possible that an investigation of the blood groups will throw considerable light on the subject," he declared in 1953, at about the time he and Clarke began their butterfly studies.[7] Clarke, as a clinician, wanted to apply their reasoning and their research techniques to medical problems. To do so, he first set up a small genetic disease clinic in the hospital at which he was working. Then, in order to devote more time to research, he decided to leave private practice for an academic appointment.

The opening up of a position as *reader*, or associate professor, at Liverpool University's department of medicine provided a welcomed opportunity—which he seized. At that time, in the mid-1950s, clinical genetics was a new field of medical inquiry. It was also one that farsighted scientists could see would be of growing importance —and the trustees of the Nuffield Foundation, which continued to support Sheppard and Clarke's butterfly work, also agreed to support their human studies.

Clarke began at once to probe the interaction between blood groups and human disease. An early co-worker with him in this effort was a young physician in the department of medicine, Dr. Richard McConnell. A soft-spoken, agreeable man, whose rosy cheeks and rimless glasses lent to his face the cheerful countenance of a friendly bank official, McConnell had had considerably more contact with clinical blood work than any of the other members of the small group that began to grow up around Clarke. He bent his efforts to the research question of whether ABO blood groups had any influence on the incidence and severity of duodenal ulcers— and eventually found that they did.

Clarke and Sheppard meanwhile continued their butterfly breeding experiments and their quest for a method, and for a man, to pursue the human analogue to their swallowtails' mimetic supergene—the Rh factor.* The man they found was Ronnie Finn.

* Sheppard's familiarity with British theories of genetics, and especially the *supergene* concept, led to their study of blood. Ironically, the supergene, which was attacked violently by Wiener, eventually came to be regarded as, at best, inadequate, and in part inaccurate, even by Race himself.[8] Yet, even if Wiener had been right and Fisher wrong about the genetics of Rh, one can ask whether Wiener's formulation could have attracted Sheppard to his fruitful pursuit of Rh and ABO. "It may be wrong that Rhesus is a supergene," Clarke would comment years later. "But it was a useful idea, and one we believed at the time—and that's how we got to Rhesus." Sheppard would add that recent genetic knowledge renders both Wiener's and Fisher's theories archaic.

# 15

## Ronnie Finn

WHEN DR. RONALD FINN first met Cyril Clarke early in 1958 he was twenty-seven years old. He aspired to be, like Clarke, a specialist in internal medicine. Like Clarke, he knew next to nothing about the clinical problems of erythroblastosis, and in fact had never participated in an exchange transfusion on an erythroblastic infant.

In most matters social and professional and in temperament Clarke and Finn were far different from each other. Finn's family had recently arrived in England, having emigrated from Eastern Europe. He had been born, raised, and educated in Liverpool in modest circumstances and had won his medical degree, M.B., Ch.B. —Bachelor of Medicine, Bachelor of Surgery—from Liverpool University's medical school. He was a bright, boyish, ordinary-looking man who dressed plainly and may already have manifested a modest predisposition to plumpness.

In the British system, the Bachelor of Medicine degree—which earns its bearer the title *Mister*—qualifies a man to practice medicine. But medical rank and status are won by earning an M.D. degree. In Britain, unlike the United States, this is a difficult postgraduate chore, and is required for advancement into an academic position—a prestigious goal that Finn longed to attain. To win his M.D., a man had to conduct a substantial research project under the direction of a senior faculty man and present his findings in an acceptable thesis.

Finn had returned to the university to write his thesis. Clarke was assigned to be his advisor. Finn later would see himself as having been, at that moment, "just a bright boy," seeking entrance to the world of established medical men. He came to Clarke empty-handed, needing and seeking a thesis project. The authoritarian, Germanic model of education was much in evidence in England's graduate medical departments, and Finn had steeled himself to the task of carrying out an assigned piece of research.

For all his advance resolution, he nevertheless might have been forgiven his acute dismay upon learning from Clarke that his thesis topic was to be "The Relationship of ABO and Rh." "I, at the start, knew nothing at all about Rh," Finn would say later. "And I knew nothing about genetics. They—Professor Clarke and Dr. Sheppard —put me on this project. They said, 'Would you like to repeat Philip Levine's study and extend it?' "

Such a venture promised small direct return in internal medicine, the specialty in which Finn worked, and might later hope to teach. Still, self-confident in his intellectual abilities and determined to succeed, he was not inclined to give up without first trying his hand. He accepted the assignment.

Mostly what was wanted, he later would recall being told, was a duplication, in the Liverpudlian population, of Levine's study of ABO "protection" and the several attempts that had been made to explain it.

All prior investigations of ABO's role in Rh-incompatible pregnancies had been *retrospective*; that is, they were based on case histories already on file in hospital record rooms. As Finn would recall his assignment, Clarke felt there might be something to be learned from a *prospective* study, in which Rh-incompatible pregnancies were followed while in progress to find out whether, as one might predict, those that were ABO-incompatible produced fewer sick babies. As Finn understood his task, it was to re-explore and perhaps extend scientific understanding of Rh genetics. It had "nothing at all" to do with finding new ways to treat or prevent Rh disease.

Finn approached this task with few clinical preconceptions or hortatory notions about rhesus disease—a fact that he later would see as having been of singular advantage. Clarke recommended *Blood Groups in Man* as a basic text. Finn bought the then-current third edition, and studied the short, key passages on ABO and Rh that had been set as his point of departure.[1]

Finn accepted as his initial chore the routine and undramatic—but by no means easy—task of establishing statistically the true incidence of Rh disease in the Liverpool area. He set up headquarters for his thesis research just down the corridor from Clarke's office in the newly opened medical school building in Ashton Street, opposite the storybook Victorian structures of the Liverpool Royal Infirmary. Since he needed to continue his house calls and hospital medical practice by day, he often appeared at the school only late in the afternoon—and then stayed late into the evening. McConnell, who like Finn was a bachelor at that time, also stayed late, working on his project—ABO blood groups and ulcers.

To arrive at workable incidence figures for Rh sensitization and erythroblastosis, Finn analyzed admissions at several hospital obstetrical services in Liverpool, in conjunction with a genetic survey that Clarke had recently completed on Liverpudlian blood group distribution. The statistics yielded no surprises. But Finn, in thinking about them, nevertheless found them surprising. They showed that only 1 in every 20 Rh-incompatible deliveries in Liverpool yielded a baby with erythroblastosis.* Despite their Rh incompatibility with their mothers, 19 of every 20 babies at risk escaped illness: Their mothers had *failed* to become immunized against them. It was this fact, above all others, that first set Finn's mind to turning, and, three years later, he would start his thesis by saying: "One of the most puzzling features of erythroblastosis is that it occurs in only 5 percent of Rh-negative women at risk."[2]

From the salient fact that few are stricken while many are spared, it followed, Finn decided, that other mechanisms besides ABO incompatibility "must exist for the prevention of Rh immunization." It would be the main object of his life for the next couple of years to determine by what other means this majority was protected.

Finn's fixation on the 95 percent of threatened pregnancies that did *not* end up in trouble may seem an obvious lead, but in fact it prompted him to prospect a trail that most practicing Rh experts had ignored. Serologists, obstetricians, and pediatricians, called upon to diagnose and manage the illness, naturally focused their

---

* Different testing methods, by different investigators, using different patient populations, have yielded different incidence figures for Rh sensitization and for erythroblastosis. Thus, Ronnie Finn's initial finding was that 5 percent of pregnancies at risk resulted in sick babies. In later analyses at Liverpool, the risk rate would rise closer to the 10 percent that Vince Freda was to find at Presbyterian Hospital in New York City.

attention on the sick babies—the 5 percent—and their mothers. Finn, with absolutely no clinical responsibilities in erythroblastosis, thus was free to follow his imagination in the opposite direction— toward an understanding of the 95 percent who did not get sick, in order to better understand why they had been spared.

Statistically, the relative infrequency of Rh-incompatible matings that were also ABO-incompatible meant that no more than 20 percent of the babies who were spared could be said to owe their survival to the protection afforded by double incompatibility. Nonetheless, it had seemed clear to many investigators that a more precise understanding of *how* ABO incompatibility protected, and *how well*, might be valuable knowledge.

Levine, it will be remembered, had analyzed the ABO blood groups of the fathers and mothers of erythroblastic infants and had found that fewer were ABO-incompatible than might have been anticipated—in point of fact, 25 percent instead of the 35 percent ABO-incompatible matings that occur in the population as a whole. Nevertheless, ABO incompatibility could hardly be called absolute "protection" against erythroblastosis, since one erythroblastic pregnancy in four (25 percent), was ABO-incompatible.

There was a flaw in this study, however, which several researchers, including Levine, would later remark: he had analyzed the ABO status of the *father* vis-à-vis the mother. Yet clearly, it was the ABO status of the *fetus* vis-à-vis the mother that mattered—and that might be different. ABO-*in*compatible parents can conceive an infant that is ABO-compatible with its mother.

This can occur because each individual parent carries two ABO blood group genes, but passes only one on to each offspring. Thus a group A father may carry two genes for A so that his *genotype* is:

AA.

Or, he may carry one gene for A and one gene for O, in which case his genotype is:

AO.

When his blood is tested it invariably is group A, because A is dominant and O is recessive.

A mother who is group O has two identical recessive genes:

OO.

When a group A father and a group O mother conceive a child, one of two things can happen. If the baby gets an A gene from its father and an O gene from its mother,

$$A \times O,$$

it will have the genes AO, the blood group A, and be incompatible with its mother.

But if the baby gets an O gene from its father and gets a second O from its mother:

$$O \times O,$$

then it will have the genes OO and will be blood group O. Its blood cells carry no antigen that would cause them to be quickly destroyed once they got into its mother's circulatory system. This fetus, unlike its father, is ABO-compatible with its mother, and hence will not be protected from a coexisting Rh incompatibility with her.

Most group A individuals are of the genotype AO. Since half the offspring of a mating between an AO father and an OO mother will produce OO offspring compatible with their mothers, it was difficult to judge, on the basis of parental blood types alone, how many Rh-incompatible pregnancies were not being protected because of a flaw in the ABO "protection" mechanism and how many were not being protected because the fetus in fact was ABO-compatible with its mother.

A much more accurate—and dramatic—estimate of the strength, or efficacy, of protection provided by ABO incompatibility became available when enough cases could be collected of the rare matings in which the father was group AB and Rh-positive and the mother group O and Rh-negative.

| FATHER | MOTHER |
|--------|--------|
| AB     | OO     |
| Rh+    | Rh−    |

In these marriages the offspring must get an A or a B gene from its father, and will invariably be either AO or BO; i.e., group A or group B. In either instance it will be ABO-incompatible with its mother.

Levine had been on the lookout for such cases. Yet as late as 1955 he could report to a meeting in New York of the Columbia University Seminar on Genetics and the Evolution of Man that he had not found even one clear-cut instance in which a group AB father and a group O mother had given birth to an Rh-incompatible erythroblastic infant.[3] When the fetus' ABO incompatibility with its mother was guaranteed by the fact that its father was group AB, it was virtually 100 percent protected against Rh sensitization and erythroblastosis!

Others confirmed this striking finding in surveys in which the number of sick babies born to families where the father was AB and the mother O—designated as AB × O mating—was compared with the number of sick babies in which the father was O and the mother AB. In the latter, O × AB matings, the mother has neither anti-A nor anti-B antibodies, and hence her fetus will always be ABO-compatible with her. If ABO afforded no protection, then one could expect that AB × O and O × AB matings would produce an equal number of erythroblastic infants. In fact, Finn would find, in one report on 1,742 Rh-sensitized families there were 29 cases of erythroblastosis in unprotected O × AB combinations, but no cases at all in protected AB × O matings.[4] In Liverpool, he would eventually uncover more than a dozen erythroblastic births in unprotected O × AB families, but only one in an AB × O mating.

The action of an O mother's anti-A and anti-B antibody clearly was so enormously effective in destroying A and B fetal red cells that in the unquestionably protected AB × O matings, Rh sensitization rarely—if ever—occurred. In the first report published on the Liverpool Rh research, this is stated strongly, in conditional terms: If Race and Sanger are correct, and ABO-incompatible cells are destroyed in the maternal circulation before they can immunize the mother against the Rh antigen, then an Rh-negative woman of group O married to an Rh-positive AB man is unlikely to bear any erythroblastic offspring since each child is bound to be incompatible in the ABO system.[5]

Ronnie Finn was now deeply immersed in Rh. His thinking had been shaped by Clarke and Sheppard, by Race and Sanger, by Levine—and by his own fixation on the fact that while many pregnancies are in jeopardy of Rh sensitization, few actually are struck by it. Two foreign investigators would also decisively influence him. The first was Finnish. The second was German. Finn later would say that, without them, his thinking about Rh would never have advanced beyond the academic, investigative stage.*

---

* Interestingly, both the Finnish and the German research, and the approaches they suggested to Finn, would be overlooked by Vince and John, in New York, until after they had formulated their own plan to prevent Rh sensitization with injections of anti-Rh gamma globulin.

The work in Finland was known to Sheppard and Clarke before Finn entered the picture. A key part of Ronnie Finn's thesis assignment was to try to confirm it in Liverpool. The Finnish investigator was Dr. Harri Nevanlinna, the scion of a distinguished Helsinki family. He had won his colleagues' respect for his service in World War II: Overcoming shortages, he transfused battlefield casualties with blood collected in soft-drink bottles. Nevanlinna had graduated from medical school in 1948 and had gone to work for the Finnish Red Cross. He was trained as a pediatrician; his bent was to population immunogenetics—and his choice for a thesis topic had been Rh.

Erythroblastosis was far more common in Finland than in England or the United States, due to genetic factors and differences in family size. It was also a quite severe disease in the late 1940s. Exchange transfusions had just been introduced and would provide some relief; previously the death rate in sensitized pregnancies had been 70 percent.

Nevanlinna, who was twenty-eight when he started his thesis, had realized—a full decade before Finn and Vince Freda—that the theories advanced in the medical literature to explain how and why Rh sensitization occurred were poor, at best, and probably incorrect. He was "amazed," he would say later, to find that Levine, Wiener, and the other great first-generation Rh experts had "paid attention only to the sick babies of the immunized mothers," and had ignored "the preceding, healthy infants. They had no interest in the *mechanism* by which immunization occurred." It was precisely that problem that keenly interested Nevanlinna.

He chose as his axiom the observation that erythroblastosis rarely occurs in first pregnancies. From this, he reasoned, Rh immunization requires not one, but two separate and distinct stimuli, in two pregnancies. The first, the primary stimulus of antigenic red cells, primed, or "sensibilized" the mother's antibody-producing mechanism—but did not result in the production of antibody that would harm the baby. "The primary importance of the first pregnancy in the immunization process had no doubt mostly been overlooked," Nevanlinna declared. "The Rh antigen must escape from the fetus during the first pregnancy (or delivery), resulting in a change in the mother's mode of reaction."[6]

Now primed, when next this mother's immune system was subjected to Rh antigen, she would become *immunized*. She would have a secondary, or *immune*, reaction, manifest in the production of antibody that would cross the placenta and injure the baby.

It was Nevanlinna's intuition that it was the first, primary stimulus that was the key to Rh sensitization: once it occurred, all subsequent Rh-positive pregnancies were foreordained to produce antibody and the consequent destruction of the fetus' blood. If this were true, moreover, any explanation of why immunization and disease did *not* occur in most pregnancies would have to focus not

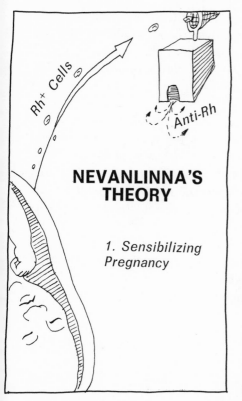

**NEVANLINNA'S THEORY**

*1. Sensibilizing Pregnancy*

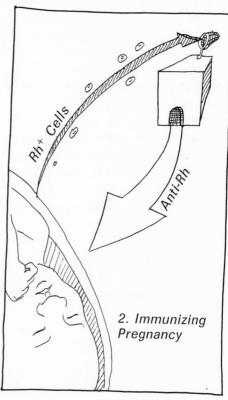

*2. Immunizing Pregnancy*

on the pregnancy of the moment, but on the woman's *preceding* pregnancy.

Nevanlinna's argument may well be the most subtle, sophisticated, and prolix blend of clinical medicine, immunogenetics, and mathematical logic in the entire Rh corpus. His conclusions, however, are crystal clear—and simple. He confirmed his intuition on the determinative role of the first antigenic stimulus by studying 21 women who had had Rh-incompatible blood transfusions and then had given birth to Rh-incompatible babies: 19 of the 21 babies suffered hemolytic disease; most cases were severe or fatal. This demonstrated, Nevanlinna said, that once a primary stimulus occurred—and most women clearly were susceptible to it—the subsequent pregnancies almost invariably would be severely affected. Previous theories that it was a slow buildup of antibody in the mother that eventually caused erythroblastosis could now be discounted. Once a primary stimulus occurred, the next stimulus would provoke a strong immune response—it was an "all or nothing" phenomenon.

If this were so, and if Levine and the others were right when they said that even the tiniest amount of blood would trigger the secondary, immune response, in the pregnancy that produced a sick baby, then why was it that only a small fraction of women at risk received primary sensitization in any given pregnancy? What protected the others?

Since the unknown factor that seemed to prevent this primary stimulus seemed to operate in a relatively uniform manner in various national groups, Nevanlinna reasoned that it must be a genetic determinant—as Wiener and Levine both suspected. The ABO protection first hinted at by Levine seemed the most likely explanation —except that, in keeping with his two-pregnancy theory of sensitization, Nevanlinna realized he would have to look both at the pregnancies that produced the secondary, immune response with sick babies and *at the prior, sensibilizing pregnancies that preceded them.* No one had ever done that before.

Nevanlinna did. The results were dramatic:[7]

|  | CHILDREN ABO-INCOMPATIBLE WITH MOTHER | CHILDREN ABO-COMPATIBLE WITH MOTHER |
|---|---|---|
| *First sick child* | 17 | 15 |
| *Last healthy child* | 11 | 39 |

Among the first-afflicted children in the Rh-incompatible families, 17 were ABO-incompatible with their mothers and 15 were ABO-compatible. In other words, the purported protective mechanism of ABO incompatibility was absolutely inoperative in pregnancies that produced families' first erythroblastic babies. The "protective" effect was similarly absent in second and subsequent sensitized pregnancies, for in this group 16 children were ABO-incompatible with their mothers while almost the same number were ABO-compatible. Nevanlinna could conclude that "ABO incompatibility evidently has not inhibited the manifestation of immunization" in the already-primed pregnancies that actually produced ill infants.

Only when he looked at the healthy children born immediately *before* the first sick child in each family could he find evidence— striking evidence—of ABO incompatibility's protective role: among the 50 next-youngest brothers and sisters of erythroblastic babies, 39 were ABO-compatible with their mothers while only 11 were ABO-incompatible. "Hence," Nevanlinna declared, with emphasis, "the inhibitory effect of A and B properties has acted upon the so-called sensibilisation stimulus"—the pregnancy before the first sick child.

Usually, though not always—i.e., 78 percent of the time—the sensibilizing pregnancy was one that was not protected by ABO incompatibility between mother and fetus. Once sensitization had occurred, however, it made absolutely no difference whether the next—the *first affected*—fetus was ABO-compatible or incompatible, for ABO incompatibility would not protect it. The mother invariably would get her second, immunizing dose of its Rh-positive cells, make antibody, and make it ill. The only time that ABO protection was operative—and, hence, *the time when sensitization must be occurring*—was the pregnancy before the first sick child appeared. As Clarke, in Liverpool, later would quip: "It's the baby that's all right that does the damage!"

Finn, in Liverpool, and Vince Freda, in New York, later would find fault with Nevanlinna's theory that two kinds of stimuli—a primary, sensibilizing stimulus and a second, immunizing stimulus —are needed for antibody production. But once they learned of his work, neither would ever doubt that, brilliantly and painstakingly, Nevanlinna had fixed the events of the *preceding*, visibly unaffected pregnancy as the juncture at which the fate of each as-yet-unconceived baby was irrevocably set.

With the exception of Race and Sanger and the Liverpool group, Nevanlinna's peers and elders in the Rh and blood communities reacted poorly to his theories. Having spent five years on Rh, failing to see new avenues which he might fruitfully pursue, faced with growing administrative demands at the Finnish Red Cross, and attracted to new research ventures—Nevanlinna dropped Rh. Little did he know then, in 1955, that he had made a brilliant contribution.

Finn, three years later, was gripped by Nevanlinna's findings, and he attempted to repeat Nevanlinna's investigation in the families of erythroblastic babies whom he was keeping track of in several Liverpool hospitals. This meant attempting, through interviews in the mother's home, to ascertain the ABO and Rh blood types of each of her children, as well as of her husband.

Data of this nature can be surprisingly difficult to obtain and verify. Neither patients nor their families are eager to be stuck to "give" blood when there is no obvious benefit in return, which certainly there was not from Finn. People suspect that doctors are spying out things that are none of anybody's business. They believe, correctly, that blood studies can bring to light illegitimate conceptions as well as unreported abortions and stillbirths.

By late 1958 Finn had investigated 91 families into which Rh erythroblastic babies had been born. As Nevanlinna had predicted, there were far fewer protected A $\times$ O matings than unprotected O $\times$ A matings. But because of difficulties in documentation, Finn was able to determine the blood group of the "sensibilizing" fetus with certitude in only 14 of the families. In each and every one of the 14, however, this last healthy fetus in fact was compatible with its mother—a finding that was even more clear-cut and striking than Nevanlinna's. Finn found it fascinating to plot each family's childbearing history, marking an *I* in his notebook for each ABO-incompatible fetus and a *C* for each that was ABO-compatible; *X* marked a sensitized pregnancy with a sick child. A family's successive pregnancies might be *I, I, I, C, X*, or *I, C, X*, or just *C, X* if the disease appeared in the second child. As long as the preceding pregnancies were *I*'s with no *C*'s there was little or no danger for the baby that was coming. But when *C* came up, even though the baby was entirely well, then invariably it was the very next pregnancy that was *X*.

"All the data are therefore consistent with an ABO-incompatible fetus giving complete protection against Rh sensitization."[8] This conclusion appears in the first report of the Liverpool Rh work, late in 1958, for which Finn shares authorship with Clarke, who is senior author, Sheppard, and McConnell, whose serologic knowledge and suggestions Finn was finding more and more helpful as he plunged deeper into Rh protective mechanisms.

If all Rh-incompatible pregnancies were also ABO-incompatible, Finn thought to himself, then the problem of erythroblastosis would no longer exist. But not more than 20 percent of at-risk pregnancies were so protected. What usually protected the others?

It made sense to Finn that in most instances the placenta had stood up against penetration of fetal cells into the mother. Hence there had been no antigenic stimulus, and no dangerous immune response. But there was no way to *prove* this. Two decades after Darrow and Levine had postulated that passage of fetal cells into the mother caused sensitization, Race and Sanger still had been forced to concede that while large numbers of "fetal cells have on several occasions been clearly demonstrated in the maternal circulation, . . . whether or not placental bleeding is the usual cause of maternal immunization by a fetus is not known."[9] Neither was there a practical way known to find out.

# 16

## *"Then the Penny Dropped!"*

FATE—or perhaps it was only what Finn later would call "fortuitous coincidence"—here played a card for Liverpool. What she provided was a method for measuring, with a fair degree of accuracy, the number of individual fetal red cells present in a test tube of mother's blood. Finding these cells is not unlike finding a few scattered grains of sugar in a teaspoonful of salt, since under the low-power microscope—the stage upon which the drama of fetal bleeds is enacted—a fetal red cell is visually indistinguishable from the thousands of maternal red cells that surround it.

The technique that would make the odd fetal cell stand out clearly for counting had first been worked out by Dr. Enno Kleihauer, a young researcher in the pediatric clinic at the University of Freiburg, in West Germany. He had published his technique in a German journal in 1957.[1] Kleihauer had no interest in erythroblastosis. He did want to be able to find fetal red cells in adult blood. To do so, he exploited the fact that the stuff of fetal red cells differs chemically from that of adult red cells. By carefully manipulating the chemical composition of the fluid in which a sample of mixed adult and fetal cells was suspended, Kleihauer succeeded in leaching the dark red hemoglobin out of the adult cells, while leaving the chemically different fetal hemoglobin behind, inside the fetal cells. Under the microscope, only the ghostlike empty outer membranes of the adult red cells remained; the sharp pink spots of hemoglobin in the undamaged fetal cells stood out sharply and clearly by contrast. By counting the number of fetal cells on a microscope field, it was possible to calculate the ratio of fetal to maternal cells in the sample and estimate the total number of fetal cells present in the five or so quarts of blood that fill the average woman's vascular system.

A Canadian saw Kleihauer's original paper and guessed his test's potential. Pediatrician Dr. Alvin Zipursky of the University of Manitoba in Winnipeg—the site of Canada's leading Rh research center —set out at once to study transplacental bleeds with the new test. While Rh did not play a part in his experiments, Zipursky successfully established the Kleihauer test's accuracy in quantifying fetus-to-mother bleeds. He reported his work in *Lancet*.[2]

It was from Zipursky that Finn first learned of Kleihauer's technique. Its impact on the Liverpool investigation is clear from the fact that McConnell, a full decade later, would clearly remember the morning early in March 1959 when Clarke strode into the laboratory waving aloft the new issue of *Lancet*: "Crickey!" he exclaimed. "Here's what we've been waiting for." With the Kleihauer test Finn might demonstrate that women with effective, unbreached placentas which did not leak fetal red cells did not get sensitized to the Rh factor, while women in whom fetal cells could be found had placental leaks and would become immunized to Rh.

It was agreed that Finn would begin doing Kleihauers on the Rh-incompatible pregnant women whose bloods he was studying. He would have assistance from one of Britain's most highly regarded laboratory technicians, Mr. W. T. A. Donohoe, who had recently been brought into the Liverpool department of medicine at McConnell's suggestion.

Finn and Donohoe quickly found that despite its seeming simplicity, the Kleihauer test required excruciatingly exact technique: The chemicals had to be made up immediately before being used; storing them ruined the results. A slight deviation in the angle at which a Kleihauer slide was held under the water tap for washing could result in too little of the adult hemoglobin being washed away or too much of the fetal hemoglobin going along with it.

Counting cells on a blood slide, moreover, is akin to counting stars in the sky—much depends on the plane on which the viewer focuses his eyes and the acuity of his vision. To standardize the counts, Finn took the average number of fetal cells found in four three-minute counts from each patient's blood as her "fetal score."

With the test's chemistry now under control, he next examined, unlabeled, 50 blood specimens from adult males—who presumably would not have any fetal hemoglobin in their veins—that were mixed among 50 specimens from recently delivered women. A total of four three-minute "counts" were made for each individual's blood. Finn found no more than 0.5 "fetal" cells, on the average, in any of the male bloods. To assure a safe margin for error, he therefore set a score of 2 fetal cells per three-minute scan as the base line for proven transplacental bleeds in women. He calculated that a fetal score of 5 meant that a total of 1 ml, one-fifth of a teaspoonful, of fetal blood had entered the maternal circulation. Then Finn began using the Kleihauer test to study the blood of Rh-incompatible women.

By now it was the spring of 1959; Finn had become completely caught up in his project, for with the Kleihauer test there beckoned before him the possibility of resolving once and for all the mystery of why only a small percentage of Rh-negative women become sensitized to the Rh factor. This was a mystery that Levine, whom Finn had come to regard as the doyen of Rh research, had been the first to penetrate when he suggested that ABO blood groups influenced Rh. It would be an honor if he, Finn, could end the mystery by proving that the dominant protective mechanism in the majority of Rh-incompatible pregnancies was the leak-resistant integrity of the intact placenta. The "rhesus project" had become the dominating interest in his life. According to his own testimony later, Finn awoke thinking about it in the morning; turned and returned it in his mind while going about his professional tasks of the day; and still had rhesus in mind when he fell asleep at night. The Kleihauer slides were keeping him in the laboratory later and later each evening. He had a special key made so that he could enter and leave the university after everyone else had gone home. In the department, Finn was beginning to be called "the night shift."

A bachelor with few responsibilities outside his practice and the thesis research, Finn would toil on his project six nights a week and on weekends. It was essentially solitary work at this stage, he would later say: There was no one else at his level in the department who knew much—or cared much—about Rh. Clarke listened carefully to his progress reports and, as his patron, provided access and entree to patients and resources needed for his research. But it was not in discussions with Clarke or in bull sessions with colleagues in the department that the work moved forward. Years later Finn would say, "Professor Clarke and I were very much in the relationship of master and pupil. We didn't really talk about much of anything." Moreover, as McConnell would recollect later, the rhesus work commanded little interest because most department members, including Clarke, shared Race and Sanger's view that this was a clinical problem about which not much more could be done.

Finn kept his counsel. His single-mindedness in pursuit of his project began to concern his family. His mother, like mothers everywhere, reminded him, helpfully, that his closest boyhood and medical school friend—hadn't they graduated together?—was already married and settling down in a fine private practice. Yet here was her Ronald, spending his nights locked away in the laboratory instead of going out looking for a nice girl to wed.

But Finn was adamant—and determined. He sensed he was on to something, and would pursue it. He examined more and more bloods, from more and more newly delivered Rh-negative women —as many specimens each week as he could find and process. Fairly soon it began to be apparent that transplacental bleeds large enough to leave more than two fetal cells in any one field were quite uncommon. At most, these bleeds occurred in 10 to 15 percent of pregnant women.

For the first time in his project, Finn was beginning to stake out new territory. Unlike Zipursky, he was correlating his Kleihauer findings with the ABO and Rh status of mother and fetus—this was something that no one else had thought to do.

His data, though sparse at first, were quite gratifying: In the one mother in ten in whom he could find fetal cells, indicative of a transplacental bleed, the fetus was ABO-compatible with the mother. But if the fetus was ABO-incompatible with the mother— and hence protected—no fetal cells could be found.

Peering into his binocular microscope night after night, slide after slide, Finn began to anticipate that when the fetus and mother were ABO-incompatible, he would find no fetal cells in the maternal blood. Here, before his very eyes, was the first confirmation in patients of Race's hypothesis that ABO incompatibility "protects" a mother from Rh sensitization because the antigenic fetal cells get destroyed by maternal anti-A or anti-B antibody— before they can sensitize her to the Rh factor.

Finn was not seeing fetal cells in the ABO-incompatible mothers because any that had gotten into them had been quickly destroyed. But if fetal cells could be seen, then the fetus and the mother were ABO-compatible; no protective mechanism was operative. The dark refractile fetal red cells on his slide meant that some, at least, of these mothers would become sensitized to the Rh factor. Slides without cells were from mothers who were protected—they were safe from Rh sensitization. If only the slides with fetal cells could be changed—if they could be freed of the fetal cells—they too would be "protected": the jeopardized mothers would have the same, almost perfect protection as mothers blessed by ABO incompatibility with their fetuses. The protective mechanisms against Rh sensitization would be extended from the 20 percent of women who were naturally protected to 50 percent, or even perhaps close to 100 percent if ways could be found to destroy the sensitizing doses of fetal cells!

Finn's mind had subconsciously bridged the gap from a study of natural "protective mechanisms" to possible methods of duplicating natural protection in women who did not naturally have it. What would have to be done to remove the fetal cells on the Kleihauer blood slides? What would have to be done so that none of the Kleihauer blood slides showed fetal cells—so that *all* women might be protected?

It came to Finn's mind that a way to destroy the fetal cells he was finding in mothers' bloods was to inject the mothers with an antibody against fetal hemoglobin. An antifetal hemoglobin antibody would have the virtue of acting selectively; it would not damage the mothers' red cells, which contain adult hemoglobin; it would attack only the invading fetal cells. But Finn doubted that an antibody against fetal hemoglobin would be effective since it would be unable to penetrate the cell membrane to get at the hemoglobin inside; moreover, the real target was not the hemoglobin inside the red cells but the Rh antigen sites on the outside surface.

"Then the penny dropped!" Finn later would say. If not antifetal hemoglobin, then perhaps antibody that would home in on the Rh antigen sites themselves and destroy them, along with the fetal cells upon which they were borne. *Anti-Rh antibody* might destroy fetal red cells before they could cause sensitization. Then the Kleihauer slides for ABO-compatible women would be as free of fetal cells as the Kleinhauer's for ABO-incompatible women. Most, or even all, of them might be protected against Rh sensitization.

Dr. Finn, analyzing Kleihauer slides, realized that if blood of new mother that contained many dark fetal cells (left) could be treated so no fetal cells appeared (right) she would be spared Rh sensitization and her next baby would not be ill. (*D.R.Z., 1969; Kleihauer slides Courtesy Dr. Finn.*)

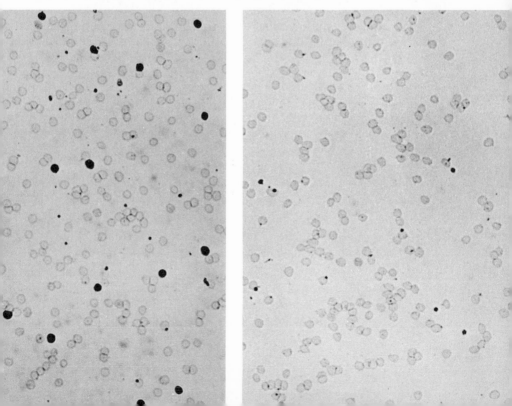

Unlike Vince Freda and John Gorman, who would arrive at the same endpoint a few months later by an altogether different route, Finn had not reached the idea of prophylactic anti-Rh injections through give and take in conversation. His recollection, many years later, would be that he came on the idea alone and by himself—and that it had dawned on him slowly over a matter of weeks or even several months as he moved slide after Kleihauer slide across his microscope's stage for its critically timed three-minute appearance. ABO-incompatible slides showed no fetal cells and were protected. Slides that showed fetal cells were ABO-compatible and unprotected. Destroy the fetal cells that show up on unprotected slides, and then the women behind these blood samples will also be protected. Antibody that mimicked anti-A and anti-B was needed. Anti-Rh would do it.

Later, Finn would feel that the idea had not occurred in a flash. Rather, it was the opposite of Archimedes, who, upon seeing the water rise when he stepped into his bath, realized that the same method would measure the volume of the King's crown—his assigned task—and had exclaimed "*Eureka!*—I have found it." For Finn there was no *Eureka!* and in retrospect he would say that he probably had the solution to his problem in mind for some time before he became consciously aware that he had it. He would picture himself as a thoroughly illogical, nonmethodical thinker.

"But I am a dreamer—and there is a close link between creative thinking and scientific thinking. I spent the whole of my childhood in a dream world, and I still do this—dream. And that's how this work was done. I'd spent several years thinking, speculating about this all of the time; it dominated my life. I thought about it all the time.

"I am a dreamer. I live in a world of my own. I don't need company. I don't need people. I could quite happily live on a desert island with my thoughts and a few books. And it was in an illogical, dreamlike way that I got to it. I must have permuted these thoughts—Levine's ABO protective mechanism, Nevanlinna, destruction of fetal cells—a million times in my mind and finally they came together. It was not done in a logical cold-blooded way. I think this dreaming is the way scientific creativity is done."

True to this unmethodical manner of thinking, Finn kept neither diary nor notebook in which to write down his idea. The exact date he became aware of it is unrecorded.

Given the slow rate at which Finn was able to collect significant cases and the tedious labor of the Kleihauer test, he accomplished his key thinking quickly—certainly within a year. What is known is that by February 18, 1960, he had formulated the idea, for that is the date he first gave voice to it in public.

The occasion was a postgraduate education program that Clarke had arranged for Liverpool medical practitioners at their local professional society, the Liverpool Medical Institution. Several men in the university's department of medicine described work they had in progress. Finn prepared a rather stiff historical review of erythroblastosis, drawn largely from the library work he had done for his thesis; in the seventeenth century, he related, the midwife to Marie de Médicis, the French queen, had described several interesting cases of what would later be known as erythroblastosis.

Finn touched briefly on Levine, Race and Sanger, and Nevanlinna, including his own confirmatory study, and described the Kleihauer test. "Using a modification of this method," he said, "we have been able to demonstrate that fetal cells can often be found in the maternal blood in compatible matings following delivery, but we have never been able to find them in incompatible matings." Then turning to the meeting chairman, Finn said: "Mr. President, may I conclude on a highly speculative note . . . ? We have found that about 10 percent of women have over 1 ml of fetal blood in their circulation following delivery. It is very likely that this will lead to the production of antibodies in a high percentage of cases, and from this small selected group of women will arise the future cases of erythroblastosis. We are investigating this point at the moment, but if the hypothesis proves correct, then examination of a primigravida's blood following delivery will enable us to predict with a high level of accuracy the likelihood of erythroblastosis in a further pregnancy.

"It might then be possible to destroy the fetal cells with a suitable antibody, and so prevent the future development of erythroblastosis, thus imitating the natural protection afforded by ABO incompatibility."[3]

In a summary of the meeting, the *Lancet* two weeks later published Finn's proposal, leaving unspecified—as he had in his written text—the determination of what would be "a suitable" antibody.[4] One could speculate that by this point in time Finn had not decided on anti-Rh antibody over antifetal hemoglobin. But McConnell, who shared the podium with Clarke, Finn, and other members of their department, would remember, years later, that regardless of what Finn had *written*, he *said* "anti-Rh antibody" in his speech.

Finn's proposal surprised McConnell. Though his rapport with Finn was perhaps the best of anyone's in the department, this was the first he had heard of the prevention idea. And it surprised him further—though not pleasantly—that Finn had chosen to blurt it out before an audience of medical practitioners, who were not at-tuned to "far-out" new ideas, rather than save it for a meeting of highly qualified academic researchers. "He's got nerve saying that out loud; it's speculation," McConnell said to himself. But what surprised McConnell the most—and did please him—was the sense, as he thought about it, that Finn's proposal really was a very good one.

# 17

## *Surprises*

A FEW MONTHS LATER Finn did present his proposal to a group of research-oriented colleagues, as McConnell wished he had done in the first place. His audience was the British Genetical Society. The time was July. Finn now specified, in his "highly speculative" peroration, that the best antibody for destroying Rh-positive cells in a mother's blood might be "a powerful anti-Rh."[1]

His auditors did not stand on their chairs and cheer. McConnell, who attended the meeting with Finn, would remember that "all the big-time geneticists treated us as harmless lambs. Why, men had spent their lives on Rhesus! And yet, here we came, rank amateurs, who were not even serologists!" The whole thing seemed too improbable to be believed.

Finn's talk was not published, so John and Vince, in New York, never read it, although they were by then embarked on the path to a similar solution to erythroblastosis. No one knew at the time how close the race would turn out to have been. In retrospect, however, it seems clear that the idea of using anti-Rh arose in Liverpool several months before it occurred to Vince and John.

In Finn's two talks, the key part of one of which had been published in the *Lancet*, and in the *BMJ* report a year later, Liverpool clearly had priority of publication.

Ironically, the man who might have been a closer competitor to

Ronnie Finn than even Vince and John, but whose efforts largely were to be forgotten, was the Chicago immunologist, Kurt Stern. Finn's talk to the British Genetical Society in July is the first documented reference to his plan that specifies "anti-Rh" antibody, and at that time Finn had done nothing experimentally to demonstrate that it would work. Yet only a few weeks later, in August, Stern told the American Association of Blood Banks, in San Francisco, that his experiments, then fully completed, showed, as stated in his abstract in the meeting program, that "injection of Rh-negative recipients with Rh-positive ABO-compatible red cells previously coated *in vitro* with anti-Rh antibody . . . failed to produce Rh sensitization even after exposure to the antigen."[2]

This essentially was the experiment, and the result, needed to confirm Finn's—and Vince and John's—proposal, with the qualification that the Rh antigen and anti-Rh antibody would have to be injected separately to duplicate a fetus-to-mother bleed and an intended antidote. Stern had mixed the two substances before injecting them.

Stern nevertheless had taken an important step toward proving the antibody's protective potential. Had he realized this, and said so then, having done a key experiment, his claim would at least have equalled Liverpool's. But Stern did not realize what he had achieved. When he learned of Liverpool's labors, nine months after his San Francisco talk, he played the game as a gentleman; he staked no retroactive claim.[3] There was something else that neither Stern nor Finn could know in the summer of 1960: In the months immediately ahead Stern would, also unwittingly, lend a lifesaving hand to the Liverpool project.

Finn knew that experiments would be needed to determine if, in fact, anti-Rh injections would forestall immunization in Rh-negative men who were deliberately exposed to the Rh factor. Yet he made headway with the idea only slowly in his department. McConnell, who may have been the first to see promise in his proposal, would remember a Saturday morning in 1960, possibly in the spring, on which he and Finn were alone together in the laboratory talking about Finn's idea. McConnell picked up the telephone and placed a call to Clarke, at his home in the suburbs.

"We must get on with this," he remembers saying. "We must get some volunteers. I think it will work!"

Was it ethical? Clarke wanted to know. Would it be proper to inject men with the Rh factor? It might prove harmful if any of the men subsequently needed a transfusion, and was inadvertently given Rh-positive blood! An expert consultation was needed.

The following week, Clarke and McConnell went down to London to visit Race and Sanger.

"It's a jolly good idea!" Race later would recall saying.

"*You* thought it up!" he would remember Clarke replying, in allusion to Race's theory of ABO protection, which Liverpool hoped to duplicate with anti-Rh. Race, not having pursued the idea himself, declined credit.

"The problem will be in getting the volunteers," he predicted. But once they had been found, and had consented to participate in the experiment, Race could see nothing unethical in exposing them to the risk of Rh sensitization.

"What form of antibody would you use?" Clarke wanted to know.

Race replied that since the anti-A and anti-B that were destroying fetal cells in ABO-incompatible pregnancies were predominantly of the 19S form, a 19S anti-Rh would be the one to use.

Finn, meanwhile, who also favored 19S, had two major roadblocks to think his way through. One was the experts' belief that sensitization occurs *during* pregnancy, through continuous small transplacental leakage of fetal blood. If true, it would be foolish to administer antibody at delivery; the damage would already have been done.* Finn, like Vince in New York, now had strong motivation, absent in other investigators, to rethink the problem of when sensitization does, in fact, occur—with the hope that what he *wanted* to be so, namely, that sensitization occurs at delivery, *would*, in fact, be so.

While Vince at first based his hopes in part on clinical intuition, Finn, who delivered no babies, came to this conclusion through analysis of his Kleihauer slides. By February 1961, when he reached the end of this study, he had examined the blood of 256 newly delivered mothers. He had detected fetal bleeds of 2 or more cells per three-minute scan in about 15 percent of them.[4] This was a far higher percentage than would be expected to become newly sensitized to the Rh factor; Finn had calculated, it will be recalled, that 5 percent of all pregnancies at risk result in a "bad" baby, and he now estimated that only about 2 percent occurred in previously unsensitized women. While this figure later would turn out to be

---

* The idea that this protection might be provided *during* pregnancy was never seriously entertained at Liverpool because of the risk to the fetus.

far too low, it fit nicely with the thesis Finn wished to prove with his data.

Of the 256 women, he followed 97 who were Rh-negative mothers of Rh-positive fetuses to see if they would develop anti-Rh antibodies in the postpartum period. All were previously unsensitized to the Rh factor. Three of the 97 had had large bleeds of 20 ml or more—or five teaspoonsful—of fetal blood.

Antibody studies done several months postpartum showed that two of the three women—or exactly the anticipated 2 percent—had in fact become sensitized to the Rh factor. Among the other 94 women, who had had smaller bleeds, only one became sensitized—under anomalous circumstances.

If the rare huge bleeds would account for the observed incidence of sensitization, then there was no need to postulate that slow leakage caused any part of it. More important, truly large bleeds seemed much more likely to occur while the juncture between the fetal and maternal circulations was being ripped and torn—at delivery—rather than during the previous, relatively quiescent, period of pregnancy. All of Finn's reasoning, moreover, confirmed—and was confirmed by—the one fact about erythroblastosis that nobody questioned: The disease rarely occurred in the first pregnancy. Finn now could see clearly that this was because sensitization rarely occurs until the moment pregnancy ended. "If the antigenic stimulus occurred early in pregnancy," he declared, "one would expect that the instances of the disease would be more common in first pregnancies. This argues that the episode of sensitization usually occurs . . . during the process of labor . . . when the utero-placental juncture is subjected to severe trauma."[5]

There was one final advantage to the big-bleed-at-delivery theory of sensitization: Not every woman would have to be treated with anti-Rh antibody. In fact, if a threshold could be established for the amount of fetal cells necessary to cause sensitization, then it would be possible, by doing Kleihauer tests on each Rh-incompatible woman at delivery, to pick out the two or three in every hundred who stood at risk of sensitization. They alone would need treatment with the cell-destroying anti-Rh antibody.

Another roadblock seemed far more difficult to surmount. That was the problem of how the injected anti-Rh antibody would be able to find the few fetal cells, lost in oceans of maternal blood, to destroy them. An ABO-incompatible mother's serum, for example, was filled with natural anti-A or anti-B antibody, ready to pounce on intruding A or B fetal cells. But any reasonable amount of anti-Rh antibody that might be injected—whether as gamma globulin or as high-titer anti-Rh serum—was bound to be swallowed up and lost in the mother's circulation. *

"At first," Finn declared a year later, "the anti-Rh seemed an attractive idea. But on further consideration of the dilution factors, it seemed to have very little chance of success. If you consider that there is 5 ml of fetal blood present, [each fetal cell] would be separated from its neighbor by thousands of adult cells. Even if the antibody were powerful, this would be like looking for a needle in a haystack.

"If we were to give 10 ml of even a powerful antibody, it would be diluted by at least five liters of maternal blood . . . and this might even involve diffusion through 20 liters of extracellular fluid. It is hardly conceivable that even a powerful antibody would retain any significant potency after such dilution, especially against a widely dispersed target.

"With these considerations, we almost gave up the whole project, but owing to the attractiveness of the idea, we decided to test it, although confidently expecting a negative result."[9] Clarke, meanwhile, had decided to go ahead.

"When I spoke at the Medical Institution, in February, I was a voice crying out in the wilderness of Liverpool," Finn would recall much later. "I don't think anybody took much interest in me. By November, Professor Clarke was deeply interested." In a short communication that they sent to the British journal *Nature*, Clarke, McConnell, and Sheppard subscribed with Finn to the proposition that "it may be possible . . . to destroy the circulating fetal cells by administration of . . . anti-Rh and thus prevent immunization [to the Rh factor]."[10]

Finding subjects in whom to test the proposition was proving to be a problem, as Race had predicted. Prison medical authorities whom they approached demurred: British law prohibits prisoners being used for research purposes. "A prisoner," quipped McConnell, "is not a volunteer!"

---

* Finn hit on the idea of using purified anti-Rh gamma globulin in 1960, and so stipulated in a draft of a paper he was preparing for publication.[6] In editing in proof, this specification was deleted.[7] As a result, Vince, John, and Bill would gain credit for the proposal to use gamma globulin instead of serum, which they first published a year or so later.[8] Since no anti-Rh gamma globulin was available in Liverpool, plans went forward for testing Finn's theory with anti-Rh antibody-containing serum.

Clarke next proposed that they approach Liverpool's chief blood banker, Dr. Dermot Lehane. Liverpool had been badly hit by German bombing in World War II, and had been a staging center for Allied troops, many of whom were wounded and needed blood. Lehane had set up an immensely successful blood program, tapping thousands of donors to sustain untold numbers of Allied combatants and wounded civilians—as well as German prisoners held in the area. Lehane had maintained his program intact after hostilities ended, but he had never allowed his donors—most of whom were blue- and white-collar workers and municipal employees—to be used for research. McConnell doubted that Lehane would allow them to be used for the Rh experiment.

Clarke, a consummate politician, presented the matter to Lehane. He agreed to help.

The first injections were made on March 23, 1961. The initial six volunteers were Liverpool policemen. All were Rh-negative. They got a potentially sensitizing dose of 5 ml of Rh-positive blood cells which had been tagged with radioactive material so that their concentration in the blood could be measured later by assessing the radioactivity of a blood specimen. A half hour later three of the men got 10 ml of serum that contained anti-Rh antibodies. Because of problems in the preparation, the serum contained both 19S and 7S antibodies.

The sensitizing agent had been injected. A potential antidote had been given to three of the men to seek it out and destroy it before it could cause damage. But even if the antibody did catch up with the red cells, it was not at all clear to the Liverpool investigators *how* the "fetal" cells were to be destroyed. Nor, if this succeeded, how their destruction would prevent Rh sensitization. In fact, their confidence and willingness to proceed without a clear-cut rationale for *how* the purported protection would operate is one of the more remarkable aspects of their endeavor.

Race, in presenting his hypothesis to explain how ABO incompatibility protects against Rh sensitization, had spoken of the "invading cells" being "eliminated." Natural anti-A, for example, which is 19S, catches up to a group-A fetal cell in a mother's blood and eats holes through its cell membrane so that its hemoglobin leaks out and it is destroyed; such a cell can be visualized as a water-filled balloon hit by a charge of buckshot.

Since fetal cells destroyed this way by ABO incompatibility do not provoke Rh sensitization, Finn had decided that in destroying a fetal cell one also destroys the antigens it carries. As he conceived of this situation when he first presented his theory at the Liverpool Medical Institution early in 1960, if an ABO-incompatible red cell crosses the placenta into a mother, "it will immediately be destroyed. . . . The theory then postulates that any Rh antigen carried by that red cell will [also] be rapidly destroyed, and thus there will be no time to stimulate the mother's antibody system [to make anti-Rh]. No [anti-Rh] antibody will be produced, and therefore, erythroblastosis will not occur."[11]

Similarly, Finn felt, if one substituted for anti-A some other antibody, such as anti-Rh, its mode of action when injected would be to "destroy the fetal cells"—thus "imitating the natural protection afforded by ABO incompatibility." In this original simple scheme, to destroy the fetal cells in the mother's circulating blood with a 19S antibody meant that one was destroying the antigen that they carried.

But Finn was not altogether sure of this line of reasoning, which no less an authority than Nevanlinna had dismissed almost with contempt. "In our opinion," Nevanlinna had declared, "no observation supports [Race's] theory [of ABO protection]; also, why a rapidly eliminated red cell should act as a poorer antigen than a red cell that remains longer in the maternal circulation remains an open question. The contrary explanation might serve just as well."[12] Rapid removal of antigenic cells or cell fragments might concentrate them in the blood-cleaning organs—the liver and spleen—which are also the sites where new immunities are created!

Finn voiced his doubts in his thesis, which he completed in March of 1961; it would be judged several weeks later. He wrote: "It is not absolutely clear why the rapid destruction of fetal cells in the maternal circulation should not be followed by the production of [anti-]Rh antibodies. This disruption [destruction] of the Rh antigen molecules in the maternal circulation, the predominant sequestration of such [fetal] cells in the liver, and the short duration of the antigenic stimulus, are possible explanations of this phenomenon."[13]

A whole new rationale now appeared—from Kurt Stern in Chicago. No one in Liverpool had heard his talk in San Francisco, and publication of his report was still some months in the future. But the 1960 blood bank meeting had been a special occasion honoring Landsteiner, and Ruth Sanger had been there and had carried the meeting program with Stern's abstract in it home to London. Notic-

# THEORIES OF ANTIBODY'S ACTION

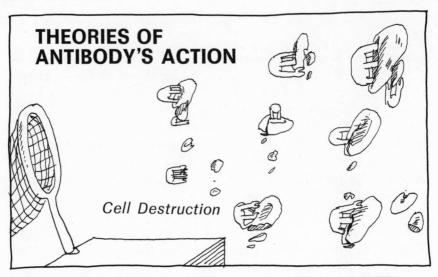

*Cell Destruction*

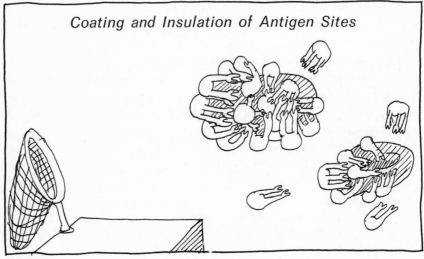

*Coating and Insulation of Antigen Sites*

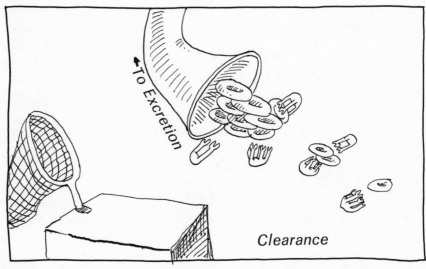

*To Excretion*

*Clearance*

ing that Stern's experiments closely paralleled those proposed in Liverpool, she sent Clarke a copy of the abstract.

Its influence on Clarke, Finn, and their colleagues can clearly be seen by comparing the manuscript of a communication they submitted to the British journal *Nature* on November 30, and the published version which appeared the following June 3; they had received Stern's abstract in the meantime. In November they wrote: "It may be possible . . . to *destroy* the circulating fetal cells by the administration of gamma globulin from serum containing anti-Rh, and thus prevent immunization."[14] (Emphasis added.)

By June they had amended the text to say: "It may be possible . . . to *inactivate* the circulating fetal cells by the administration of anti-Rh and thus prevent immunization.

"Using Rh-negative male volunteers, we have already shown that the administration of Rh-positive cells followed half an hour later by anti-Rh, results in these cells being *coated* with the antibody. In view of the results of Stern . . . it is hoped that this coating will prevent Rh-sensitization."[15] (Emphasis added.)

Stern, it may be recalled, had coated Rh-positive cells with 7S anti-Rh antibody. As Finn read his results, this coating of the antigen sites with antibody tended to insulate them from the host's immune system, preventing sensitization. At the same time, 7S antibody clumps together the cells it attacks, so that they will be quickly filtered out of the bloodstream either in the liver or in the spleen—much as a baker's sieve clears flour of lumps which, if left in, would ruin a dough. McConnell pointed out that British transfusion specialist Patrick Mollison had shown that Rh-positive red cells, pretreated with 7S anti-Rh antibody, would begin to be filtered out of a person's bloodstream within seconds after they were injected.[16, 17]

The heavier the antibody coating, the quicker this happened. With a very heavy antibody burden the red cells might be "cleared" in a few minutes, or an hour at most. Red cells with relatively lighter coatings of antibodies remained longer—hours, or even days—during which time, Finn and McConnell felt, they continued to be dangerous; the quicker they were cleared out of the bloodstream and removed from the body the better.

Mollison's work suggested a second reason why rapid clearance of fetal cells might forestall Rh sensitization. Cells with heavy antibody coatings are removed quickly, in the liver. Cells with lighter coatings are removed less quickly, in the spleen. McConnell would come to feel this was of special importance, since the spleen is filled with immunity-inducing, or *reticuloendothelial*, cells. Fetal cells that were sequestered there might well trigger an immune response. The liver, on the other hand, has relatively few immunogenic cells. So there might be clear advantage in using a potent anti-Rh antibody to remove fetal cells quickly and safely via the liver rather than slowly and dangerously via the spleen.

There were thus several rationales for the hopefully preventive action of the antibody that Finn had injected into the Liverpool policemen: destruction of antigenic cells and antigen, blocking of the cells' Rh antigen sites, and clumping of the cells so that they would be sequestered and rapidly "cleared" from the circulation. Any one, or all, of these modes of action might be operative, and might prevent Rh sensitization—and the fact that Stern's prisoners had not become sensitized seemed to Finn a good omen. "When we knew about Stern's work," he would recall, "we knew the anti-Rh injections would work."

Results from the tests on the policemen at first seemed good. Natural 19S anti-A or anti-B will remove close to 100 percent of incompatible A- or B-type cells from a woman's circulation within a day. By the end of 48 hours the mixed 19S and 7S anti-Rh seemed to have successfully found and removed from the policemen's circulations about 50 percent of the Rh-positive cells they had been given. Delicate immunologic studies, set up by technician Donohoe, showed that many of the remaining antigenic cells had been found by the antibody and were coated with it, as might have been hoped.

Tests to determine if any of the "protected" policemen or any of the controls had in fact become sensitized to the Rh factor were scheduled for two months after the initial injections. But Finn's thesis was due, and he could not wait for these results. Having changed the title from the assigned topic of interaction between ABO and Rh to "Preventive Mechanisms Against Rh Haemolytic Disease," he turned it in to Clarke in April, after more than three years of labor.

May of 1961 would prove to be one of the most unsettling months of Ronald Finn's life. His thesis reviewers, in addition to Clarke, were the chief of the Liverpool University department of medicine, Lord Cohen of Birkenhead, and Robert Race, from London. They approved the thesis—though without special commendation—and Finn was awarded the coveted degree of Doctor of Medicine (M.D.).

At the very moment he won his M.D. degree, Finn lost his doctoral project. Henceforward, the Liverpool Rh research would no longer be one man's thesis but a team effort of the department of medicine under the direction of Cyril A. Clarke. Even the report Finn now was preparing for publication in the *British Medical Journal* failed to indicate the extent of its indebtedness to his thesis project.

The May 27 *BMJ* report—which was so to shock John and Vince a few weeks later—listed Finn as senior author, followed by Clarke, Donohoe, McConnell, Sheppard, and Lehane.* [18]

Finn, meanwhile, approached an important change of venue. For several years, younger members of the Liverpool department of medicine had been going to the United States to gain a year's experience working at Johns Hopkins University in Baltimore, Maryland, where geneticist Dr. Victor McKusick had started one of the world's first centers for the study of medical genetics. McKusick had a project that required a blood-grouping laboratory, and, as McConnell would recall the situation, had written Clarke asking if one of his junior men would like to spend a year at Johns Hopkins helping to set one up. Clarke nominated Finn, and Finn accepted—with the proviso that he might continue his Rh studies. McKusick in turn accepted Finn and his proviso.

Finn's departure was set for September 1. The month of May, so far, had had its ups and downs but, by and large, it seemed to Finn that he might relax and congratulate himself on a job well done. His thesis was finished and approved; the proofs were read and returned for the *BMJ* report; a year in America was coming.

Then the bomb fell. The antibody tests came back on the three "protected" policemen. One had become sensitized to the Rh factor. Others soon would be. A second group had been injected with antigenic red cells and protected with antibody, so that already six

---

* The editorial in the same *BMJ* issue, seconding the hope that prevention would be possible, was a prestigious accompaniment to the first publication of a new therapeutic proposal.[19] *BMJ* editorials are written by experts in the field under comment. The author's identity is, by the rules of the game, a closely guarded secret; investigators do not comment on their own research. Whoever wrote so favorably about so new an idea must have known the thinking of Finn and his colleagues quite intimately. One British blood expert who would have fit this description was Robert Race. He would later deny, with a smile, that he was the author. A second expert familiar with the Liverpool work was Ruth Sanger.

men had received anti-Rh antibody. While colleagues—and competitors—around the world read in the *BMJ* of Liverpool's seeming success, the Liverpool experiment turned into a shambles. By August, five of the six "protected" men were sensitized to Rh—far more than among the unprotected controls! Instead of preventing immunity, the anti-Rh injections in fact appeared to have enhanced the possibility of its occurrence.

The Liverpudlians were struck dumb. At the moment that Vince, John, and Bill were confounded by Liverpool's triumph, Liverpool was reeling with defeat.

"I remember we could have shouted for joy when the man who was doing our isotope studies first rang up with the early test results and said that we had gotten clearance," Clarke would recall. "Then we were thrown in the depths when we found out, months later, that we had gotten enhancement."

"We were rocked back on our feet!" McConnell would remember. Sheppard, who had designed the experimental protocols for the volunteer study, would say "it was a considerable blow to get exactly the reverse" of the anticipated results. Finn was "disturbed" —their plan "was not going to work."

It seemed reasonable, as they discussed it, to drop the whole project forthwith. Clarke later would count it their "finest hour" that they decided not to do so. There seemed just enough promise in the results—and just enough possibilities left unexplored—to try to continue, though the confusion and ambivalence they felt could not be concealed. Finn revealed his state of mind in a letter to Stern late in August:

Further to the information given in the *BMJ* article, we now have data on four groups of volunteers. The results are remarkably constant in that 10–20 ml of antibody leads to the destruction of up to 60 percent of the injected donor cells. One could hardly expect this to provide any protection, and in fact, some of our "protected" subjects have become sensitized. More recently we have increased the dose of a relatively weak antibody (titer 1:4 in albumin and saline) to 50 ml and have succeeded in destroying 100 percent of the donor cells within 48 hours. We have no antibody results yet for this group, but we are hopeful that some protection will ensue.

It is generally accepted that incompatible Rh-positive cells are removed to the spleen, and it is therefore difficult to explain why sensitization [usually] does not take place. Rather surprisingly our preliminary results tend to suggest that moderate reduction in the life span of injected Rh-positive cells actually increases the risk of Rh sensitization. We have wondered whether this is not due to a more powerful antigenic stimulus as the total volume of injected antigen is destroyed and hence enters the reticuloendothelial system over a shorter time.

This raises the interesting possibility that a time factor may be of importance. Thus in the case of ABO incompatibility and your own work, it is just possible that owing to the very rapid destruction of donor cells the antigenic stimulus may be operative for too short a time to enable the reticuloendothelial system to initiate antibody production. These thoughts are of course completely speculative, but I would nevertheless, appreciate your comments.* [20]

Based on the Liverpool team workers' interpretations of what had gone wrong, there were two new avenues to pursue: Finn centered his critique on the inadequate potency of the antibody they had used. While 19S anti-A antibody would clear a moderate dose of group A fetal cells completely in 48 hours, their 19S anti-Rh antibody had cleared only about half that amount—allowing the rest to disappear slowly enough to initiate sensitization. His suggestion was to increase the dose and potency of the antibody used for injection. McConnell concurred in Finn's notion that an antibody that would clear most of the cells—say 95 percent—in a day or so would probably still provide protection. While he had been a firm advocate of the 19S preparation, he now argued strongly that, in view of Stern's apparent success in preventing immunity with 7S antibody, they too should use pure 7S.

Stern's moment of hidden glory had arrived. As Finn later would recall it, it was McConnell's insistence on the untried option—7S anti-Rh antibody—raised by Stern's experiment that in Liverpool now made the difference between stopping and going ahead.

Sheppard, who was in charge of designing the experimental protocols for the human trials, agreed—reluctantly—to change two variables, increasing the antibody titer and changing from 19S to 7S, both at the same time. With these changes, the work went cautiously forward—buoyed by Finn's certainty that somehow he was right and Clarke's willingness to gamble on a long shot even though their first bet had failed.

The imprint of their initial—and in McConnell's word, "shocking"—setback would, however, pervade their every subsequent

* Stern had initiated the correspondence when he saw Finn's reference to his AABB abstract in the *Nature* report of the Liverpool work. He promised Finn a copy of his full report when it was published.[21]

thought and decision. Sheppard would design each succeeding experiment "cunningly"—the adverb is Clarke's—so that it would return the absolute maximal amount of information possible with the absolute minimal possible exposure of nonsensitized humans to the Rh factor. Henceforward, Liverpool's watchword would be: Caution.

August ended. The day-to-day routine of finding and injecting volunteers and following their clearances and titers now was assigned to another young internist in the department of medicine, Dr. John Woodrow. In Britain and in the United States the hard conceptual task of conceiving a solution to the Rh problem had been completed. The problem ahead, as Finn embarked for Baltimore, was: Would it work?

# 18

# The Road to Sing Sing

"ANOTHER BLOW has struck," John Gorman had written in a letter to his parents in Australia, late in June. The first blow had been his certification examination for the American Board of Pathology: John had flunked badly the section on hematology—his specialty— and would need to repeat it. The second blow was Liverpool.

"That article in the *BMJ* in May—look for it—has completely scooped our idea of using antibody to prevent sensitization. They describe experiments on volunteers and project the entire plan of attack. We are too late. We can only . . . follow their instructions and get it done. Looking back, I got very little encouragement with that idea—so I must make sure the same thing does not happen with the I.I. [immuno*in*competent] cell."[1]

Utterly discouraged as they were, neither John, Vince, nor Bill was ready to give up. Besides, John pointed out, *he* couldn't stop: He was bound by contract with the City of New York beginning the following week, July 1, to spend $60,000 of municipal taxpayers' dollars to develop an Rh prophylaxis. Wiener, too, felt they should continue: The Liverpool people had done an experiment and had published their results. Now the New York group should do *its* experiment to see what *it* would find—it was far too early to discount surprises.

John was destined never to spend even one minute in the blood laboratory preparing anti-Rh antibody for injection—as he had promised, in his grant application, to do. His penchant for creative thought always would be perfectly matched by his dislike for lab bench labor. When it came to manufacturing anti-Rh antibody preparations, Bill would be responsible for all failures and all successes. John's first expenditure, when his grant monies came, was to hire a secretary to check out the references for his I.I. clone theory paper.

The Liverpool paper seemed convincing. No one in New York found reason to question the success of red cell clearances or the hoped-for prevention of Rh sensitization that they seemed to imply. Liverpool and New York had an identical Rh prophylaxis plan and almost-identical justifications for it, and for a while at least the similarities would seem more striking than the differences between them.

This was especially true for Vince. Months before he read the Liverpool paper, he had interpreted the idea of "ABO protection" as confirmation of John's proposal that passive antibody injections would prevent sensitization to the Rh factor (*AMIS*). But subsequently, Vince had come to regard the anti-Rh antibody injections both as an expression of *AMIS*, following John, and as a direct method to destroy fetal cells, as did Liverpool.*

This duality in Vince's thinking appears clearly in the NIH grant application he had filed just before the Liverpool paper appeared. In one passage which appears in identical form in John's grant, Vince speaks of ABO protection and the hoped-for protection from Rh sensitization in terms of *AMIS*: "Levine has established that if an Rh-negative mother has a preexisting circulating [anti-A or anti-B] antibody directed against the baby's red cells . . . then sensitization to Rh by pregnancy is extremely rare. . . . This may be a very similar phenomenon to those [other examples of *AMIS*] cited."[2, 3]

But in another passage which is not duplicated in John's grant Vince wrote: "It is hoped that the [anti-Rh] antiserum will destroy those fetal cells which escape into the mother at the time of labor, and thus prevent the fetal Rh factor from *initially* sensitizing the mother, much as an incompatibility in the ABO system protects the mother from Rh sensitizations."[4] Vince's rationale here is identical to Liverpool's. Clearly, his thinking in part was close to theirs. Subsequently, while John would stick closely to the *AMIS* explanation, Vince would occasionally cite red cell "destruction" or "clear-

---

* Liverpool was wholly unaware of *AMIS* as a reason for what they were doing.

ance" as the operative principle of New York's Rh prevention plans. "Needless to say," Vince wrote to a colleague in August, "the basic idea proposed recently by Finn *et al.* was hatched in our little brains at least six months before his article appeared—but this is now 'sour grapes.' "[5]

At the same time that Liverpool advanced the idea that cell destruction and/or clearance would prevent sensitization, the *AMIS* principle also received strong new support that considerably bolstered Vince's hope that giving the injections after delivery of the baby would be soon enough to provide protection. John's boss, McKay, found the new evidence in a report in the highly learned *Journal of Experimental Medicine.* "It looks like you're on the right track!" he exclaimed, as he showed it to John. What John saw was an extremely long and extremely detailed experimental study entitled: "Antibody formation: The suppression of antibody formation by passively administered antibody."[6] *AMIS!*

John was astonished. The author was no stranger. He was an immunologist, Dr. Jonathan Uhr of New York University. John had met him the previous winter at the University of Melbourne where he had been working with Macfarlane Burnet. Uhr had also been a medical school classmate of Vince's at NYU. Oddly, from wholly different directions their paths now crossed again, at *AMIS*.

John and Vince immediately went to see Uhr. They learned from him several important new pieces of information. They learned for the first time that *AMIS* had originally been formulated as a theory by Harvard pathologist Theobald Smith in 1908.[7] Many others had studied it. Uhr himself, they learned, was excited by *AMIS* because he sensed that it was an important immunologic regulatory mechanism that controlled antibody production—a possibility which his colleagues had largely overlooked.

The idea that *AMIS* might be clinically useful apparently had not occurred to Uhr; he certainly had never thought that it might prevent Rh disease. But Uhr's basic discoveries about *AMIS* electrified John and Vince, whose aim was wholly practical.

In his experiments, Uhr had used antidiphtheria antibody injections to prevent animals from being immunized by diphtheria antigen injections. On the key question of timing, he had found that the protective antibody was equally effective when given *after* the antigen, even many days afterwards, as it was when given before. As Vince summarized this valuable piece of information in an addendum he was drafting for his NIH grant application, even "if the antibody was given five days after the primary antigen injection, there was complete suppression of [immune] response."[8]

This meant that in the delivery room Vince would not have to hurry, hypodermic syringe at the ready, to give the protective anti-Rh antibody to the mother the instant the umbilical cord was cut. It might do to wait hours, even days after the baby's birth to give her the anti-Rh prophylaxis. More important, an injection given after delivery might provide protection against fetus-to-mother bleeds that had occurred during gestation as early as several weeks before.

John and Vince asked Uhr: "Will *AMIS* work with Rh?"

The immunologist later would recall replying: "I think it's a good possibility!"*

Uhr was an encouragement for Vince, John, and Bill. So was Stern, whose paper from the previous summer's AABB they now saw and read for the first time, when it appeared in print in August.[9] They were as struck by it as Clarke, Finn, and McConnell had been. "He came right to the brink," John would later say. "I couldn't believe that he couldn't take the next step.

"But I knew, when I read it, that we'd succeed!"

At Ortho, Bill had pushed forward with fractionation. He had been dissatisfied with the first experimental batch of anti-Rh gamma globulin he and Hans Hager had made. The method they had employed, using ammonium salts to separate the gamma globulin out of the blood serum, yielded material that had potent anti-Rh activity. But this method failed to separate the 7S anti-Rh gamma globulin fraction from the 19S fraction. Because 19S can carry hepatitis, the federal government had forbidden its use in humans. Hence, for the present, a preparation that included 19S could not even be tested.

Pure 7S would be needed. Ortho's huge commercial fraction plant and also its smaller pilot plant were capable of making it. Instead of using ammonium salts, these plants precipitated gamma globulin fractions out of serum by *alcohol fractionation*; at criti-

---

* Uhr may not have felt as encouraging as he sounded—and sometimes remembers himself sounding. Recalling his talk with Vince and John in another context, at a conference of fellow immunologists, he later said: "I was tempted to discourage them . . . but I did not."[10] He explained that he did not doubt *AMIS'* ability to *prevent* immunization. But he then accepted Levine's classical view that immunization occurred during pregnancy, by slow transplacental leakage of fetal cells, and he knew that attempts to use antibody injections to *suppress* immunization, once it had occurred, had not proved notably successful.

cally determined subzero temperatures alcohol will remove various of the individual gamma globulin fractions from serum. Unfortunately, the smallest batch that could be processed, even in the smaller pilot plant, was several gallons of serum—more than Bill could quietly divert to his need.

To accommodate the liter or so that he could lay hands on, Bill labored late for several evenings building a miniature alcohol fractionation setup on his lab bench. In this crude system, a bucket of dry ice served as coolant.

When Vince and John came to Ortho to see Bill in mid-August, he could report that in his experiment he had obtained an apparently pure and quite potent anti-Rh antibody preparation. Satisfied that this could be achieved, Bill now was preparing to broach the project cautiously to his superiors.

Bill went first to his immediate boss, Glen Hill, whose respect for him had, if anything, increased in the six years since he had brought him to the company. "If you think it's worth doing, I'll back it on your say-so," Hill, in effect, said. He helped Bill obtain additional bags of anti-Rh serum, and at the same time carried the Rh prevention idea to Ortho's administrative heads—some of whom were skeptical, to say the least.

"There was no one here who would believe it would work," Hill would say later. Bill would add: "We were told to drop it. It wouldn't work!"

But they prevailed. Later they would say that Ortho encouraged and "supported the project to the extent that data justifying it became available." Hager, who returned from abroad in early autumn, would recall:

"Ortho felt that with all crazy scientists, you had to let them play if you wanted to get work from them. They went along—hesitantly. It took some persuasion."

Ortho decided to go ahead in August and assigned supervisory responsibility to assistant research director Dr. Heron Singher, a biochemist. He was an imposing, corpulent, severely-crippled man in his forties who perambulated, painfully, Ortho's sprawling plant with the aid of steel crutches and a motorized wheelchair.

Singher was an iron man, a scientist of the old school who played his cards close to the chest and rarely, if ever, confided in outsiders. No thought nor fact passed his lips that was not guarded by considerations of scientific skepticism, industrial security, and a manifest distrust of nonscientists, especially writers.

Bill, as a scientist, perhaps benefited from the more positive, protective side of Singher's nature. He later would recall Singher encouraging him at the start, saying: "If the project makes sound logical sense to you as an immunologist—or, even if it has loopholes—then pursue it, if it will be useful to humanity."

A dinner was arranged in New York at the new and elegant Four Seasons restaurant to introduce the Ortho leaders to John and Vince. Bill did not attend. John arrived on time to meet Hill and Singher. Vince had a patient in labor whom he could not leave, and though the three men waiting for him dallied long over drinks, they had to dine without him.

Recapping the evening's events in a long letter to Australia, John wrote:

"Ortho decided they would help us get enough anti-Rh serum to run a fairly large trial on Rh-negative volunteers. They are going to get 12 liters and process it into gamma globulin so that the volumes that have to be injected can be small.

"They will package it and test it for sterility, pyrogens, etc. On the market this much Rh grouping serum would be worth $100,000, but supply exceeds demand. This study should show whether we can get good protection against Rh sensitization. . . . They will have it ready in 2-3 months and the study will then take another six months. If we get encouraging results, it will unloose a tremendous amount of research using actual Rh-negative mothers."[11]

Vince, meanwhile, pushed ahead with testing plans for the anti-Rh injections. By mid-July he had compiled a list of prisons in and near New York City where they might find "volunteers."

Sing Sing prison—the fabled "Big House" of criminal lore—in Ossining, "up the river" on the east bank of the Hudson, seemed the best choice: Its inmates stayed put long enough to participate in experiments that might continue for months or even years. Vince wrote to the Warden, Wilfred Denno, explaining that he and John were developing an Rh prophylaxis which would require testing in forty Rh-negative men before it could be used on pregnant or newly delivered women.[12] Denno was dubious:

In reply to your letter of September 15, informing me that Dr. J. Gorman and yourself are presently engaged in a research project which has to do with preventing hemolytic disease of the newborn, but that before you can attempt to work with pregnant mothers the experimental procedure must be tried on approximately 40 male volunteers (Blood Type Rh-negative), and that you would like to meet with me during the see whether or not another research project may be undertaken in the first week of October, and that Friday, October 6, is a satisfactory date for Dr. Gorman and yourself, I wish to advise at this time that this institution contemplates going into at least one and perhaps more than one research project in about six weeks.

However, I will consult with the Senior Physician at this institution to near future, which I doubt very much, and also to take your request up with the [New York State] Commissioner of Correction. . . .[13]

Fortunately, Sing Sing's senior physician, Dr. Harold W. Kipp, had received his medical training at Columbia, and John's chiefs suggested that he be contacted directly. This John and Vince did. Kipp was favorably impressed; the young men seemed to him to be "sincere" and "ambitious." Their project had intrinsic merit and had the added advantage that they would do most of the work, with little of the responsibility being left to the prison medical staff.

Kipp went with John and Vince to see the warden. Denno was disturbed that a lot of blood seemed to be required from a lot of men. Vince explained that only a few tablespoonsful would need to be taken for testing. When they left the warden, Kipp suggested it might be helpful if they could do with fewer men. Would twenty be enough? John and Vince agreed that it would.

Kipp told the warden: "After our interview . . . I sat down and discussed their problems in more detail and feel that we can proceed with their proposed experiment, if it meets with your approval and the Commissioner's. . . .

"I feel that if we can proceed with the experiment it will be of benefit from a medical standpoint. . . ."[14]

Several days later Vince again heard from Sing Sing: The project had been approved.

# 19

## Roadblock

JUST AS VINCE was winning New York State's approval to test in its lawbreakers the anti-Rh antibody that Ortho had agreed to make, he was losing, at the hands of the federal government and the medical establishment, his bid for funds to finance the venture. Early in autumn word came via the grapevine that NIH had denied his grant request; shortly thereafter, this was confirmed by letter. No reasons were given.

Vince was furious. He bided his time a bit, then launched himself vigorously into what was to be the first of a long series of skirmishes with the medical Old Guard, which seemed honor bound to resist his ideas.

NIH's granting procedures are widely hailed as being exemplary mechanisms for the allocation of public monies to private research. They are designed to minimize political pork-barreling and administrative favoritism in the awarding of federal research funds. Decisions rest largely on the judgment of the applicant's professional "peers," chosen because they are well-respected, well-established members of the medical research community. These peers meet periodically, usually at NIH headquarters in Bethesda, Maryland, in study sections of twenty members. Since they often must pass on the plans of men whom they know—and who well may be chosen next year to pass on *their* research requests—these deliberations are among the government's most carefully guarded secrets.

By 1961 federal grants through NIH had become the major source of research funds. Medicine had warm friends on Capitol Hill and in the White House: In 1961 alone, NIH allotted more than a half-billion dollars in grants to medical researchers. Compared with the tight money situation that was to prevail at the decade's end, its opening years were a researcher's bonanza.

Vince's grant application had been denied by the NIH Study Section on Human Embryology and Development. Shortly thereafter, Vince happened to run across a largely favorable review of the Liverpool experiments that had been written by the reigning dean of American obstetricians, Nicholson Eastman, who had just retired as chief of obstetrics at the Johns Hopkins Hospital in Baltimore. Eastman, Vince had heard, played an influential role in the study section. Vince's slow burn flamed into a long—polite—letter to Eastman. He asked why he and John had been denied money to pursue a plan similar to the one that Eastman had found to have merit in Liverpool:

For several months we labored over the grant application in every respect. We consulted many authorities until it was decided that whatever risks were involved ( e.g., infectious hepatitis, etc.) were at a minimum and were well compensated for by the possible value to the patient and the potential of the study. The grant application was revised and amended until it satisfied the critical reviews of Dr. Wiener, Dr. Levine. . . .

The grant application was submitted to the NIH (HED section) only after it was thoroughly reviewed and received the approval of these and other experts. The grant application was submitted to NIH before Finn's article appeared (thus we could not quote his article) and of course was rejected by the HED section council some six months later. I gather that the application was rejected because it was considered too chancy and that it was too confusing in parts. Apparently what was quite clear to the experts who previously reviewed this application had only confused the Council. . . .

I confess I was pretty well stunned when the application was flatly rejected without so much as a single comment or suggestion for revision. . . .[1]

Vince enclosed a copy of the grant request with his letter. Eastman replied:

As I trust you know, I am not a member of the Study Section on Human Embryology and Development, my term having expired almost two years ago. Hence, I cannot speak with any first-hand information about the reason for the rejection of your application. Having followed your own work for a number of years, it would have been my thought that your name alone on an application would well nigh ensure its acceptance. Moreover, having read your application and being acquainted with the problem involved, I really cannot understand what happened. . . .

I was very much upset about what you had to say and endeavored to ascertain through various sources as to what could possibly have happened to your application. One person from whom I had hoped to have an answer to your question was out of town at the time and I have had other difficulties in securing an explanation of what happened from my inquiries. . . .

About the only result that has come from my inquiries is that you might be able to get an explanation . . . from Dr. Samuel Moss, NIH Division of Research Grants. Just how much information Dr. Moss is permitted to give out, I do not know; but it would do no harm to write him.[2]

Rather than write, Vince drove down to Bethesda to talk to NIH officials. He learned from them that Eastman's successor as HED study section chief was the man who also had recently succeeded Eastman as chief of obstetrics at Johns Hopkins, Dr. Allan Barnes. Vince also learned that one of the two members responsible for thoroughly reviewing his grant—as a basis for the full panel's decision—was a pediatrician, Dr. Wolf Zuelzer, from Detroit. Zuelzer's recommendations might be expected to have carried special weight with the study section, for he, unlike the grant's other reviewer, was an expert in Rh disease.

Zuelzer and his close collaborator and co-worker in Detroit, Dr. Flossie Cohen, were respected figures in the Rh research community, whom Vince and John later would come to know well as doubters and critics. Zuelzer himself, in fact, would later characterize his laboratory as a "wasp's nest of skepticism" with regard to bold, unproved plans to effect Rh disease—plans that seemed to him to fly full in the face of his own clinical experience and Cohen's painstakingly detailed program for first finding out the basic mechanisms and natural history of the disease.

A tall, distinguished-looking, somewhat preoccupied man, Zuelzer had been born in Germany, had trained in Berlin and in Prague, and had received postgraduate education in pediatrics, pathology, and blood in Boston before stopping off, on his career's course, in Detroit. There, somewhat to his own surprise, he had stayed.

He had become a prominent member of the pediatric establishment in Michigan and in the United States. In Detroit he held the title of Director of the Child Research Center of Michigan, and he was professor of pediatric research at nearby Wayne State University. He was soon to join the editorial board of the powerful and conservative journal *Pediatrics*.

As the principal "peer" to evaluate Vince's grant application, Zuelzer, then fifty-three years old, disapproved its presumptiveness perhaps more than he disliked the specific proposals—some of which, including *AMIS* and amniocentesis, he later would say he was willing to see supported, albeit on a far less ambitious scale than Vince proposed. Years later, seated at his desk in Detroit, with his original file on the grant open before him, Zuelzer would explain that preference was allotted by NIH study sections to those applications that were distinguished by their "clarity of ideas," and which promised to focus heavily on the "theoretical aspects of a situation and on the basic mechanisms" of a disease.

By contrast, "grandiose claims for influencing clinical medicine very often were tossed out," Zuelzer would say. Vince had boldly asserted that his primary aim was "to determine whether it is possible to prevent the initial sensitization of Rh-negative mothers by . . . injection of Rh antiserum in the third stage of labor."[3]

Besides being too bound up with clinical problems and the treatment of patients, Zuelzer found Vince's application "wordy" and faulted by "naive reasoning"—the work of a bright young man handicapped by "lack of any clear immunologic background in the Rh field.

"The proposal was hazy in theory and tended to be in a hurry clinically—factors that tended to mitigate against it."

Zuelzer also found good reason in recent research findings of his co-worker Flossie Cohen to doubt Vince's blunt and undocumented assertion that anti-Rh antibody injections, or any other measures taken at the time of delivery, would intervene soon enough to prevent sensitization.[*] Cohen, like Ronnie Finn in Liverpool, had been developing methods to find and measure fetal bleeds in a mother's circulating blood. Her method differed from the Kleihauer test:

---

[*] Zuelzer accepted the notion that lowering or blocking a mother's anti-Rh antibody production might control the disease. Several years earlier, he had himself attempted just such a feat by injecting women with the then-new "miracle drug" ACTH. The ACTH had failed to help.[4]

antibody against a particular red cell antigen—for example, anti-A or anti-B—was bonded to a dye that would glow under ultraviolet light. The antibody then was mixed into a specimen of red cells in which only a few—perhaps one cell in 100,000—carried the specific antigen with which it would react. The antibody would find and stick to these scattered red cells. Then, when the sample was viewed under UV light, these cells alone would show up as a greenish glow, while the 99,999 other red cells around them which had not picked up the dyed antibody remained invisible.

This work was still very preliminary. But Cohen felt her results already were completely at variance with assumptions upon which, she felt, Ronnie Finn and Vince Freda based all their hopes: that antibody injections at delivery would be in time. Cohen had gone far enough to be able to prove that Rh-positive fetal red cells appeared in mothers' blood three or four, or more weeks *before* delivery.[5] If these tiny bleeds could cause Rh sensitization—and, unlike Finn and Freda, Cohen assumed that they could—then injecting mothers with anti-Rh antibody at delivery was too late to be helpful. (Her criticism is based largely on the "cell clearance" rationale for how the anti-Rh antibody was supposed to work. Throughout, Cohen and Zuelzer would see this as the principal rationale both in Liverpool and in New York. They would tend to ignore *AMIS*, which, as Uhr had shown, might not require the protective antibody to be given until days after the Rh-positive cells got into the mother.[6])

Despite all of these problems, Zuelzer had not dismissed Vince's application wholly out of hand. While the $100,000 Vince requested for five years seemed too much for an untried man with an untried idea, Zuelzer felt that the prevention plan did warrant testing in male volunteers. He recommended that a pilot project "should be supported in prisoners, and if that works out, they should come back and ask for more money to carry it on in women." He also approved Vince's amniocentesis study.[7]

Zuelzer forwarded his recommendations to HED study section chief Barnes. Zuelzer did not attend the group's mid-September meeting at which his and the second reviewer's views formed the basis for a vote on Vince's grant. The second reviewer apparently was at least as critical as Zuelzer, for the study section's pink summary sheet of its action notes, Zuelzer later would say, "that as far as the preventive approach to hemolytic diseases is concerned, this is an interesting approach. But the study section was concerned with the specific assumption that sensitization occurs only at labor, and also was concerned with the risk of hepatitis from the antibody injections."[8]

By majority vote, Vince's request was rejected—*in toto.* Federal tax dollars would not help launch Rh prevention research in New York.* Apparently, to praise faintly, as Zuelzer had, was in fact to damn a new man with a new idea—even at the moment of greatest government largesse medical research had ever enjoyed. Vince lost because his project was considered less valid than others against which he was competing for the available funds. What sort of research did NIH favor? In the period 1957–1967, one of NIH's largest outlays for research on diseases of the fetus and newborn, which includes erythroblastosis, was the Collaborative Perinatal Research Project. It has already cost about $100 million.[9]

The Perinatal Project's aim was the direct opposite of Vince and John's. They sought funds to advance a specific idea for dealing with a specific disease. The Perinatal Project had the non-goal-oriented goal of generating enormous amounts of data that might reveal links between parental and gestational factors and a wide range of diseases. Data were to be gathered from 50,000 pregnancies at more than a dozen hospitals. The babies were to be followed until they reached age eight.

In one year before 1961, the Project's budget had been approved through the HED study section. In 1961, when HED denied Vince's request for $20,000 a year for five years, the Perinatal Project got $6 million from NIH. (Ironically, a bit did indirectly support Vince: Columbia-Presbyterian participated in the Project; its institutional grant paid part of his salary.)

So many data were gathered through the Project that the NIH computers and biostatisticians were swamped. Differences in medical and data-gathering methods among the various participating hospitals threatened to invalidate the entire effort. Two institutions dropped out. Criticism forced the Project to be restructured in mid-course. Many of the data had to be discarded.[10] A congressional investigation was threatened.

The Perinatal Project, and its cost, continued into the 1970s. While useful data undoubtedly has—and will—come from it, a

---

* The Liverpudlian Rh investigators had already won modest financial support from NIH's counterpart in Britain, the Medical Research Council, as well as from the Nuffield Foundation, an important private fund, and from the Research Committee of the United Liverpool Hospitals.

1969 progress report by project chief Dr. Heinz Berendes fails to disclose a single advance made against a major disease on the basis of project data.[11] In 1970, Dr. Berendes declined to respond directly to an explicit request that he specify any such advances; he cautioned that "an appraisal of the results of this program at this time is premature. . . . The follow-up of our population is not complete and therefore any analyses thus far are largely preliminary and incomplete."[12]

Whether in time the Perinatal Project would justify its cost and effort, time alone would tell.

# 20

## Finn in America

FINN, MEANWHILE, unbeknown to John, Vince, or Bill and as yet wholly unaware of who they were or what they were doing, had come to the United States—bringing the lion's share of Liverpool's Rh research with him. Beginning in September, the Johns Hopkins Hospital in Baltimore was to be his base of operations for a year.

In agreeing to work at Johns Hopkins under medical genetics chief Dr. Victor McKusick, Finn had asked to continue his red cell clearance studies in human volunteers. McKusick consented.

As far as salary was concerned, Finn later would say that Mc-Kusick arranged for him to be paid out of grant monies from the National Institutes of Health. Thus, the same month that NIH turned down two Americans it began paying a salary for an Englishman to work in an American hospital on an almost identical project.

Finn's experiments fell outside the scope of the genetics department's resources, so McKusick sent him to work with the smooth young chief of the Johns Hopkins blood bank, internist Dr. Julius Krevans. Krevans "frankly doubted" that Finn's Rh prevention plan would work, and in a note to McKusick he had said: "I am not as convinced as Dr. Finn is of the potential use of this technique in preventing hemolytic disease. Nevertheless, it shows imagination and competent experimental design. . . ."[1]

In September, face to face, Krevans raised the objection that sensitizing fetus-to-mother bleeds occurred throughout gestation,

205

so that preventive measures applied at delivery would not be in time. Finn replied: Why was it that women failed to become sensitized during their first pregnancies? His Kleihauer data, he added, showed that sensitization was usually associated with a big fetus-to-mother bleed, at delivery—which meant that steps then to clear these cells quickly from the maternal circulation might be in time.

Finn was candid with Krevans concerning the failures in Liverpool with the low-dose antibody injections, but said that sensitization had not yet occurred with the larger, more potent doses now being tested. Nonetheless, it was still too early to say for certain that the improved clearance times—most of the red cells now were gone within 24 hours—would also forestall immunity to the Rh factor. Finn could see two alternatives, Krevans would later recall: Either the entire protective concept was in error, and the Liverpool group was barking up the wrong tree; or the initial failures could be laid to low dosage, and might be overcome with larger, more potent antibody injections.

Impressed with Finn's grit and the rationale of his work, Krevans agreed to help develop the experimental data that would decide between the two alternatives. The two internists moved quickly together to set up a series of red blood clearance studies in prisoners at the nearby Maryland Penitentiary.

Bill Pollack, meanwhile, processed an initial batch of 7S anti-Rh antibody for use in prisoners at Sing Sing. To do so, he first had to find, among the dozens of blood shipments logged into Ortho's receiving room each week, a bag of sterile human serum with a high titer of anti-Rh antibody. One morning, a 12-liter bag of Rh-sensitized Rh-negative serum arrived that seemed to Bill to be suitable. He took it, and he and Hans Hager processed it.

After he had completed his labor, the 12 liters of serum had dwindled to less than one liter of pale yellowish fluid, which he and Hans Hager sealed into 33 vials of 10 ml each. Hager fretted: "We're not even going to have enough to do the sterility checks!"

He almost was right. Of the 33 vials, 22 went for testing the material and assaying its strength. To Bill's surprise, the batch passed all tests for purity. He also was more than a bit pleased to discover that it was enormously potent. John would assess its 7S anti-Rh antibody titer at a near-astronomic 64,000.* If weak anti-

* The enhancement-inducing anti-Rh antiserum used in the first Liverpool experiment had a titer of 64.

body enhanced rather than suppressed immunization, as Bill feared —and as Liverpool, unbeknown to him, apparently had already discovered—then it was in Bill's skilled hands that hopes for a potent and effective preparation now rested.

John meanwhile had completed his essay on the immunologically *in*competent cell. He read it to the annual blood bank (AABB) meeting in Chicago early in November. "My paper on the theory was well received," he wrote home to Australia.* "Most people said that they got the idea. It was a very good meeting with nearly everyone in the blood banking world there. Did not make the newspapers at all, however."[3]

John's next project carried him, temporarily, far afield from Rh, in the direction of home: He had won an NIH grant to study a rare, genetically determined enzyme disorder called G6PD deficiency, in the aborigine population of New Guinea. The week after the blood bank meeting, he flew west from New York toward the Land Down Under—where hot summer was just starting. Following his trip to New Guinea and Christmas with his family, he would return, via Europe, after the New Year.

Thanksgiving week, Bill sent Vince the first vial of 7S anti-Rh antibody.[4] Just before Christmas Vince injected it into the buttock of a dying cancer patient at Delafield Hospital who had agreed to volunteer for the experiment.[5] This was the first time potent 7S anti-Rh gamma globulin had been injected into a human muscle; there was no guarantee that it would remain effectively intact and behave in the body as anticipated. Blood samples drawn periodically showed that the antibody required about eight hours to migrate from the muscle, where it might safely be injected, to the bloodstream, where it might be effective. The man had no demonstrable adverse reaction to the material—the first test of its safety in humans had been passed.

Early in the new year, Vince finally solved his money problem. He followed John's example and applied to the City of New York's Health Research Council for a grant. Wiener, his mentor, a tough master but a good man to have in your corner, sent a handwritten recommendation:

---

* John published the *in*competent cell theory in 1964.[2]

I hold Dr. Freda in the highest esteem, and consider that he is most worthy of your backing. . . .

He early showed his inclination for original investigative work, and I was able to observe him closely because on three of his 12 or more publications we collaborated. His work in the blood grouping field has showed him to be both an imaginative and a careful investigator. . . .

I personally have the highest regards for Dr. Freda as a person and a scientific investigator, and I am confident that any investigation he undertakes is bound . . . to advance the subject and will benefit mankind in general.[6]

A few weeks later, Wiener scrawled a one-sentence note to Vince: "Did you get the grant?"[7]

He did.

Clearly, the view of Zuelzer and the NIH study section was not the last word on Vince and his work. HRC chose to believe the local expert. Its grants review committee decided his work warranted a "high priority" and awarded him $50,000 for a three-year period.[8]

The Sing Sing plans moved ahead frustratingly slowly.* After six weeks of conferences and negotiations, Warden Denno notified Vince that the experiments had been cleared by the New York State Commissioner of Corrections. The State Attorney General, who is charged with protecting prisoners' rights, also approved.

Vince worked out, with State officials, a long and complicated release form that each prisoner would have to sign, in eight places, attesting, among other things, that "he was aware that he faced a risk of allergic reaction, and that allergic reactions sometimes caused death—though, he had been assured, all precautions would be taken to minimize such a risk." Each man would state he was volunteering freely and of his own volition, and would attest that he had been informed that the experiment's purpose was to determine the effect of high-titer anti-Rh gamma globulin on small injections of Rh positive blood as part of an attempt to discover a cure for hemolytic disease of the newborn which kills many babies each year and can cause many others to be seriously crippled or mentally retarded for life.

Bill completed work on the material, resealed it in 5 ml vials, and on February 13 dictated a letter to John: "Under separate cover I

---

* The first published word of the New York group's work appeared early in 1962, in Columbia-Presbyterian *Annual Report* for 1961.[9]

am going to send you 22 vials of sterile anti-Rh gamma globulin (each vial containing 5 ml) together with 10 ml vials of unsterile vialing residue . . . to serve as controls in your subsequent titrations and to save you having to use the sterile product. Hope all goes well!—Bill."[10]

Bill was not wholly satisfied with the fact that they now had a testable 7S anti-Rh antibody preparation. He, like John, continued to feel that a preparation which could be given only after delivery would miss the mark. But while manufacture of the 7S material was proving to be a relatively standard procedure, making the 19S fraction, which he and John favored, was not. As he got deeper into its problems, he found them to be legion. For one thing, there was far less 19S in a given volume of serum. What there was was far more difficult to extract. When extracted, the material was potent enough—at first. In fact one batch turned out to be the most powerful anti-Rh antibody Bill had ever handled. But when he put it aside to pick up some other more pressing task, and then returned to it several weeks later, the titer had fallen to nil. An antibody fraction that had no shelf-life could hardly be made into a commercial preparation. Bill and John considered using still another part of gamma globulin, the so-called Porter fragments, which, like 19S, also do not pass the placenta.*

Bill and Hans Hager also found, as their work progressed, that protein-dissolving enzymes that are normally present in blood could not be separated from the gamma globulin by fractionation. In whole blood, chemical antagonists kept these enzymes in check. But the antagonists vanished during fractionation, leaving the sought-after gamma globulin—whether 7S or 19S—vulnerable to degeneration.

Fragmentation of this kind was commonly encountered in most if

* Named for the basic researcher who first made them, Dr. Rodney Porter, then of the National Institute for Medical Research, London. He, and an American, Dr. Gerald Edelman of Rockefeller University, working independently, showed that the Y-shaped 7S gamma globulin molecule could be cleaved into four pieces when treated with protein-dissolving enzymes, including the meat tenderizer, *papain*. The enzymes eat away the bonds that hold the parts of the molecule together.

While the intact 7S molecule crosses the placenta from mother to fetus, one of the fragments—conveniently, the one that combines with antigen—for the most part does not. Thus, if only this Porter fragment of 7S anti-Rh antibody were injected into the mother, even during pregnancy, it might nullify Rh-positive cells that entered her circulation, but not jeopardize the fetus. The basic research on gamma globulin structure that Vince, John, and Bill hoped to apply, clinically, would win Porter and Edelman the Nobel Prize for Medicine a decade late, in December 1972.

not all commercial gamma globulin. It did not impair the globulin's ability to prevent diseases like measles—the purpose for which gamma globulin was most commonly used. But this breakdown definitely did decrease the anti-Rh titer of both the 19S and 7S fractions. Bill later would find that while this fragmentation rendered the 19S material impotent against the Rh factor, peculiarly, it actually strengthened the anti-Rh activity of the 7S fraction.

Just at this juncture, New York first learned of Liverpool's initial reverses of the previous spring. The ill-tidings came by mail early in March 1962. Two immunologists from Columbus, Ohio, wrote to the British journal *Nature*. On the basis of experiments they had just completed in rabbits, they warned: "There are certain dangers inherent" in the injection of anti-Rh antibody "which could result in more rapid immunization or a higher probability of immunization," rather than protection. In short: enhancement. Investigators Carl Cohen and Wayne Allton, Jr., said their results showed that "immunization can be remarkably enhanced if complexes of antibody and red cells are introduced into a recipient. . . . There is danger," they concluded, "in overlooking the comparative aspects of immunization work, especially when attempts at generalization may lead to increasing the probability of erythroblastosis fetalis."[11]

It was a warning that the New York workers would not soon forget.

The Liverpool team had responded, in *Nature*, by confirming that the Ohioans' findings in rabbits "are generally in agreement with ours in man." Eight of nine men who got the "small" 10 ml dose of anti-Rh serum along with Rh-positive red cells had by now become sensitized to the Rh factor. But in later experiments in which three men had been given 20 ml doses of antiserum and three others had been given 50 ml, none had become sensitized. Cautious grounds for hope remained.[12]

In Baltimore, Finn and Krevans were pushing ahead rapidly. They had already injected several dozen prisoners, using the larger antibody doses. It was too early to draw any conclusions, but none of the men had as yet become sensitized.

Finn, meanwhile, was eager for the approbation of American Rh experts, and the expert of experts whose approval he most sought was Philip Levine—whom he looked upon as the Grand Old Man of rhesus research and the progenitor of his own prevention plan. Memories are muddled on how their meeting first came about, but it is likely that Krevans, who had contacts with Ortho through the Johns Hopkins blood bank, set up the appointment. He recalls going with Finn to Ortho to see Levine and remembers Levine as being essentially negative to the idea of anti-Rh antibody prophylaxis—as, in fact, he had been with Vince.

But Finn, who viewed himself as "a descendant of Levine," came back with an entirely different impression, perhaps precisely because admiration and feelings of kinship had prompted him to make a greater effort than anyone else had to convey his ideas to the master. Moreover, Finn stressed that his own thinking on the protective powers of ABO stemmed directly from Levine's 1943 observation that ABO incompatibility conferred "protection" against immunization to the Rh factor. "This is your finding, from whence we began," Finn explained. Levine, he remembers, was fascinated, after he carefully explained his prevention plan, a step at a time. Finn later would recall that Levine would listen to one idea or sentence, then say "Stop! Go through that again." Finn would repeat what he had said, carry his argument foward a step, and again Levine would interrupt: "No, do that bit again. . . . Now, I've got it!"

Between talks Levine took Finn through the Ortho research laboratories, and in the course of their tour introduced him to one of the promising younger staff scientists, Dr. William Pollack.

Bill might well have been flabbergasted to find himself suddenly shaking hands with a member of the Liverpool team. If so, he perhaps decided that now was not the time for sharing secrets, for Finn later would recall that Bill listened politely while he spelled out some of Liverpool's ideas, and said naught of his own. "Bill Pollack was very devious," Finn would say later. "I spoke to him, gave him my ideas, but in no way did he indicate that he was interested in this at all." Asked later if he recalled the meeting, Bill would say no.

Finn spent the weekend as house guest of the Levines, continuing their conversation on rhesus. He would remember Levine as the only Rh expert "who ever gave me the time of day. He said it was fascinating—he was impressed and interested—though he didn't say it was going to work."

In fact Levine felt interested enough to tell Finn that other Americans should hear his proposal. Levine was a participant in an ongoing seminar in human genetics that met regularly at Columbia

University in New York. Would Finn present his work to the seminar if Levine arranged it? Finn would. Levine said he would arrange it.[13]

What Levine himself knew about Bill's Rh project at the time is unclear. He failed to mention it to Finn, and either had not yet been told, or, like Bill, was not saying. The mystery is mirrored in a letter Levine wrote, just after Finn's visit, to an obstetrician in Germany: Dr. Jörg Schneider, of Freiburg, had read Liverpool's paper in the *BMJ* and had decided to pursue the indicated path to Rh prevention. Schneider had written to Levine asking his views and Levine, in reply, commented cryptically: "There has been increasing interest in the concept of Finn et al. . . . I believe he would be interested in your suggested program [to test it] in animals."[14, 15]

Whenever it was that Levine did find out about the Rh prevention work in progress at Ortho, it is clear that Bill and his associate failed to win from him the same interest that Finn would claim to have achieved in a weekend's visit. "He did not take a very active part in it," Hager would remember. "He would not participate in the discussions. He was on the periphery—like an interested observer. Nor did he lend his people to do any part of the research. Not at all."

All approvals necessary to test Bill's preparation had come. On a Friday early in May, Vince and John drove north to the dead-end stop at the top of Hunter Street in Ossining, New York. By prearrangement with senior physician Kipp, they were passed in to Sing Sing and escorted to the prison hospital. At the guards' station at the door, a bronze plaque appropriately proclaimed: "In this building Science and Charity and Thrift join hands to help the prisoner and the people."

A flyer had been circulated to recruit volunteers: "There were no dramatics involved in this," Warden Denno later explained. "These guys just saw the notice and volunteered. There was none of that movie stuff. None of that goes on here. . . .

"No promises were made to them whatsoever. The experiment had nothing to do with their release, or any possible parole, and they understood that. Nobody could make that kind of promise."[16] (The only allowable gratuities would be cigarettes at Christmas and ball-point pens, which, Vince found to his surprise, were in short supply and in great demand.)

Nine men participated in the first experiment. All were Rh-negative. John separated them into two groups—four "treated" and five "controls." Vince then gave each of the "treated" men 5 ml of anti-Rh antibody preparation. The controls got nothing. A day later, Vince and John returned to Sing Sing and drew blood for testing from each of the "treated" men.* Then they injected all nine

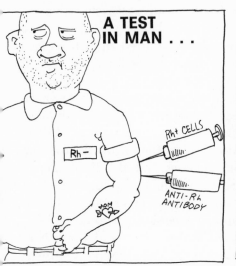
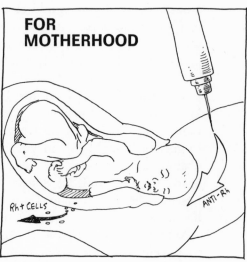

of the men—the four "treated" and the five untreated "controls"—with 2 ml each of Rh-positive blood. John had drawn the red cells from a Columbia medical student who was a regular, and apparently hepatitis-free, donor at the blood bank. Thus, each prisoner now had the equivalent of a sensitizing fetus-to-mother bleed of Rh-positive cells, and half of them had been "treated" with hopefully protective passive antibody.

Four weeks later, the process would be repeated, and it would be repeated a total of five times. In the second and successive months, blood samples would be taken to determine which, if any, men had become sensitized to the Rh factor.

Sensitization would be easy to document in the controls, since any sign of antibody would signify that it had occurred. But the treated men were being injected with an antibody which normally

---

* Giving the antibody first, *before* the red cells, reversed the order of events in pregnancy, when the protective anti-Rh antibody would have to be given *after* the antigenic fetal bleed. But this order permitted Vince and John to be sure that the injected antibody would appear, in potent amounts, in the men's bloodstreams.

might remain in the bloodstream for up to six months. So there would be no way to tell for sure, for many months, if antibody found in their blood was a residue of treatment, or represented instead a treatment failure. However, changes in antibody levels from month to month would provide at least some clues as to the antibody's source.

Unlike Liverpool, John and Vince planned no tests to see how quickly the antibody would clear the Rh-positive red cells from the men's bloodstreams. The one and only test that seemed relevant to them was whether or not the antibody neutralized the Rh antigen on the red cells so that they would not cause Rh sensitization.

The time had arrived for Liverpool and New York to meet. Wiener heralded the event. A week before the first Sing Sing injections, Vince had received from him a "Dear Vincent" note: "Tried to get you tonight to call your attention to the enclosed Program: Columbia University Seminar on Genetics and the Evolution of Man, May 14, 1962 at 8 P.M. 'Some Thoughts on Rh Hemolytic Disease,' by Dr. Ronald Finn, University of Liverpool."[17] Levine had kept his promise to provide Finn an American platform.

May 14, a Monday, was a tense day for Vince and John. Now they would see, and perhaps speak, to a rival who had bested them, in the first round at least, without having known then—or yet—that he had done so. Vince, feeling frustrated that their own attempts had stirred so little interest, was especially irritated that people who had not heeded his and John's plan were now eager to hear it from a stranger—Finn.

For Finn too, the day was not without tensions. He was a stranger to New York. He drove up in the afternoon from Baltimore, got stuck in traffic, and arrived at his hotel in midtown with little time to spare. He quickly washed and changed to his evening suit—to find, to his chagrin, that he had not brought along what he needed to keep his trousers from falling.

"Braces!" he exclaimed impatiently to the surprised bellboy who answered his call for room service. "I need a set of braces. Quickly!"

The bellboy looked blank. Only by pantomiming his need could Finn get it across to him. "Ah, I see!" the bellboy exclaimed. He hurried out to a late-closing men's store to buy the daft English doctor a pair of *suspenders*.

At Columbia, Finn summarized his thesis, which he augmented

with results from the experiments on men in Liverpool and Baltimore. Finn could foresee the testing of perhaps 75 men with the larger doses of 7S antibody-containing serums that they had switched to after their initial mishaps. Buoyed by his own optimism and the promising early results in Baltimore—3/44 (3 out of 44) men sensitized among the controls, compared to 0/35 sensitized among men who got Rh antigen plus antibody protection—Finn glibly glossed over the previous year's failures: "One of the most interesting things that has come out of this study is the marked enhancement of sensitization (12/48) in the volunteers in whom there has been a less-than-complete removal of the Rh-positive cells. . . . There seems little doubt, however, from our results that there is no danger of enhancement if the fetal cells are completely cleared."[18]

Finn finished. There were questions, and now, as members of the audience crowded up to talk to the speaker, it was time for John and Vince to come forward and say, in effect, "Did you know that there are other people? That we. . . ."

Finn did not know. He was surprised. He was not dismayed.

Vince and John approached him unassertively. Finn would later indicate that he felt they had entered the Rh field as a result of reading his *BMJ* paper. Since he already had published his work and they had not, he did not see them as rivals or equal claimants. In fact, it would only be many years later, when he was shown a copy of Vince's grant application, date stamped on receipt by NIH, that Finn would accept that Vince, independently, had conceived the key idea that protective antibody injections at delivery might be in time.

Vince and John drove Finn back downtown after the meeting. They stopped in Times Square so that he could purchase some phonograph records. They had a bite to eat, and continued their conversation, and then renewed it the next day.

Finn, feeling his priorities were firmly established, felt free to share his thoughts and data with Vince and John, whom he found to be agreeable persons. With John, who like him was British, he found it especially easy to establish a friendly rapport. They told him about Sing Sing and their use of 7S anti-Rh gamma globulin rather than antiserum. He counseled them to optimal protective dosage—as a hedge against enhancement—and pointed out that the Sing Sing data would be only partially valid since the prisoners there were getting the protective antibody *first,* and then the antigenic red cells—the reverse of what could be anticipated to occur in women.

John ascertained from Finn that he was unfamiliar with Theobald Smith and the *AMIS* principle, and hence had no idea of its potential applicability to Rh disease. Rapid destruction and/or clearance of the antigenic Rh-positive red cells was, in Finn's mind, the way that anti-Rh antibody provided protection.

Of all the New York accomplishments, Finn was most interested in the gamma globulin preparation. Could he have some to test? Vince and John explained that it was very scarce and in short supply—and could only be used by them, at Sing Sing, under the protocols set up between Ortho and the United States government. Nevertheless, they said they would try to get him a vial.

All things considered, it was a very cordial encounter.

In a "Dear Ron" letter posted a week or so later, John told Finn that a spare 5 ml vial of gamma globulin, left over from the sterility testing, was on its way by mail. "Let us know," John wrote, "what kind of titer you get with it and whether it clears red cells rapidly."[19] John and Vince were to hear far more of the 5 ml vial of material than John could possibly have guessed as he posted his letter—and the context would not be pleasing.

In the wake of Finn's visit, Vince and John had another meeting with Ortho officialdom. In two letters to his parents in Australia, he recapped the month's highpoints:

The Sing Sing project is going well. We have finished our second series of injections. So far no results. . . .

Finn visited us two or three weeks ago. . . . He has scooped the publicity pool for our idea of preventing sensitization to Rh with antibody, and he wants Ortho to make gamma globulin for him also. . . .

They [Ortho] took us out to dinner . . . We are expanding our supply [of] gamma globulin. Ortho is going to make us a large batch for $4500 and we are submitting a new grant request to Washington, possibly for over $100,000. . . . They discussed making Porter fractions out of this antibody for us as these might be suitable to give to the pregnant mother. . . .

Ortho is very enthusiastic about this project now—chiefly because of Finn's work.[20, 21]

# 21

## Sing Sing

FINN, too, was enthusiastic. He and Krevans had wasted no time in injecting the vial of 7S gamma globulin that John had sent them into a Baltimore convict, along with 5 ml of Rh-positive red cells. "Your gamma globulin has proved a great success," Finn wrote back in a hand-scrawled letter a week later. "The [reduction of] red cell survival equals the best we have achieved with 50 ml of anti-Rh serum."[1] In six hours the gamma globulin had cleared 92 percent of the injected red cells from the man's blood; 98 percent was gone in twenty-four hours. If clearing red cells was the way to prevent Rh immunization—and Finn still felt that it was—then here, clearly, was the machine to do it.

But not all the news from Baltimore was good. "On the other side of the picture," Finn wrote, "we have just observed a woman who has developed antibody postpartum without [having had] any demonstrable hemorrhage at delivery—and you will remember that we had previously had a similar case. This has given us food for much thought, and I just wonder what percentage of women are really sensitized at delivery. It would seem to us that the timing of sensitization is becoming the most critical point in the story. . . .

"It would seem well worthwhile to follow Rh-negative women with the Kleihauer in the last trimester, perhaps weekly, to see if we can pinpoint exactly what percentage become sensitized at delivery, within two weeks of delivery, and earlier. Vince's Rh . . .

clinic would be ideally suited to this type of study, and I hope to get this going in Liverpool in the fall."

Finn was near the end of his American sojourn. Clarke had written to say he would send John Woodrow, who had taken over the Liverpool experiments in Finn's absence, to carry on in Baltimore when Finn returned home. Johns Hopkins agreed to the plan, and one sunny Sunday in August Finn and Woodrow rode the Greyhound bus to New York for Finn's farewell—and Woodrow's get-acquainted—visits.

John met the bus and brought Finn and Woodrow to his apartment. They sat on the terrace, drank beer, and talked about the work in progress. Vince, who had a woman in labor, failed to appear. Socially, the afternoon was highly successful: John Gorman and John Woodrow commenced a friendship that would continue quite actively for the whole of Woodrow's one-year American sojourn. Both men were bachelors and footloose, and Woodrow frequently would come to New York, stay with John, and the two of them would party it up together. Their camaraderie marked the high point of rapport between the Liverpool and New York groups—which was shortly due for a serious setback, as a result of the 5 ml of gamma globulin Finn had tested and had been so impressed with.

Even on that August Sunday, John Gorman's recollection later would be that—given their competing interests—the conversation on Rh was not altogether comfortable. John said he was going to Mexico City the following month to present their preliminary Sing Sing results to an international hematology meeting. In their last talk with Ortho, he explained, it had been suggested that New York now put its work on record—a claim should be staked. Singher and Hill planned to attend the blood meeting with Philip Levine and felt it might be a good place to give a paper. Of the three New York researchers, John, as a blood banker, was the appropriate one to present it.

Finn said that he, too, had considered going to Mexico but that this was his last month in America, and he was eager to go sightseeing in the West.

Woodrow, while hopeful, was far less sanguine than Finn about the work in progress. While his doubts had failed to impress John in New York, where Finn's optimism had brightened the day, they became clearly and disconcertingly evident when John Gorman and Vince returned the visit, in Baltimore, a month or so later. Finn and his optimism had departed, and they were met in the blood bank by Woodrow and Krevans—both of whom, John later would recall, wore long faces; they attributed their gloom to the as-yet-unfathomed danger of enhancement. In fact, it was at this get-together, with Finn absent, that the magnitude of the enhancement menace Liverpool had encountered first really struck home to Vince and John.

It was true, Woodrow told them, that they were getting fewer cases of enhancement with high doses of 7S antibody than they had with low doses of combined 7S and 19S material. Nevertheless, sensitization still occurred fairly commonly when the protective antibody dose was only 10 ml of 7S antibody-containing serum. In one or two cases men who had gotten the large 50 ml protective dose along with 5 ml of antigenic red cells had become sensitized. It was disturbing—very disturbing. Even though they seemed now to be protecting many more men than they sensitized with the antibody injections, and even though the antigenic stimulus was extremely large—bleeds of 5 ml occurred only once or twice per 100 deliveries—still they were dealing with a sensitization that occurs naturally only in one of every ten pregnancies at risk. Protection that extended to less than 100 percent of threatened women might be tolerated—and, in fact, everybody anticipated failures. But even if only one percent of women *not* destined to become sensitized did in fact become so as a result of the treatment, it would have to be discarded as worthless. It would violate medicine's cardinal injunction: *Primum non nocere.* The primary concern is to do no harm.

Woodrow was less convinced than Finn and McConnell by the "terribly naive" notion that the antibody injections might protect women by rapidly moving the antigenic red cells from the bloodstream to the spleen—which is where, it seemed, the antibody would take them. "My God," he would say later, "the spleen is the *last* place you want them!" Clearance might be a measurable consequence, but it was the antibody's role in coating and insulating the red cells' antigen sites that would provide the protection, if anything would: "You had got to get shucked of the idea that it's simple clearance that does it!"

Initially, Woodrow had felt that Finn's insistence that labor was the sensitizing event was simply "wishful thinking"—and he as yet lacked facts that would convince him differently. He still believed in the project. He hoped it would work. But he had doubts which only hard work could resolve.

Worrisome as Woodrow's second thoughts from Liverpool might be, John and Vince could take heart from the fact that, clearly, the race was far from over: Problems remained to be solved, and, despite Finn's ambition to push on quickly to a clinical trial in Rh-negative women, the question of who would get there first seemed more open than it had been for quite a while. Vince could find cheer in the fact that whether the protective mechanism was red cell clearance or prevention of immunization, Finn himself had said that Bill's gamma globulin, because of its terrific strength, might well be the only preparation potent enough to ensure protection instead of enhancement. And the anti-Rh gamma globulin was New York's contribution—the claim for which John nailed down, once and for all, in his talk in September to the International Society of Hematology's Congress in Mexico.[2]

Publication of their abstract in the Congress program marks John, Vince, and Bill's first formal appearance in print in advocacy of anti-Rh antibody as an Rh preventive. More than two years had elapsed since Finn's first formal presentations to the Liverpool Medical Institution and the Genetical Society.[3, 4] By the rules of the research game, then, "priority of publication" for the use of anti-Rh antibody clearly belongs to Finn; credit for the idea of using gamma globulin, rather than serum, and the rationale of *AMIS*, rather than cell clearance, belongs clearly to John, Vince, and Bill.

Beyond its publication priorities Liverpool, from the start, sustained preeminence in terms of the quality, influence, and circulation of the journals in which it published. The International Hematology Society Congress in Mexico was a special event, for blood specialists, and the proceedings, published two years later, could not have sold many copies since only 500 were printed.[5] Vince's first detailed publication of their work, late in 1962, appeared in a local Columbia organ, the *Bulletin of the Sloane Hospital for Women*, with a circulation of only a few thousand.[6] Finn and Clarke, by contrast, first published in *Lancet*, the *British Medical Journal* and *Nature*, three of the world's top-rated medical and scientific publications.[7, 8, 9] Vince and John did not reach their equivalent until many years later. The fault, if one exists, was largely their own. Vince had access to the important *American Journal of Obstetrics and Gynecology* through his chief, Howard Taylor, who then was its co-editor. John wanted to publish aggressively, both plans and actions, as Liverpool was doing. But Vince insisted that they publish only results—and, in major journals, only major results. So they waited.

It could not yet be said with certainty that the Sing Sing experiment was a success, John told the Mexico meeting. But the blood antibody levels in the "protected" men were remaining rather constant, suggesting that theirs continued to be harmless, passive immunizations while the titers in the unprotected men, several of whom already were actively immunized, varied widely.

The 1962 blood bank meeting was held in Memphis, Tennessee— in a racially-segregated meeting center. John stayed home in protest, as did many other blood bankers. Vince, meanwhile, submitted for publication the first full report on their prevention work and his antepartum clinic. He had now diagnosed fetal erythroblastosis in 50 cases on the basis of amniotic fluid assay, which, he said, "may be the most important diagnostic tool available . . . in the most serious of Rh cases." Vince also revealed that he had defied current practice and used the new technique as a guide to premature induction of labor in several cases. These developments, along with their progress on the Rh preventive, led him to conclude, with characteristic optimism, that "the attack on erythroblastosis fetalis is gaining momentum, and it is possible that in the next few years we may see a marked shift in emphasis from management of affected babies to prevention of the disease itself."[10]

By year's end, in fact, there was clear reason for cheer about Sing Sing. Each of the 9 prisoners had been given up to 5 shots of antigenic Rh-positive blood. Four had been "protected" with an anti-Rh antibody injection each time. As this "passively administered" antibody slowly disappeared from their veins, it became evident that all 4 had been protected from sensitization; but 4 of the 5 unprotected controls were strongly sensitized. John wrote home to Australia:

Vincent Freda and I are in a very good position with regard to the Rh [work] now—we have beautiful results from Sing Sing—showing complete prevention of sensitization of our protected prisoners. We are reporting this at the Federation [of American Societies for Experimental Biology] meetings at Atlantic City in April, and have a manuscript just about ready for *Transfusion*, the blood banking journal.

Vincent had lunch with Wiener, who discovered the Rh factor, on

Friday, and Wiener said it was beautiful work. Moreover, the antibody preparation that Ortho made for us is now in great demand and Krevans from Johns Hopkins and Finn in England want some also.[11]

Vince wrote Warden Denno, saying the results had been highly favorable, and warranted a continuation of the experiments in a larger group of men. Denno wrote back:

In reply to your letter of February 26, 1963, informing me of the results of the research study on preventing Hemolytic Disease and that these results are both positive and very exciting but that in view of the fact that it was only possible to study a small group of volunteers (4 prisoners received this new reagent and 5 prisoners acted as controls), that before you can try this reagent on pregnant mothers you must enlarge your study to 20 volunteers (10 will receive the reagent and 10 will act as controls), and that as you now have an adequate supply of this extremely expensive preparation to carry out your program, that you would like to continue this research project for an additional period under the same conditions that you have been conducting it in the past, and that the only difference would be the number of volunteers in the study (20 instead of 10), and requesting permission to be allowed to continue your study, I wish to advise that permission is granted. . . .[12]

The primary problem to be dealt with was *enhancement*. To take this danger well into account, in their second Sing Sing experiment John, Vince, and Bill greatly increased the antigenic stimulus against which the antibody would have to compete. Instead of getting 2 ml of antigenic red blood cells as in the earlier experiment, each prisoner would get 10 ml in each injection.

In the first experiment, the protective antibody had been given *before* the antigenic red blood. The real test was whether antibody would protect ex post facto—*after* a fetus-to-mother bleed. So, in the new experiment the red cells would be given *first*, followed, a day or so later, by antibody. Vince and John later would recall that Warden Denno had qualms about setting up an injection schedule that would bring them back to the prison to see 20 or more men at regularly scheduled intervals of 24 hours; someone might seize the opportunity to use them as part of a prison break. Could they extend the interval? What about 48 hours? "Why don't we go whole hog?" Vince said to John. "Let's make it *three* days, or 72 hours, from antigen to antibody. If we can get protection after that long a delay, we can be sure it's working!" John and the warden agreed to the three-day interval.

For all its ironbound order that brought keeper and kept to co-operate in a generous, humanitarian act, Sing Sing was a place of smouldering, savage violence. The Irish-born technician whom John had hired to do the lab work on the prisoners' blood, Miss Nancy Treacy, could not, as a woman, enter the gates to draw the specimens. On only one of John and Vince's more than seventy trips "up river" did she go along: It was a winter's day; snow had fallen the previous night; and she joined John in the morning to see the snowfall on the branches and landscape on the way up the Hudson to Ossining. Freshly cleaned and dusted with snow, the suburban countryside reminded her of home. Miss Treacy remained in the parked car, outside the prison gates, while John entered for the day's injections. She was startled, a few minutes later, to see him running from the gate, back toward the car. "Let's get out of here!" he exclaimed, pale and shaken. "Someone stabbed somebody in there with a knife. He's dying!" They drove back down the Hudson in silence.

Woodrow, meanwhile, working in the Maryland Penitentiary, and Finn, back home in Liverpool, using free volunteers, plugged ahead with their injection programs. By spring, Clarke decided the time was right to submit a new report. Their last publications had indicated all but total failure with the low-dose 19S antibody injections. Their new 7S data were considerably better. The Liverpool team now had grown to nine authors, headed by Clarke. Finn, now one among the many members of the team, saw the paper only after it had been written.

Liverpool reported that when they used high doses of 35 to 50 ml of plasma containing 7S anti-Rh antibody, only 3 of 21 men had become immunized, after up to 4 antigenic stimuli of 5 ml Rh-positive blood each. But half of the unprotected controls had become sensitized.[13]

Three sensitizations in about eighty exposures is about the normal rate of Rh sensitization in women at risk, so from one point of view these results were not so good. Still, it was apparent that enhancement was no longer occurring, for at least this was not *more* than the normal number of sensitizations. Moreover, as Sheppard, who designed the experiments, would later point out, 5 ml of Rh-positive blood is a huge antigenic challenge; only one or two women in a hundred would get that much fetal blood leakage; most would get far less. Perhaps Liverpool was on the right track after all.

The Liverpool team now repudiated the idea that they were duplicating ABO protection, their original rationale, and shifted instead toward Stern's explanation that the Rh antigen sites on the injected red cells were blocked by the injected antibody. The enhancement in the early experiments, they suggested, might have been due to the fact that 19S antibody takes the antigenic cells to a more immunogenic part of the immune system—as Woodrow believed—or, perhaps, transported the antigen to the immune centers where, dangerously, it broke free—as prisoners, led captive to headquarters, may do added harm if they escape their bonds.

In the paper in the BMJ, Clarke fired a shot that would shake the banks of the Hudson. "We are not entirely happy about giving whole plasma or serum," he wrote, "since it is not without risk of producing hepatitis. This difficulty can be overcome by using a concentrated gamma globulin preparation containing only 7S anti-Rh antibodies. We tested such a preparation and found that 5 ml given intramuscularly was much more powerful in producing clearance than 50 ml of high-titer antiserum given intravenously."[14]

The tested preparation, of course, was the vial John and Vince had given to Finn the previous spring—a fact that Clarke neglected to mention in his text. Only in small print, in the Acknowledgments, which included "Thank you's" to Liverpool dock workers and the medical staff of the Maryland State Penitentiary, did Clarke thank Bill Pollack, Ortho, Gorman, and Freda—in that order—"for allowing us to test a sample of high-titer anti-Rh in the form of gamma globulin."

Vince was furious. Clarke had published on the efficacy of their preparation before he and John and Bill could do so! Their first report to a major scientific body on the Sing Sing results was scheduled for the following week. Clarke did not indicate that the New York group had independently thought up and made the Rh-preventive his group had tested—perhaps he did not believe that they had. Cordiality would continue between the two groups, but a seed of conflict had been sown over the issue of whether Clarke and Liverpool had title to essentially complete credit for the Rh preventive, or whether New York had staked a late though independent claim that gave it the right to a share of the credit.

The moment had arrived, however, when New York had data with which to blow its own horn. Vince's presentation had been set for Atlantic City, four days after publication of Liverpool's second BMJ paper. Public relations officials for the huge annual gathering of the Federation of American Societies for Experimental Biology had fastened upon his report as one of perhaps a dozen among the 3,000 or so scheduled for delivery that were worthy of being touted to the newspapers. A photographer was sent to Vince's lab; in her photo, Vince guardedly displays a vial of their experimental preparation (see page 88). A news release was written and, for the first time in his career, in Atlantic City, Vince met the press.[15]

The reporters clearly were attracted by this personable, competent-sounding young obstetrician whom hardened convicts had agreed to serve—in motherhood's interest. *The New York Times'* soft-spoken medical writer, Harold Schmeck, Jr., talked to Vince, and the *Times* carried the story the next day.[16] So did the wire services and newspapers around the world.[17] A medical newspaper headlined the proposition: "Anti-Rh Gamma Globulin May Bar Erythroblastosis." If the Sing Sing results continue to look good, Vince was quoted as saying, clinical trials would start in a year to "prove whether our theory is valid."[18]

One who read the press accounts from Atlantic City was an old friend of the Freda family, who wrote to congratulate Vince for the "blessed" discovery he had made for mankind.[19] Vince thanked him, cautioning: "Although our research has made a significant move forward, we are still quite a few years away from actually solving the problem. There is no guarantee that we will succeed, and I would say the odds are only about 50-50 that we will. But these are excellent odds for any research study."[20]

At Atlantic City that spring the work, for the first time after three years, took on a frightening though exhilarating sense of reality. "We're really selling the project, for the first time," exclaimed John, who, with Bill, had joined Vince and his wife, Carol, at the meeting. They had driven out of town for a celebratory dinner at a restaurant in Smithville Village, a reassembled collection of eighteenth-century New Jersey stores and homes that had been turned into a shopping and dining center. "John," someone exclaimed, "all you need now is a wife!"

The Rh establishment and, in particular, the pediatric blood specialists, remained far less impressed than the newspapermen had been. The following week, Fred Allen, Jr., came from Boston to deliver a formal lecture at Columbia on "Attempts at Prevention of Intrauterine Death in Erythroblastosis Fetalis."[21] His talk may stand as the most complete catalogue, for all time, of the unsuccessful attempts—including several of his own—at novel, daring, and even quite cunning methods to prevent erythroblastosis. All, Allen added, already had failed or looked as if they would.

Allen completely ignored the home team in his talk at Columbia, although John felt that in a private talk, off the dais, he was far more encouraging than he had been several years earlier when John had tried to "peddle" their anti-Rh antibody plan to him. In his lecture Allen did deal with Liverpool: "It has recently been proposed that Rh-negative women be given anti-Rh antibodies deliberately in an attempt to destroy fetal Rh-positive cells as they enter the maternal circulation. This proposal was not based on sufficient experimental evidence, and there are theoretical reasons for believing it an unwise procedure, though the matter is certainly not settled."*

If Allen was willing to wait and see, the pediatric opposition elsewhere had hardened, especially in Detroit. In submitting their results for publication in *Transfusion*, Vince asserted that the question of when sensitization occurred still had not been resolved—but that the evidence, as he and Finn could see it, was that it occurred only at delivery. One of the anonymous reviewers of the paper took issue with this point of view, saying that, probably, sensitization took place much earlier.[22] Acceptance of Vince's paper was delayed. The critical reviewer appears to have been Zuelzer. In August, the month that Vince's paper was finally accepted by *Transfusion*, Zuelzer and Flossie Cohen had submitted to *Blood*, a competing publication, a detailed, documented report covering more than five years of research on transplacental passage of fetal red cells into mothers' bloodstreams.[23, 24] The results directly contested the assumptions upon which the New York and Liverpool prevention programs were based.

Cohen had used several methods for counting fetal cells in maternal blood, in order to resolve the discrepancies between the amounts and timing of fetal bleeds that she had found, compared to the results found by Finn. His "Model-T" method, the Kleihauer test, had detected fetal cells in only 20 percent of women. In his counting system, he disregarded—as "no fetal bleed"—all scores of less than one fetal cell per 10,000 adult red cells. As a result, he figured that countable bleeds occurred in only 12 percent of women.

---

* A last, and most startling, revelation about Allen's view of Rh-antibody prophylaxis would surface only five years later—for which, see Chapter 32.

Cohen's precision-tooled Detroit technique for staining fetal cells with dyes visible by UV light—certainly the "Cadillac" of fetal cell counting methods—detected bleeds as small as one fetal cell in 1,000,000 adult cells. (See Chapter 19.) Using this technique along with the Kleihauer, Cohen found fetal blood in almost half of some six hundred women whose bloods she drew at delivery. She, unlike Finn, did not discount the minute bleeds. "Some authors," she commented, referring to his work, "disregard minute quantities of fetal cells in the maternal blood. In the present study, any blood in which even a single fetal cell could be seen was considered to be 'positive,' for the significance of the transplacental passage of even minimal numbers in terms of their potential sensitizing effects cannot be prejudged. . . ."[25]

Still more telling against the Finn-Freda hypothesis that protection at delivery would be in time was Cohen's finding, from blood tests on pregnant women *before* delivery, that almost three women in ten had some detectable fetal blood in their veins by the third trimester—though exactly how much they had, on the average, she did not say. If, as Cohen believed, "the time of the first entry of fetal cells into the maternal blood is of obvious importance for the genesis of maternal immunization," then the prognosis for a preventive method predicated on treatment at delivery was poor at best.

Most devastating of all, Cohen found that labor usually did not strongly affect the fetal cell population in a mother's blood. Women who had large numbers of fetal cells at delivery usually had had them weeks or months before. Neither was there significant correlation between the length and violence of labor and the mother's fetal cell count. With words that cut, Cohen concluded: "The fact that labor is not an event of special significance has far-reaching implications for the theory of [Rh] immunization and especially for current proposals to prevent sensitization by creating passive immunity during a supposedly crucial period centering on the time of delivery."[26]

Among themselves, in fact, Liverpool and New York had become quite responsive to Cohen and Zuelzer's criticism. While Finn was anxious to press on to a clinical trial in women using 7S antibody at delivery, Clarke had insisted that he and Woodrow repeat all the Kleihauer work he had done for his thesis, using a much more rigorous counting method. Instead of analyzing four miscroscope slide fields for each woman, they would scan 100. Similarly, Vince had applied to NIH for funds to set up an automated Kleihauer slide-scanning system. He wanted relatively little money for this and for the Rh antepartum clinic. He also asked for more than $100,000 for development of alternate anti-Rh antibody preparations which might be given *during* pregnancy, in case, as Cohen and Zuelzer insisted, postpartum protection turned out to be "protection" ex post facto.

Singher had set the cost for 25 vials of 19S anti-Rh antibody at $25,000 and for 25 vials of the 3.5S Porter fraction at $168,000—or almost $7,000 a vial.[27] Vince at first combined all their financial needs into one grant application, then split it into two parts when it became clear that NIH was in no hurry to buy experimental gamma globulin preparations at upwards of a thousand dollars a vial.

Divided, Vince's request still failed. NIH turned down both applications. "Grantsmanship," Vince had remarked, "happens to be my poorest subject."[28]

Cost was not the only bar. Bill had not yet succeeded in making a suitable 19S preparation. The Porter fraction could be made, but, it would soon turn out, when it was injected into animals it was excreted almost at once in their urine. It vanished far too quickly to pose any threat whatsoever to Rh-positive cells.

If 7S antibody at delivery failed, the options now were strikingly circumscribed.

John, meanwhile, was leaving Presbyterian Hospital. He had on several occasions crossed swords with his chief in the blood bank, John Scudder. He resented the growing teaching and administrative loads imposed on his time both by the blood bank and the pathology department, to which he belonged. The Rh research, his now-promising prothrombin machine, the incompetent clone, and his other inventive endeavors seemed threatened by routine.

A job offer had come from a well-regarded private hospital on the East Side of Manhattan, Lenox Hill. They would make John assistant blood bank chief and build him a research laboratory. John accepted, and handed in resignations at Presbyterian Hospital and at Columbia.

Though he did not know it at the time, this would turn out to be a short-term move that would eventuate in long-term advantage.

Remodeling of his new quarters at Lenox Hill took longer than had been anticipated. Fortunately, for he wanted to travel, John found himself between jobs, with several months free. His parents flew from Australia to California in May, on the first leg of an around-the-world flight. John met them and they toured the West together, after which Dr. John, Sr., and his wife, Dr. Jean Grant, went on to London.

Later in the summer, John flew to England to meet them. His parents were visiting their other son, Richard Francis "Frank" Gorman, an eye specialist, and his wife, Kathryn. She was pregnant. The baby she and Frank were expecting would be their first.

In his jacket pocket John brought from New York the very latest tallies, midway through the second Sing Sing experiment, as well as the soon to-be-published full report on the first one.

One day in September, John and his parents drove up to Liverpool to renew acquaintances with Finn and with Woodrow, who had recently returned from Baltimore. John found Clarke, whom he now met for the first time, to be exceedingly courteous—and exceedingly interested in the progress of the Sing Sing work. A general discussion, which began at the medical school, continued over dinner at an Indian restaurant, chosen by Ronnie Finn.

For the doctors John Gorman, it was a homecoming of sorts: Their forebears had emigrated to Australia from a Lancashire town just outside Liverpool. Being British helped bridge the gap between New York and Liverpool; the Gormans all felt welcome. For John, Sr., as proud father, it was a special privilege and a pleasure to be present—and to participate actively—in the anti-Rh strategy session that unfolded over curry and tea.

The Gormans learned that Liverpool had come to what Ronnie Finn later would characterize as their "fallow period." Finn himself was eager to press on with a clinical trial in newly-delivered women. "We'd been a year ahead of the American group at the start," he later would say. "By 1963, they were hot on our heels— and I would have liked to keep a jump ahead of them."

Clarke demurred. "Professor Clarke governed the pace," Finn would recall later, "and he was very, very afraid of making a mistake. He has an acute sense of timing. He had the view that if we made an error, it would kill it—and him. There was a certain art of self-protection in that he didn't want it to blow up in his face. It would have killed all of us if it went wrong. Suppose that we had started clinical trials and gotten enhancement! That would have brought the wrath of the medical profession down upon us."

Even Finn himself could not wholly fault his chief's caution. Many times in that year he had remembered a warning that had been delivered by one of his medical school professors: If, in the whole of your medical career, you do absolutely no good, that's all right. But never, never do anyone any harm. *Primum non nocere.*

Clarke told John he was especially eager to see—in print—the Sing Sing results from the experiment in which the antibody was given *after* the red cells. John had these data only in note form: None of the "protected" men had yet become sensitized, although several unprotected "controls" seemed to be.

Clarke said he could see several necessary intermediary steps before the method was applied in newly-delivered women. For one thing, all tests to date had used Rh-positive red cells from adults as the antigenic stimulus. In fact, it was *fetal* red cells, which are chemically different, that cause Rh sensitization in new mothers. Fetal red cells should be tested. And they should be tested, somehow, in *women*, since, unlikely as it seemed, women's antibody response to Rh might be different from that of the men in whom all tests had been conducted. This Liverpool had started to do. Clarke would later say: "We needed to do the injections with fetal cells, in postmenopausal women, just to say we'd done it, before starting the clinical trial."

Clarke also was worried about Cohen and Zuelzer's data. John, who was equally concerned, nevertheless had greater confidence in the fall-back position—his original plan—of giving 19S anti-Rh or one of the other gamma globulin fractions before the baby was born. Clarke disliked the idea. He would say later: "I don't think we would have been keen on giving it during pregnancy." All hopes in Liverpool now were riding on Finn's beleaguered belief that bleeds big enough to cause sensitization occurred only at, or close to, delivery.

Liverpool also faced a tough practical problem. Unlike New York, they had to go outside of their group to get 19S anti-Rh gamma globulin. Clarke and Finn had both written Ortho, which either was unwilling or unable to fill their request for the material. Supply was short, and making it remained difficult; one batch that Bill had spent many weeks producing went bad and had to be discarded—delaying all work for several months. Blood experts in Britain were less convinced of the project's merit than Ortho and much time would go by before the Lister Institute, in London, could provide Liverpool with a suitably large shipment of 7S anti-Rh antibody.

John listened attentively to the Liverpool progress report and promised to keep Clarke and his colleagues abreast of the ongoing work at Sing Sing. John's father, John S. Gorman, listened attentively. No one sitting around the table that afternoon talking over the emptied curry dishes and tea glasses could have foreseen that, within a very few months, it would be the *senior* Dr. Gorman who would act to crystalize and bring to a head all the elements of their long discussion.

Shortly after the visit to Liverpool John returned to New York. John, Sr., remained, briefly, in London with his son Frank and Frank's wife, Kath, who was soon due to give him his first grandchild. By autumn, the grandparents-to-be had returned home to Melbourne.

# 22

## Heroic Help for the Fetus

WHILE JOHN WAS in England there occurred the single most breath-taking episode in the entire Rh saga.

The scene was far outside the Liverpool–New York axis. It was in Auckland, New Zealand. An X-ray room in New Zealand's National Women's Hospital. The time: a day in early September 1963.

At center stage is obstetrician "Bill" Liley. He is now thirty-four years old, and already has to his credit the development of amniocentesis into a quantifiable, lifesaving diagnostic procedure for dying Rh-positive fetuses. (See Chapter 11.)

Liley is masked and gowned. The woman lying before him on the operating table is draped for surgery. Only her protuberant pregnant belly is bare and exposed.

Liley approaches her, carrying a seven-inch long hollow needle. He appears to be starting still another amniocentesis; he has in fact needled this woman's belly before. But more is at stake now than a diagnosis. Liley knows, from the "tap" already done, that this fetus, at less than eight months' gestation, is too immature to deliver alive, but too sick to survive until liveborn delivery is possible. It is, he remarks, a "really maddening" bind.

Delicately, Liley stabs the long needle straight on, into the woman's belly. A local anesthetic keeps her from feeling its entry. Liley feels the needle point pass through the resistant abdominal musculature, then clear the uterine wall and enter the unresisting fluid-filled womb. If this were an amniocentesis, it would now be time to stop and attach a syringe, for suction, onto the back of the needle so that a fluid sample could be drawn out for study.

But Liley does not stop. Instead of carefully keeping the needle point away from the fetal body, his hand deftly guides it forward and downward until it is directly against the fetus' tiny stomach. Then, with one final thrust, he pushes the point straight on in.

In pain, the fetus squirms, but cannot wiggle away; the needle pins it to the uterine wall, against its mother's backbone. Carefully, deliberately, Liley now unstoppers the back end of the needle's hollow barrel. He threads into it a thin plastic tube. He eases the tube forward until it is inside the fetus, then pulls out the needle, leaving the tube in place. The fetus can now wiggle, with no danger it will break off the needle point inside its body.

Through the tube, Liley forces into the fetus three ounces of warm, life-sustaining red blood cells. Unlike the fetus' disease-destroyed Rh-positive cells, these cells are Rh-negative, like the mother's, and so will not be harmed by the deadly anti-Rh antibodies she is producing.

The thin scarlet fluid running into the fetus through the tube Liley is holding is the world's first successful intrauterine blood transfusion. A few weeks and another blood transfusion later, this fetus will be delivered, alive—albeit barely—by cesarean section. With the help of exchange transfusion, it will survive and thrive. The blood given to it in the uterus will prove to have been its margin of survival: Half of its red cells at birth are transfused.[1]

Liley's needle had penetrated barriers beyond flesh and death on its way to the heart of the womb: breached, too, was the metaphysical barrier between the world of life that is and the universe of life that is yet to be. A fetus had been treated, medically, as one of us.

Shattered, too, had been the barrier of medical custom. Prudence and caution had insisted until then that the womb and its contents were beyond the boundary of direct medical intervention. Strikingly, it had been with erythroblastosis fetalis that Ruth Darrow and Philip Levine, a quarter of a century before, had first disproved the age-old belief that the womb is a hermetic seal between fetus and mother. Strikingly, it was again erythroblastosis which now allowed Liley to demonstrate that medical help could be extended across the uterine barrier to aid a dying unborn baby.

Liley was first to supplement effectively a baby's blood in utero.

But, as in all of the short, dramatic war against Rh disease, others were actively pursuing similar paths; Liley's triumph over these contenders was whisper-close in terms of time. Indeed, it would turn out that one in fact did beat him. Yet Liley would

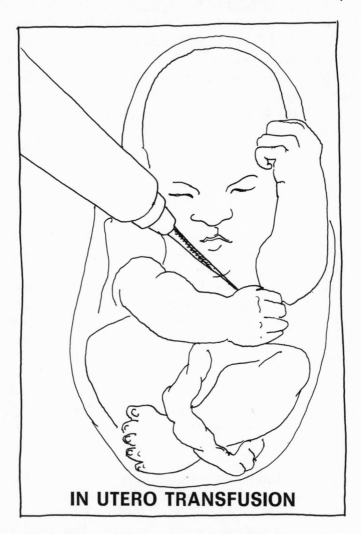

## IN UTERO TRANSFUSION

gain—and would remain secure in—triumph, because, as one among several who sensed a challenge, he provided what was by far the most effective solution.

The challenge presented itself to those courageous enough to think creatively about amniocentesis. The fluid "taps" could tell a man fairly precisely when a fetus was going to die for want of

sufficient red blood cells. The needle through which this information was obtained came frustratingly close to the fetus in need of
assistance. Why should a needle that brought amniotic fluid out of
the womb not also carry a blood supplement back *in*?

The problem was: How to do it. A hidden fetus, unlike an adult,
could not simply be given a blood transfusion into a vein. Working
blindly, from outside the womb, there was no way to find and hit a
vein with the needle.

In fact, the first man to do amniocentesis in an Rh case, Douglas
Bevis of Manchester, was the first man actually to try—and in one
case succeed in—saving a fetus by transfusing it in the uterus. He
did this in the late 1950s. Bevis did not think he could hit a fetal
blood vessel with a needle. But why not one in the placenta? At
least, it was a less mobile target. Fetal blood circulates continuously
through the stalklike umbilical cord to the placenta, firmly attached to the uterine wall. There, circulating through a jumbled
network of small vessels, fetal blood gathers oxygen as it passes
close by oxygen-rich maternal blood on the other side of the thin
placental membrane.

Bevis located the placenta by injecting the mother with radiopaque dye and examining her stomach on a fluoroscope screen. The
concentration of maternal blood vessels in the placenta made it
stand out in view. Then he pushed a long hollow needle down
through the mother's abdomen into the placenta. Blood pushed up
from inside. The needle's point rested inside a placental vessel. But
on which side of the membrane?

With the needle still in place, Bevis quickly tested the blood,
using a modified Kleihauer technique, to determine whether he was
getting fetal or maternal red cells. When he was fairly satisfied that
the needle in fact rested in a fetal vessel, he began injecting blood
into it through the needle. It proved to be a slow, frustrating business. Bevis could not be absolutely sure that he was getting the
blood into a vessel that would carry it to the fetus. Placental vessels
are close-packed; most are small. Attempting to get blood into them
from the outside proved a hit-or-miss proposition at best.

Bevis tried the method several times, and succeeded once: A
fetus that had appeared doomed was live-born; its blood carried Rh-
negative red cells like those which had been injected. But the placental route seemed too terribly difficult a way to reach the fetus.
Bevis abandoned his effort.[2]

The next to try, by a different route, had been Boston pediatrician Fred Allen, Jr. His attempt was not based on amniocentesis but on his long, innovative experience with exchange transfusion. He was prompted by one other fact: Some Rh-positive babies that are born with Rh-negative fraternal twins have a little Rh-negative blood in their veins. This occurs because early in gestation the Rh-positive fetus had absorbed, and accepted as part of itself, a bit of blood-forming, or hematopoietic, cells. If the cells could be put into remain active and functional, so that the child's blood continues to contain both Rh-positive and Rh-negative red cells.

Why not deliberately duplicate this situation in Rh-threatened babies by giving them—early on—small amounts of Rh-negative blood-forming, or hematopoietic, cells. If the cells could be put into the fetus' abdominal cavity the natural movement of fluid inside its body might carry them to the blood-forming centers in the liver. A very small supply of these hematopoietic cells might make enough Rh-negative red blood to tide the fetus over to a safe delivery.

Allen had attempted this plan, and had described the results the previous spring in his talk at Columbia, where Vince and John had heard him. Despite "formidable" technical problems, Allen said, he and his colleagues had succeeded in putting Rh-negative blood-forming tissue into two of the four Rh-positive fetuses whose wombs they had entered. But, "all fetuses were aborted within three weeks of the procedure," he added. "No evidence of survival of the donor tissue could be obtained. This method appears to be sound from the theoretical point of view, but a technologic break-through is needed."[3]

Vince, listening to Allen's account, had been neither discouraged nor dismayed by these failures. Rather, he had been encouraged in a plan of his own: to give full exchange transfusions to fetuses inside the uterus. Since his first talks with John, he had been turning over in his mind methods for getting Rh-negative blood into the fetus. His first hope had been to create a direct shunt between maternal and fetal circulations. Blood pressure differences between mother and fetus had ruled out this plan, but Vince had continued to pursue the problem in collaboration with a colleague at Columbia, obstetrician Dr. Karlis Adamsons, Jr.

They were unaware of Liley's work, and could not have known that by the late spring and summer of 1963 the New Zealander had begun to test his intrauterine transfusion method on two or three pregnant, courageous women whose fetuses already were known to be dead or close to it. Vince and Karlis Adamsons had decided to open the mother's belly, expose the uterus, cut a slit in the uterine wall, and bring out enough of the baby's body to find a vessel large enough for an exchange transfusion. Adamsons, who worked out the surgical approach, had already successfully transfused a rhesus monkey fetus in this way. The big risk in such a procedure, they agreed, was the likely possibility that surgical trauma would cause the uterus to go into contractions, causing premature delivery of the baby.

A week or so after the first news accounts of Liley's successful in utero transfusion appeared in the press, Vince described his own first attempt at fetal exchange transfusion in a letter to a colleague: "I too," he said, "have been thinking about treating the fetus in utero, but by laparotomy, hysterotomy and exchange transfusion via a fetal vessel. Not too long ago I had a private patient who was an ideal candidate in that she was only at 32 weeks and results of the tap indicated that the fetus was going to die within about a week. . . . It was decided that the first approach should be the sagittal sinus vein [inside the skull].

"I operated and Karlis assisted me and we found it technically not too difficult to make a small opening in the uterus and get very adequate exposure of the sagittal sinus without delivering the fetal head." A third colleague put a needle into the fetal vein and withdrew 5 ml of fetal blood. "Unfortunately, [he] was not able to keep the needle in place or thread a catheter into the vein. We all tried without success. The baby was severely anemic, but not yet hydropic. . . . Karlis and I would have tried to cut-down on the femoral artery [in the leg], but the mother was under deep fluothane anesthesia longer than I planned for, and because the baby was pretty good size and the uterus quite irritable I delivered the baby. . . . It succumbed from prematurity. . . . Maybe we'll have better luck next time."[4]

Vince and Karlis Adamsons subsequently succeeded, in one case, in withdrawing a fetal foot and leg from the womb, at 27 weeks' gestation. They successfully completed an exchange transfusion through the femoral artery, at the groin. Only a tiny slit was cut through the uterine wall, so the leg acted effectively as a plug against spilling of amniotic fluid.

Contrary to all expectations—including his own, Adamsons later confided—the fetus tolerated the two-hour exposure and intrauterine surgery, and the mother did not instantly go into labor. This shows, he said, that "the uterus is not an untouchable sanctuary that will expel its contents when it is entered."[5]

Nonetheless, labor occurred the next day. Vince delivered the baby. It was alive, but hopelessly premature.*

Thus Bevis, Allen, Vince Freda, Karlis Adamsons, and, in fact, several others had attempted, essentially unsuccessfully, to transfuse an erythroblastic fetus—and had failed because they could not get enough blood into the fetus without interrupting the pregnancy.

Liley, in New Zealand, had succeeded at the same endeavor— and the margin of his success was his luck at having heard of, and his creative ingenuity in having reapplied, a technique that had been known and discussed in the medical literature, albeit quite obscurely, for almost a century.

He first heard about this technique from a young geneticist who had stopped off in New Zealand for a visit, following time spent in Africa in an area where a severe blood disease, sickle cell anemia, takes a high toll, especially among infants and young babies. These tiny dying children often could not be transfused in the customary way. Their blood vessels were so thin and so fragile that they were difficult to find with a needle point; once in, the needles easily became dislodged.

Missionary physicians had found that they could overcome this problem by sticking the needle instead into a baby's abdominal cavity, in which the internal organs are suspended. It was into this much broader target that the blood was injected. Infants could absorb into their circulations enormous amounts of blood that had been transfused in this unusual way. Hearing his young visitor's

---

* An "open" intrauterine transfusion leading to live birth and the baby's survival would first be achieved two years later by an obstetrical team at the University of Puerto Rico in San Juan.[6] The method subsequently would be used, with an occasional successful outcome, in a few fetuses that had been adjudged to be too sick too early— that is, before the end of the seventh month—to be helped by Liley's "closed" intrauterine transfusion technique.[7] Vince and Karlis Adamsons later would try a still more radical approach. Instead of exchanging the fetus' blood and then resealing it in the womb, they implanted a very thin tube in the fetal abdominal cavity and brought the tube out of the mother's body, resealing womb and belly around it. Periodically, they infused fresh blood into the fetus through the tube. In their first four attempts at Presbyterian Hospital, no baby survived. But in 1965 Adamsons, operating with a colleague at a hospital in Buenos Aires, Brazil, put a tube in a fetus in its sixth month of gestation. Eight weeks later, the baby was live-born, prematurely, and was alive and appeared well at a follow-up visit to the hospital eight weeks later.[8]

account of this technique, Liley exclaimed to himself: If babies already born can take blood this way, perhaps *unborn* babies will do so too!

"We were no strangers to putting a needle into a pregnant uterus," he would say later. "Sometimes [in doing an amniocentesis] we would needle a fluid-filled, distended [fetal] abdomen. If we could do this accidentally, we decided, there shouldn't be much difficulty in doing it deliberately."[9]

It turned out that he was right. It was not necessary to hit a fetal blood vessel, only the much larger, easy-to-hit fetal abdomen. The challenge of transfusing a fetus had been beautifully, simply solved.

One other fact of fetal physiology assured the method's success, Liley would later explain: "We cash in on the fact that the fetus drinks prodigious amounts of the fluid around him—about five ounces an hour—to get him to opacify his own bowel so that we can see it. To do this, we first inject radiopaque dye into the fluid. The baby swallows it, and shortly has it concentrated in his intestine, thus showing us, under x-ray, where to put our needle."

Liley quickly treated, successfully, another sick fetus, and colleagues elsewhere in New Zealand followed his example. He pub-

Dr. Liley taught intrauterine transfusion technique to Americans during sabbatical year in New York. (*Mottke Weissman, 1964.*)

lished his first case report in the *British Medical Journal* late in 1963.[10] Within less than a year a dozen obstetricians in Australia, Canada, and the United States would repeat it in more than one hundred cases; Vince was perhaps the first in the United States to do it.[11, 12] Their collective salvage rate for mortally ill fetuses would turn out to be about one in three; only fetuses that became gravely ill before 28 weeks of gestation could not be successfully treated.[13]

"You couldn't possibly do any harm to the baby," Liley would later say, in explaining the rationale for intrauterine transfusion. "It couldn't be worse off than it already was. It was guaranteed hopeless.

"What we really are attempting to do is to buy a few weeks. We are trying to keep these [unborn] infants alive so that they can grow to the point where they have a chance outside the womb!"*[14]

---

*Those who survive do remarkably well. Of two early long-term follow-up studies, one says survivors are physically healthy and neurologically intact, albeit some of them lag in intellectual development.[15] The other, a controlled study, found completely normal development.[16]

# 23

## *Peril*

EXCITEMENT over medicine's first experimental stab at treating the unborn, and the continuing success at Sing Sing—no "protected" prisoner had as yet become sensitized—could not conceal the fact that the Rh preventive program now was severely threatened on theoretical grounds. With the exception of John Gorman, who had been skeptical of it from the start, all hope in New York and Liverpool rested on the belief that the sensitizing fetus-to-mother bleeds occurred, as in the Sing Sing experimental model, in large amounts at, or close enough to, delivery for preventive injections postpartum to be in time to nullify their effect.

The time had come for Wolf Zuelzer and Flossie Cohen to launch their most telling attack—exploding this convenient key belief. In earlier papers the Detroit researchers had confined their analysis largely to the issue of whether potentially sensitizing bleeds occurred only at delivery, as Finn and Vince Freda believed, or rather occurred all throughout pregnancy—as they themselves held. Though they had proved that 50 percent of all pregnant women had some fetal blood in their veins at delivery, it had been possible to shrug off these findings on the grounds that the tiny amounts of fetal blood involved usually were insufficient to cause sensitization; only the much larger bleed that occurred just at delivery contained enough red cells to initiate an Rh-immune response.

Now, however, Zuelzer and Cohen had correlated data on fetal bleeds with the key issue of whether the mother in question in fact later became sensitized to the Rh factor. For this, they followed 127 previously unsensitized Rh-negative women who delivered Rh-positive babies. They tested their bloods *after* delivery to see if they carried fetal bleeds, then retested them later to see if they had become sensitized to the Rh factor. In about two-thirds of the women, 79 of 127, they could find no fetal cells postpartum even with the extremely sensitive methods they had perfected. *But* 4 of these 79 women—some 5 percent—nevertheless eventually produced anti-Rh antibody.[1] This finding seemed to John to kick to pieces Vince Freda's and Ronnie Finn's hopefully constructed theory that large bleeds at delivery were needed to cause Rh sensitization: Here were four clear-cut cases in which there had been *no* detectable fetal bleed at delivery but the women nevertheless had become sensitized.

The opposite side of the coin proved still more damaging. Fetal cells were found at delivery in the remaining 48 of the 127 women. And in 4 of the 48, Rh sensitization occurred. But each of these women had only the tiniest amount of fetal blood postpartum—amounts ranging from a few thousandths of one ml to no more than half a ml each. On the other hand, 13 other women had had moderate to markedly large bleeds of from half a ml to 40 ml. But none of these big bleed recipients had become sensitized.[2]

Here was convincing evidence—devastating evidence—at last to John, that the big-bleed-at-delivery theory was "no longer tenable." Zuelzer and Cohen were clean and meticulous workers. While one might quibble with their interpretations, there was no reason to doubt their data. In their 127 Rh-incompatible pregnancies, there had been eight cases of Rh sensitization. Four occurred in women who had only tiny amounts of fetal blood in their veins at delivery. And four occurred in women who had none whatsoever. Since fetal cells must have been present in these women some time *before* delivery in order for sensitization to have occurred, the clearly evident conclusion, as far as John could see, was that fetal cells had gotten into these mothers fairly early in pregnancy and had sensitized them so that they began to produce anti-Rh antibody—which then destroyed the fetal cells in their veins. Thus, no telltale fetal cells had been present at delivery. But the four women already were sensitized just the same.

It was Bill Pollack's turn to save the day, with a major new explanation for the Freda-Finn theory of when and why Rh sensitization takes place. Although the exact date, in 1963, that he came to it is unclear, it was probably before Zuelzer and Cohen's final assault on the theory, and was probably based in part on doubts of his own; publication of their critique, early in 1964, forced Bill's new theory to center stage.[3]

Like John, Bill had always taken a fairly reserved view of the big bleed theory. Rather, he had been most attracted by the immunologic basis of the Rh prevention plan—the potential practical applicability of the *AMIS* principle. The Sing Sing results and the parallel experiments that he and Hans Hager had set up in rabbits, using a red cell antigen–antibody system similar to Rh, had by now convinced him that if they had to deal with only a single large pulse of antigenic blood—a big bleed at delivery, like a single, discrete red cell injection—they were bound to succeed.

But the big bleed seemed somehow too convenient, a straw man too ready to be knocked down. What if Levine and Zuelzer and the majority of other experts were right, and the antigenic stimulus was not one, big, easy-to-deal-with bleed at delivery but a constant slow leakage of fetal red cells going back through six, seven, or more months of pregnancy? "If red cells are indeed getting through at 16 weeks, as Zuelzer says, then there is ample time for a woman to become affected before delivery. If Zuelzer's right," Bill said to himself, "we're wasting our time!"

But Bill did not feel Zuelzer was right. Sing Sing was going too well. The animal work was encouraging. And it had been a year of· progress for his other projects at Ortho. Bill was relaxed and feeling mellow; a major setback seemed remote.

This was his frame of mind one afternoon, when, seated at his laboratory desk, he thought to ask himself the question: "When can one first detect fetal cells in the mother?"

Not knowing for sure the exact answer, Bill got up, walked next door to Levine's lab, and repeated his question aloud.

"When could one first detect fetal cells in the mother?"

"Quite soon!" Levine replied. "Quite soon after gestation."

"How soon would the fetal cells carry the Rh factor?" Bill wanted to know.

"Right from the start," Levine answered.

This was exciting. Bill sensed he had found a fruitful flaw in Levine's logic. He thanked Levine, returned to his lab, and picked up the telephone. He dialed John Gorman, in New York, to pose this problem: If the fetal cells are the immunizing factor during pregnancy, and the Rh factor appears on the fetal cells very early, then isn't there enough time for the first baby to be affected?

"Yes," John answered.

"But the first baby is *not* affected," Bill said.

"Right," John replied.

"Then it's the pregnancy itself—the fact that the woman is pregnant—that prevents her from becoming immunized to the Rh factor!" The immunizing event then must be *delivery*. It *ends* a temporary state of immunologic unresponsiveness to the fetus' blood that is induced by the pregnancy. Delivery allows the woman, for the first time, to respond immunologically to the Rh-positive cells that are already circulating in her bloodstream.

"Boy! That's a good idea," John exclaimed. "I wish I had thought of that."

Bill said it made sense in terms of the exceptional immunologic situation that occurs in pregnancy: A host, the mother, tolerates a tissue graft of foreign material, her fetus. And it made sense in terms of the unique situation in erythroblastosis, the only exception to this exception, in which the mother immunologically attacks her fetus.

Bill was suggesting that a woman undergoes a diminution in immune response during pregnancy that is either a specific toler-ance to the fetal antigens she is carrying, or, what seemed more likely, a decreased ability to respond to all *new* antigens. Neverthe-less, preexisting immunities, against disease antigens for example, obviously remained intact. A mother thus tolerated all parts of her fetus, in all of its antigenicity, as long as pregnancy continued. Afterwards, her immune system responded only to her fetus' Rh-positive red cells because they were the only remnant of it that remained viable in her body long after pregnancy ended. The fact that fetal red cells survive in the maternal circulation up to four months postpartum, and Vince's findings that some women did not become sensitized until four to six months *after* delivery, tended to support Bill's view: Fetal cells circulate in the mother *after* her protective tolerance has ended and then sensitize her to the Rh factor when their natural lifespan is over and they are sequestered in immunogenic organs, like the spleen, en route to being excreted.

Bill's bold new theory was prompted in part by published reports on changes in immune competence during pregnancy, some of which suggested that sex hormones—which then are present at

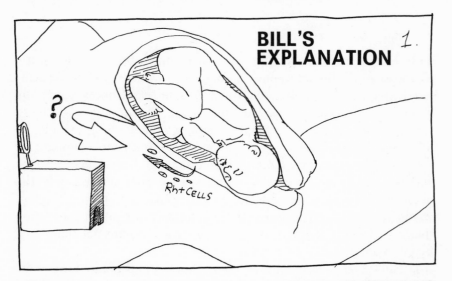

**BILL'S EXPLANATION** *1.*

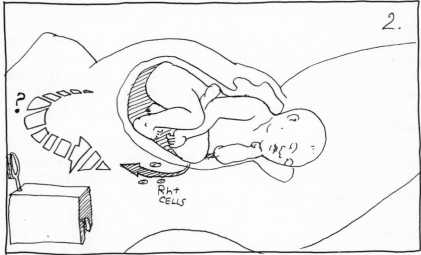

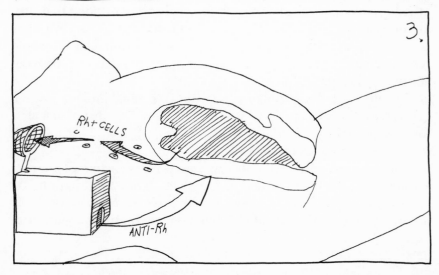

high levels—might account for the change. But the literature, when he and John subsequently dug into it, turned out to be scattered, sparse, and conflictive. However, one set of observations, by immunologist Peter Medawar, did seem to support his theory strongly: Skin grafts transplanted onto pregnant rabbits would be tolerated for twice as long as similar grafts put onto nonpregnant rabbits. This showed decreased immunologic resistance to new antigens. But if the pregnant rabbit was already sensitized to the donor rabbit's skin, say by an earlier transplant, then the graft would last no longer than usual. This tended to confirm the notion that preestablished immunities, unlike new ones, are not dampered by pregnancy.[4]

If Bill's theory was correct, then Vince and Ronnie Finn were right—and wrong—about sensitization. They were right when they said that delivery was the key moment—and hence Bill's theory supported their view that a preventive injection just after delivery would be in time. They were wrong in believing that a big bleed was the critical event—but if Bill was correct, it no longer mattered. In either case, the Zuelzer-Cohen criticism was nullified because the time of the bleed was no longer important. It was the ending of pregnancy that counted.

Bill's analysis had brought him to precisely the same juncture that Nevanlinna, Ronnie Finn, and Vince Freda had arrived at earlier: the fact that the first baby is unaffected means that events within one pregnancy are not enough to cause sensitization. Nevanlinna had therefore postulated a need for two stimuli, in two pregnancies. Finn and Freda had substituted a single bleed, *as the first pregnancy ended*, as the key event. Bill, who had not paid much attention to either Nevanlinna's or Finn's theories, decided that, like all pregnancies, the first pregnancy defended itself against new immunities, so that sensitization to a fetal antigen like Rh could take place *only after it ended*. "Something in pregnancy suppresses the immune response."

For Bill, that day's thinking was the "big breakthrough" which crystalized the situation. He would later say: "At that moment, I knew we would go to the end of the project. And I was sure it would have a successful conclusion."

John was less sure; Bill's theory was persuasive but thoroughly unsupported by direct experimental data. It seemed doubtful to him that one could successfully transfer one's hopes, mid-course, to a new theoretical justification. Remaining skeptical about postpartum injections, he reanimated his search for ways to inject anti-Rh antibody safely during pregnancy.

Vince gave credence to Bill's theory though he, like Finn, would remain reluctant to give up the big-bleed-at-delivery explanation of sensitization. He would continue to insist that the fact that no woman became sensitized in her first pregnancy strongly indicated that the small bleeds didn't matter. Bill himself retained doubts on that score, telling a colleague late that autumn: "I fear that it will be some time before any conclusions can be drawn concerning the role of the small bleeds during pregnancy."[5] But his new theory had charged him with confidence, and by early November, when the AABB opened its annual meeting on Zuelzer and Cohen's home turf in Detroit, Bill was on the offensive.

He would remember this as the first occasion at which the prospects for Rh prevention seemed real enough for experts—pro and con—to hold a private, informal meeting to discuss them. Ortho had hired a convention suite at AABB headquarters at the Statler Hilton, and this was the site for their round-table talk which, Bill would remember, included Zuelzer and Cohen, Levine, John Gorman, and Canada's leading Rh experts—Dr. Bruce Chown of Winnipeg, and several others.

John Gorman was glum because Chown, earlier in the day, had given a talk supporting Zuelzer and Cohen's earlier finding that significant bleeds—and hence, probably, sensitization—occurred before delivery. Now Chown shocked the round-table participants by saying that he too was probing the Rh prevention prospects. However, he said, he planned to follow the course John had originally proposed but which everyone else had spurned. Chown said he and his co-worker, Alvin Zipursky, would give 7S anti-Rh antibody injections, in small amounts, *during* pregnancy! Their hope was, Chown added, that an antibody dose could be established that was large enough to protectively destroy fetal cells but small enough not to harm the fetus if some antibody did pass through the placenta.

Bill felt this was an unneeded, perhaps dangerous step that ought not be taken—at least not until the safer, simpler alternative of a single postpartum injection had been fully tested and found wanting. He also found himself speaking up forthrightly, vigorously, even aggressively, against the carping at and criticism of their testing plans. Previously, in the presence of world-renowned experts like Levine and Chown, his had been a more deferential stance. Now that had changed. "I did most of the talking," Bill later would say. "I think I felt I had to convince them it would work!"

The Detroit AABB contributed one other event of note. John had previously met, in passing, a young resident in pathology at Presbyterian Hospital, Dr. Carol Rutgers. She, as he had once been, was just now assigned to the blood bank, under Dr. Scudder; an interest in blood had brought her to the AABB. She and John renewed—and strengthened—their acquaintanceship over drinks and dinner, and they returned to New York with the resolve to see each other soon again.

# 24

## "Kath"

THE SING SING TRIALS' continuing success increased John and Vince's confidence that the time fast was approaching when a clinical trial—in newly delivered women—could be attempted. But the catalyst that caused them to act came from further away—from London and Melbourne, Australia—and from closer to home than either of them could have anticipated.

While John was still in England during the summer, or, more likely, just after he had returned to New York, his father, Dr. John S. Gorman, had come to an astonishing realization: his second son, Frank, and Frank's new wife, Kathryn, who then was about three months pregnant, were Rh-incompatible. The baby they expected the following February would probably be Rh-positive. By sensitizing Kath at delivery, it might well wreak havoc among their later children.

Kath must be protected, at birth, with John's anti-Rh antibody material, Dr. Gorman, senior, decided.

To Frank, John's junior by a year, had gone the endowments of physical stature and breadth of shoulder. He was a big man, jut-jawed, with a firm, assured approach to others—outgoing where John was inward and introspective. To John's eyes, Kath, like Frank, was open and outgoing. She was a short, rather small young woman with dark hair, bright eyes, and a quickly disarming smile.

Frank was just then finishing his specialty training in ophthalmology. He and Kath were living a lightly rooted newlywed life in a succession of small flats in expatriate colonies in and around London. Frank had been "vaguely aware," since their marriage, that he and Kath had an Rh problem. But because the odds were against sensitization, especially in a first pregnancy, he was not greatly alarmed.

At first, perhaps in direct confrontation in London and later, certainly, from Melbourne by letter, Frank's father attacked his complacency. "Father remonstrated with us," Frank would remember, "saying it was too much of a risk to take to leave Kath be, without the injection. It would be a pity to miss out, since John's invention was just about ready to go."

"As time passed," the father himself would recall, "I hardened on the idea, and wrote more insistently, in a letter or two to Frank and John. Later on when I became afraid nothing would be done in time, I played with the idea of cabling John in New York for emphasis."

The senior Dr. Gorman had "no fear whatsoever" of harm ensuing from the injection. "In the 1930s," he told John and Frank, "all our children had been given pooled human serum [containing gamma globulin], for prevention of ordinary measles, without harm coming to any of them." Family feeling on the matter was not at all unanimous, however. His wife—who also was a physician—would credit Kath with considerable courage for her willingness to be the "guinea pig" who would be the first to get John's anti-Rh injection after the delivery of a baby.

In fact, Kath was hardly consulted in the Gorman family's decision-making conferences and correspondence. "No discussion was entered into with her," her father-in-law would say later, because "it seemed to me she would have to take our considered advice, having no other source. I felt it would be to our disgrace and regret if we failed Kath under these circumstances."

Frank remained diffident, but as autumn advanced toward winter, he finally agreed to the project. "It was really my father and brother who were doing it," he later would say: "I was happy to go along, but I probably wouldn't have minded too much if we hadn't." Kath, who was being at least partially kept in the dark "failed to realize"—she would say later—"that *I* was the guinea pig, as it were.

"We all took John's word that even if it *did* go wrong, the injection wouldn't have any ill effect on me—and the baby would already be delivered. So it couldn't hurt the baby."

John, in New York, confided his plan to Vince, but not to Bill Pollack or Singher at Ortho, where strong opposition—if not a flat prohibition—could be expected. Shipping a vial of the material out of the country worried Vince, not because he doubted its efficacy or safety, but because of the myriad of medical and legal restrictions under which they were testing it. He and John were the only physicians with approval to inject it, and then only in the United States. Moreover, a whole sheaf of permits might be necessary to ship a fully-tested biological product out of the country. It was inconceivable, Vince told John, that such permission could—or would —be forthcoming for an experimental preparation to be used for the first time in a clinical situation.

But Vince felt torn: "John's willingness to use it on a member of his family struck me as being some kind of an ultimate testimonial." Reluctantly, he agreed to wink at the rules and help John prepare one of their precious 5 ml vials of material for shipment to England.

Now it was mid-January. Kath was due in a month. John wrote to Frank, saying the vial was coming. Several days later, a cablegram arrived in London from New York specifying the flight and freight waybill number. John had packed the precious vial in dry ice and had driven it out to Idlewild Airport just before the takeoff. On the customs slip, under "contents" he had written: *Human serum.*

Frank phoned Heathrow Airport and ascertained that the plane was en route; it was due at 10 o'clock that evening. He and Kath had recently robbed their savings to buy a secondhand Mercedes-Benz sports car, and, after supper, they climbed into it for a leisurely drive to the airport. They had a long way to travel and the night was cold. By and by, Kath noticed that she felt uncomfortable and strange. Perhaps they had eaten too quickly. Her stomach seemed to move and hurt for a minute, then relax and lie still. "What if I'm in labor, just as we're going out to get the stuff?" Kath said. "You can't be," Frank replied. "It's too soon." They both laughed—that would be just too much of a coincidence!

The plane was already in when they reached Heathrow. Frank watched as the freight was tumbled into a bin, from which an attendant retrieved their packet. Frank remarked that the custom's charge of £2. seemed rather stiff. Then he had the packet in his hand and was carrying it back to a bench where, heavy and drooping, Kath was waiting.

Together they tore through John's careful wrappings. The dry ice gave off a small puff of "steam" as they broke the seal. Lying resplendent inside, unbroken, was the vial of injectable fluid and a second, "pilot" vial of unsterile material for cross-matching with Kath's blood.

Walking back to the car, Kath did feel distinctly awful. This was her first pregnancy. It might be too early, according to the calendar, but she knew *something* was happening—even if it wasn't on schedule.

They arrived home, sat down, and tried to fathom what was going on. It soon became quite clear: Kath Gorman was in labor. Frank remembered to take along the package John had sent as they quickly departed again to drive out to the General Hospital in the town of Barnet in West Hertfordshire, near London, where Kath had had her prenatal care. After months of planning, from three continents, the race to get Rh protection to her in time had been won by the slimmest possible margin.

Since it was midnight, the obstetrician whom Kath had told of their Rh prophylaxis plans—and who had read the published reports that John earlier had mailed to Frank—was at home in bed. The resident on duty, an Indian woman, was understandably puzzled by the odd vial of strange medication that Frank handed to her with instructions to put it on ice until it was time to inject it into his wife.

Kath labored through the night. Frank, knowing that first labors are long ones, went home to sleep, then went to work in the morning: He kept in touch with the hospital by phone. A complication occurred. The baby's head became wedged against Kath's pelvic bone and would not budge. At noon, one of the obstetricians rotated it, internally. Kath, in great pain, labored on. A half hour later her first child, a boy, Kieron Francis, was born. He was blood-type Rh-positive, like his father, Frank—incompatible with Kath.[1]

The precious vial, and the problems attendant to it, had meanwhile been turned over to a Barnet hospital pathologist, Dr. Ronald Welch. Frank had been summoned to the hospital when Kath delivered. But by the time he arrived, late in the afternoon, Welch already had taken the steps he felt necessary to familiarize himself with the contents and possible complications of the injection he had been asked to administer. He had read the reprints in Kath's chart; they described the Sing Sing and Liverpool experiments. Wanting first-hand help, he had picked up the telephone and called the department of medicine at the University of Liverpool. The Gorman family's bold self-help plan for Kath was no longer a secret.

Welch had been put through to the department's second in command, Richard McConnell, who, from the start, had been an enthusiastic backer of Ronnie Finn's Rh prevention plan. McConnell was completely surprised and, Welch perhaps sensed, disappointed. Welch himself was surprised to learn from McConnell that the Rh prophylaxis had never before been used clinically in Britain. It was a pregnant moment. As Kath herself later would say, savoring the situation: "An *American injection* was about to be given to an *Australian patient* in one of their *English hospitals!*"

McConnell knew that his group had yet to use the injection on a newly-delivered woman. So certainly this would be its first clinical test in England. Liverpool, which had originated the idea and had long held the lead in testing it, now had been overtaken at the goal line. To make matters worse, it was happening on home turf. McConnell and, when he told them, Clarke and Finn and the rest of the Liverpool team, could not help but be, at the very least, quite disappointed.

They were also gentlemen, and doctors. McConnell immediately volunteered to assist Welch in whatever way necessary, to ensure that his patient was successfully treated.

Welch asked McConnell if there was any risk. McConnell replied that there probably wasn't. He suggested that Welch send to Liverpool specimens of Kath's blood, taken just before the injection, and then again several days later, so that they could run Kleihauer tests to determine how large a fetal bleed she had sustained and how effectively it had been cleared by the anti-Rh gamma globulin. Welch gratefully agreed to do so.

When Frank arrived, Welch took him aside, told him of his talk with Liverpool, and said he was ready to give the injection if Frank would sign the requisite permission forms and releases. Frank signed.

The two men entered Kath's room together; she was half awake and uncomfortable. Frank helped her turn on her side. Welch swabbed one buttock with alcohol, then taped to it an adhesive tape "target" to mark the injection site so that he could locate it later if Kath had an adverse reaction. Then he pushed a hypodermic needle through the seal on the vial that John had sent, withdrew 5 ml of the clear, straw-colored fluid that Bill Pollack had manufactured, and inserted it into Kath's gluteal muscle alongside the target. Then he injected the liquid. It was January 31, 1964.

It hardly hurt Kath; only a tiny bump appeared where the needle had gone in. Later that night, however, she became uncomfortable. She broke into profuse sweating, once, twice, and again; urination was painful. It was unclear if either complaint, or both, had been caused by the injection; the first reaction, though not the second, had been observed in Sing Sing volunteers. Pain in urinating was a problem consistent with Kath's long and difficult labor.

Kath felt better next morning. A few days later she and Kieron Francis went home. Several days later, when Welch received the results on the two Kleihauer specimens he had sent to McConnell, there was cause for rejoicing: Perhaps because of her difficult delivery, Kath had sustained a large fetal bleed of about 3 ml of Kieron Francis' Rh-positive fetal red bood. This amount Finn long ago had found to carry a high risk of Rh sensitization. In the second Kleihauer specimen, taken 48 hours after the protective injection, the red cells had completely disappeared! By Liverpool's criterion, cell clearance, if not by New York's, Kath's treatment had succeeded.

"It looks," Frank wrote to John several days later, "as if we have been successful enough in a well-timed gamble."[2]

There the matter might quietly have ended, except that someone—it is unclear who—sensed the newsworthiness of Kath's case and tipped off a reporter for the London *Times*. On March 3, under the headline, "First Trial of 'Rhesus Baby' Serum—Woman Volunteers," The *Times* reported:

> The first practical trial of an American serum designed to prevent the birth of 'Rhesus babies' has been undertaken on a woman volunteer at Barnet General Hospital. . . .
> The idea of the new method of protection originated from the Department of Medicine of Liverpool University. The serum given is an improved American version of one [Liverpool] developed. . . .
> 'We ourselves are still investigating possible side effects of our serum on volunteers, where there is no risk of pregnancy,' a member of the department told The *Times* yesterday. The arrival of the woman in Britain with the serum [*sic*] came as a surprise to the Barnet Hospital, who asked advice from Liverpool. She is understood to be related to an American worker in the same field.[3]

John received two copies of *The Times* clipping in the mail. Frank sent one copy with a note saying: "The Liverpool boys are probably a bit hostile about your trying it out upon volunteers under their noses."[4] Clarke, in Liverpool, sent the other, with a letter that said, tartly: "I think you have probably started a clinical trial (judged by the enclosed!), and I think we shall begin one too."[*][5]

[*] Welch, perhaps a bit piqued, and embarrassed to have been caught in the crunch between Liverpool and New York, later wrote to John saying: "I was very surprised to hear that your sister-in-law is the first case in which this form of prophylactic treatment had been given, and had I known this I might have had more misgivings at the time. However, the whole case has been reasonably satisfactory from everyone's point of view to date, although clearly the proof of its value will have to await the next child. . . . There would seem to be every justification for having given this preparation and it is gratifying that there was no untoward effect."[6]

# 25

## Clinical Trials

New York's clinical trial began on March 31. Liverpool's started in May.

The two groups were using similar anti-Rh gamma globulin preparations. Their aims were identical—to determine if this antibody, injected at delivery, would keep a woman from producing antibody of her own against the Rh factor—but their experimental protocols, the plans and rules under which their clinical experiments were conducted, were quite different.

Confidence was greater in New York where John, Vince, and Bill were buoyed by the sense of having, finally, moved out ahead. They were confident that even if the injections did not work—and there was always hope that they would—they at least seemed unlikely to be harmful.

"We've done everything to those guys up at Sing Sing *except* get them pregnant!" exclaimed Vince. "Not only has there been no enhancement of sensitization, *none* of the men we've protected with antibody has become sensitized."

Confidence led the three men to design the widest possible clinical series, given their still-limited and costly antibody supplies. They decided to treat Rh-incompatible first pregnancies and subsequent pregnancies, if the woman was not sensitized to the Rh factor at delivery. No attempt would be made to evaluate how many fetal cells a woman carried in order to treat only those whose risk was greatest. All would be treated. Only Rh mothers already protected by ABO incompatibility with their infants would be excluded.

If the treatment succeeded, and the incidence of Rh sensitization was significantly reduced, then the preparation would be proven useful and effective in all previously-unsensitized mothers, regardless of how many pregnancies they previously had had, the amount of transplacental bleeding, or other factors. New York was shooting for a preventive that could be widely used, for the benefit of a mass market of three to four hundred thousand women a year—about one in every eight American deliveries.

Liverpool, by contrast, was far less confident and far more cautious than New York, whose lead Clarke had been waiting to follow. Liverpool's recent results had been encouraging, but there had been enough failures with the anti-Rh antiserum they had been using in lieu of 7S gamma globulin, for there still to be serious cause for concern about its value and safety, given the low natural incidence of Rh sensitization.

"Laboratory work and volunteers are one thing," Finn would say later. "But when you move into mothers, you don't make mistakes. So Clarke waited until New York said they were starting a clinical trial. The thing that must have tripped us over into starting our clinical trial was the publication of the American data: What I think Clarke was doing was waiting for confirmation [in males] from an independent source—and when they [New York] had confirmed our results, and said that the time is right for a clinical trial, that was the green light."*1

Finn's estimate of the situation is clearly confirmed in the letter Clarke wrote to John Gorman early in March enclosing *The Times* report on Kath.** Clarke said: "I was, of course, extremely interested to read your paper in *Transfusion*.2 I knew about the earlier part of the work [the first Sing Sing study], but the addendum was new to me. [It describes the second Sing Sing study, in which anti-

---

* What would Liverpool have done if there had been no Sing Sing data? "We'd have done a clinical trial," Finn would say, "but it would have been much, much longer [before it started]."

** Having lost the race to be first to administer anti-Rh gamma globulin to a new mother, Liverpool co-opted credit for the feat by being first to publish Kath's case in a professional journal. In a letter in the *BMJ* of April 25 announcing their forthcoming clinical trial, Clarke and his colleagues present the Kleihauer data they had obtained from the specimens that pathologist Welch had sent them of Kath's blood.4

Rh antibody given 72 hours after 10 ml of Rh-positive blood protected 14 of 14 Rh-negative prisoners from sensitization, while 6 of 13 controls became sensitized.] It looks as though the data generally strongly suggest the view that protection can be obtained, and that, using your gamma globulin, enhancement will not occur. I think you have probably started a clinical trial . . . and I think we shall begin one, too."[3]

Because of their fears, however, Liverpool's clinical trial was, in Clarke's words, "cunningly designed" to obtain maximal answers with the exposure of minimal numbers of women to anti-Rh gamma globulin injections. Geneticist Philip Sheppard planned the experiment, whose major difference from that in New York was the selection and treatment only of women facing a "high risk" of sensitization. Blood samples from all Rh-incompatible women who delivered in five Liverpool maternity hospitals were studied, each day, by Kleihauer technique; only those women who had large fetal bleeds of 2 ml or over were injected, or selected as untreated controls.

Sheppard introduced another exclusion: Only mothers in their first pregnancy would be treated. By avoiding women with prior pregnancies, they might have less of a chance of treating, unsuccessfully, women whose immune systems in some way earlier had been primed against the Rh factor but who were not as yet demonstrably sensitized.

Besides its protective value of subjecting to the risk of treatment only women whose risk of sensitization was greatest, Sheppard's plan would provide an answer with fewer injections than New York's, since Liverpool's Kleihauer studies showed that most Rh sensitizations in fact occur among the relatively few women who have big transplacental bleeds. "We ought to be able to detect a significant difference between the [treated and untreated] groups much sooner than if we took all Rh-negative mothers with Rh-positive babies, regardless of the fetal cell count," the Liverpool group declared.[5]

Most "cunningly" of all, perhaps, the Liverpool experiment avoided counting—and hence, avoided counting as failures—the most worrisome cases described by Zuelzer and Cohen, namely those women who allegedly became sensitized, but did *not* manifest a fetal bleed postpartum. Zuelzer and Cohen's data suggested that these women become sensitized late enough in pregnancy not to harm their babies but too late for postpartum injections to protect them from becoming sensitized. The antibody they produced would destroy all fetal cells in their bloodstreams, giving them low Kleihauer scores that would exclude them from Liverpool's "high-risk" trial.

How many women would be needed? Liverpool estimated that 70 "high-risk" mothers would have to be treated and compared with 70 untreated high-risk controls. New York estimated that its all-inclusive experiment would require at least 200 treated women and 200 controls.

How successful did the clinicians in New York and Liverpool believe they might be? On that question there was some degree of agreement, at least between John Gorman and Ronnie Finn. Both were deeply worried by Zuelzer and Cohen's attack. Finn himself now was finding that among women who sustained fetal bleeds the antigenic cells were detectable *before* delivery in one-third of cases. He felt, and John felt, that the anti-Rh injections, given at delivery, might, if they were lucky, prevent about *two-thirds* of all Rh sensitizations.

It was toward suppertime on March 31 that Vince injected the first woman in the New York clinical trial; she was a patient in his Rh antepartum clinic who had delivered several hours earlier. Ironically, it was a few hours later, on April 1, 1964, three years after he first asked for it, that the United States government's National Institutes of Health began, for the first time, to support New York's Rh prevention effort. Vince and John's grant would provide $15,000 annually for three years. Shortly, however, it would turn out that New York's need for research money had yet to be adequately resolved.

Two weeks later, when Vince, John, and Bill again presented the work to the annual "Federation" meeting, this time in Chicago, they concealed the fact that the clinical trial had started. The combination of Sing Sing prisoners, mothers, dead babies, and attractive young researchers nevertheless again brought them a good press.

One newspaper reader was not impressed: John's former boss at the Presbyterian Hospital blood bank, John Scudder, took Vince to task for holding out "illusive hope by implying that the mother can be protected by the administration of an artificial antibody preparation. This," Scudder declared, "you have not proven."[6] Vince sent Scudder's charge to John, at Lenox Hill Hospital. In a covering note, Vince said: "I agree with the Jesuit Fathers that after the age of seven, one cannot mold character. So I am not trying. Hell!"[7]

The contretemps with Scudder might fail to merit notice, except that, less than a month later, John Scudder was no longer director of the Presbyterian Hospital blood bank. John Gorman was.

John had been dissatisfied at Lenox Hill, where the research facilities he had wanted had not been provided. At Presbyterian, Scudder had submitted his resignation. The need to find a replacement for him had been raised in the hospital's blood bank committee, on which Vince still represented the obstetrics department, and he vigorously—and successfully—lobbied for John's appointment.

The Old Order was changing. "I am happy about this, as it is a great chance," John wrote home to Australia in mid-May in a letter that started with still more momentous news: "I will be getting married to Carol. . . . No date is set. . . .

"The work is going well. The gamma globulin still appears completely effective as no one protected with it has made antibody up to last Wednesday. . . ."[8]

There was one other, less pleasant development. John's three-year grant from the Health Research Council of New York had run out. He had applied for a renewal. "My grant application was turned down yesterday for the Rh work," he wrote. "This shows the capriciousness of the granting system as this was a far stronger application than the one three years ago, when it was approved by the same agency. This means scrambling for money from other sources."[9]

Other sources continued to be unhelpful: The National Foundation–March of Dimes—which badly needed a winning campaign for the '60s to equal its polio vaccine success of the '50s—had turned down a request for a technician's salary.

More and more, Ortho began to pick up the tabs for expenses that others would not pay. Vince and John would explain their need for materials or manpower at one of the formal meetings held periodically with Bill and with project director Singher, research chief Hill, and others. When a decision was reached that a request was valid Singher would quickly get the money; this was a "magical ability," John decided.

Liverpool's clinical trial had begun in May. By midsummer, when the British Medical Association convened its annual meeting, in Manchester, Clarke could report that three women thus far had been treated.

The American Association of Blood Banks met in August in Washington, D. C. The New York group had by now injected 20 mothers, none of whom, it appeared, had yet become sensitized. There was a high sensitization rate among the controls. John and Glen Hill were approached at the meeting by a canny, cheerful, egg-bald pathologist from Long Beach, California, Dr. Elmer Jennings, an AABB past president. Jennings wanted to know how to prepare potent anti-Rh material so that he could start an Rh-prevention project of his own.

Hill, who had already undertaken the task of finding obstetricians to test the anti-Rh material in their patients—and who was being rebuffed by most of them, who said it was an impractical and foolish plan, which they would test only if paid handsomely for their trouble—was delighted by Jennings' genuine interest. Would Jennings test Ortho's material under the existing protocols? Jennings would.

One obstetrician, New Yorker Dr. John Queenan of Cornell, asked to take part. Clarke, meanwhile, was getting doctors in Sheffield and Leeds to join the Liverpool trial. In Baltimore, Finn and Woodrows' former host at Johns Hopkins, blood-banker Julius Krevans, prepared to start a trial using Ortho gamma globulin to treat "high-risk" patients according to the Liverpool experimental plan.

The obstetrics establishment remained uninterested. Vince's chief, Howard Taylor, suggested one day that he submit the Rh work to an annual essay contest in obstetrics research. "You're sure to win, Vince," Taylor said.

Vince rewrote their most recent report, including the latest Sing Sing results, and submitted it anonymously, as required, under the Wieneresque pen name, *R. H. Factor*. Several weeks later it was returned, with a note saying that there already were so many fine submissions that R. H. Factor's could not even be considered by the judges.

The 1964 AABB meeting had been held early in order to permit participants to fly on together to a world blood meeting in Stockholm, Sweden, over the Labor Day weekend. Vince attended, stopping off in Liverpool en route. He was cordially received. In Stockholm, Woodrow presented Liverpool's data; Vince described New York's: Several dozen women now had been treated in the two clinical trials, with no sign of failure.[10, 11] Nevertheless, the reports were skeptically received. In the discussion that followed, Vince would later recall, "Zuelzer was the most outspoken skeptic."

In September, Presbyterian Hospital became the world center for Rh research. John was back. Amniocentesis pioneer John Robertson of Edinburgh came to work for a year with Vince. And intrauterine transfusion inventor Bill Liley of New Zealand arrived to do experimental surgery during a sabbatical year.

In November they were all invited to attend the world's first—and secret—meeting of intrauterine specialists convened at a Stowe, Vermont, ski lodge by University of Vermont pediatrician Dr. Jerold Lucey. The meeting initiated the new science of fetal study, diagnosis, and care—or *fetology*—whose only clinical application thus far was Rh disease. Rh prevention was on the program. Vince and John now had more than 30 injected patients. None showed signs of sensitization.[12] But, Vince cautioned, only after six months, when all signs of the injected antibody had disappeared, could one say with confidence that immunization had been prevented.

In the same month, November, Liverpool looked at their data and discovered, "unexpectedly," that after only six months, "some preliminary results seem worth reporting": fetal cells in all six of the "high-risk" women they had treated had cleared rapidly and none showed any sign of having become sensitized. But three of eight untreated "high-risk" women already were sensitized.

These results appeared on January 30, 1965, as Liverpool's third report to the *British Medical Journal*—under the names of ten Liverpudlian team members.[13] A few weeks later, on February 23, John told the New York Academy of Medicine that now 33 mothers had been treated at Presbyterian Hospital and there were 54 controls.[14] Jennings, in California, had also started.

Liverpool, John said, could prove efficacy with fewer women and less gamma globulin than New York could—although they, too, would need confirmatory antibody studies at six months, followed by successfully unsensitized second pregnancies. "In Liverpool," he added, prophetically, "if no immunizations occur in 25 protected mothers, and if the expected 8 of 25 unprotected control mothers become immunized, effectiveness of the gamma globulin may be considered virtually proved."[15]

The next month, March, McConnell went to Sheffield to the British Society for Hematology. He said 4 of 15 untreated control patients had, in fact, become sensitized; an equal number of injected mothers had not.[16]

The same month, in an exchange of letters with Clarke, John

reported that 36 New York women had passed the six-month mark. None in the treated group had become sensitized. The figures are still "too small" to be conclusive, he said—"but, at least, no failures."[17]

The scorecard now shifted, for a brief but significant moment, to the pages of the *Lancet*. An editorial reporting favorably—and optimistically—on the Rh work had dwelt at length on Liverpool, but failed to mention, even in passing, Vince, John, and Bill's efforts.[18] They replied, setting forth their claim that "in 1960, quite independently of the Liverpool group, we began a program in New York to see whether passive immunity could be used to prevent immunization of mothers to the Rh factor."[19] So far, they added, 147 mothers had been added to the study in New York and Long Beach. No results were claimed.

Clarke and Sheppard responded, immediately, in a letter published August 14.[20] Success, which but a year earlier had seemed an illusory hope, now appeared possible, and stakes that then were hardly worth contending for now were stoutly asserted. They reminded their readers of Ronnie Finn's now long-forgotten talk to the Liverpool Medical Institution, more than four years before, and the key excerpt that had appeared in *Lancet*. "Although we in Liverpool were the first to publish both the idea of giving passive antibody . . . and the results of experimental trials," Clarke and Sheppard now wrote, "it is Gorman and his colleagues who should have priority for the suggestion that anti-Rh gamma globulin should be used."

The Liverpudlians reiterated the merits of their experimental plan, adding sharply: "We have some useful data from as few as 56 patients, whereas Gorman and his colleagues give no indication that the 107 patients in their trial have yet produced any information."*[21]

Beyond its affronts, Liverpool's latest up-to-the-minute results were electrifying to John Gorman. He read them in *Lancet's* airmail edition, which reached him at a vacation house in Martha's Vineyard, Massachusetts, a week later. Three to six months after injection none of Liverpool's 27 protected women had become sen-

---

* Krevans of Baltimore, meanwhile, who was using Ortho's anti-Rh gamma globulin, was assigning all creative credit to Baltimore and Liverpool. He presented these views in August to a press conference for science writers at the Jackson Laboratory, in Bar Harbor, Maine. The newsmen's stories that resulted relegated John, Vince, and Bill to nameless also-rans.[22] Vince was furious.

sitized. But 9 of 20 protected control patients had. Statistically, these were "highly significant" results, John decided. The chance of their occurring due to chance alone was less than one in 500.

These results—no women sensitized of 27 treated; 9 sensitized of 20 untreated—fulfilled the criteria for success that John had stated the previous spring; only a full six-month follow-up was wanting.[23]

John had been summoned to Ortho by phone for a planning meeting and flew down for the day, leaving Carol behind in Martha's Vineyard. His brain raced higher and faster than the slow-droning airplane. At Idlewild Airport, he rented a car and drove quickly to Ortho.

"I was walking around, telling everyone 'It's working!' " John would later say. " 'It's proven! You should all be jumping up and down with excitement!'

"But they weren't!

"I remember telling it to Bill Pollack, Singher, Glen Hill, everybody: 'It's working! . . . And nobody's getting very excited.'

"There was a lot of lethargy. It hadn't sunk in!"

Business completed, John drove thoughtfully back to the airport, flew to Boston, missed his connecting flight to Martha's Vineyard when he stopped to buy a magazine, and did not get home until morning.

# 26

## Secret Meeting at the Waldorf

A PRAISEFUL LETTER WAS POSTED IN NEW YORK to *Lancet* commending Liverpool for being first with promising, if premature, results. Meanwhile the stage had been set for a statistical reckoning of all clinical trials in Britain and North America.[1] The occasion, appropriately, was the retirement, at age sixty-five, of Ortho's Director of Immunohematology, Philip Levine—upon whose work, if not encouragement, these efforts were based.

First, on September 9, came the dedication of a new laboratory building, named for him, at Ortho's plant in Raritan, New Jersey. The following day, Ortho set up a cocktail party and banquet luncheon, and held a symposium in Levine's honor under the aegis of the New York Academy of Sciences. The following morning, a Saturday, Singher would take advantage of the attendance in town of important Rh specialists to convene a small, secret workshop to review the Rh results.

From London, Robert Race and Ruth Sanger flew to New York for the ceremonies for Levine, as did Tibor Greenwalt, the soon-to-be appointed medical director of the American National Red Cross Blood Program. Wolf Zuelzer came from Detroit. Fred Allen attended, and also John Gorman's former boss, John Scudder. Also invited, as recommended by Ortho's public relations advisors, was Alexander S. Wiener; hope was expressed that the aging rivals would lay down their blood feud.

In fact, a news reporter, Miss Judy Ramsey of *Medical World News*, was able to coax Rh's two opposing pillars to stand together for a photographer's camera—a feat she later jokingly would say was a major coup in her journalistic career (see photo, page 41).[2]

The feud, however, was not buried. Levine, surrounded by admirers and adulators, could afford to be gracious—and perhaps was. But the day's official utterances, obviously, tended to lionize his role in Rh; Bill Pollack set the tone for the day by asserting that "the human Rh factor" was "the discovery" of Levine and his then co-worker, Rufus Stetson.[3]

Wiener walked out angry. A day or so later, newswoman Ramsey, who with Ortho's help was writing a profile of Levine, received a phone call which the Author, working at the next desk, in part overheard, and which Miss Ramsey discussed with him when it was over. Miss Ramsey related that the voice had said: "This is the Medical Examiner calling." New York's Chief Medical Examiner, Dr. Milton Helpern, was a powerful figure in the city's health and law enforcement communities, and he commanded considerable respect from the press. According to Miss Ramsey, Helpern, who was Wiener's boss, feared that his expert employee would suffer a nervous breakdown if the Levine version of The Creation appeared as Writ in the pages of *Medical World News*. He asked: Would Miss Ramsey be responsive to Wiener's side of the story?

Wiener himself had gone home to pen a candid—and true—addendum to a book he was writing: "The problem may seem trivial to others, but to the individuals involved, the priority for discoveries they have made are of considerable importance."[4]

Typical of the encomiums offered to Levine upon his retirement was the declaration of an Academy of Sciences official: "The untold number of human beings, throughout the world, who, but for his work, would have died on battlefields, in accidents, during childbirth and surgery, today constitute a living memorial to the career of Philip Levine."[5] Vince, discussing the Rh work, added, aptly if inelegantly, "If the road ahead appears to be clearer than it did previously, it is only because we have all been standing on the shoulders of such giants as Philip Levine."[6] Almost in the same breath, Vince aggravated Singher by recalling that, at the start, he and John had "enlisted" the help of Bill Pollack at Ortho, who then had "prepared" the 7S anti-Rh gamma globulin. With success now beckoning, Bill, Singher, and Ortho saw themselves much more as prime movers than as "enlisted" men.

Dr. Levine, with Drs. Gorman (left) and Freda, greets well-wishers at his retirement party. Below, he joins Ortho colleagues Dr. Pollack (left) and Singher
to hear invited speakers praise his achievements. (*Al Giese, 1965.*)

Serious business came Saturday morning: Singher convened the closed conference on "Anti-Rh Globulin" in a hotel room at the Waldorf-Astoria Hotel. Levine, on his first day as Ortho's emeritus immunohematology chief, attended. So did Zuelzer and Greenwalt. Vince, John, and Bill came, and Hans Hager. Jennings was there from California. John Queenan from Cornell came. Canadian Alvin Zipursky of Winnipeg was present. Finn had been invited, from Liverpool, but could not attend. Krevans also had been invited, but a colleague, Dr. Andrew Montague, came in his stead, bringing the Baltimore and Liverpool data. In addition, John Gorman had suggested that the Author, at that time a reporter for *Medical World News*, be present. Ortho at first agreed, but at the last moment Singher vetoed the invitation, so this reporter spent the day pacing the hotel's green-carpeted corridors outside the meeting.

During and after the conference, Ortho officials all declined to say what had transpired. The clinical investigators, however, were visibly elated as they emerged from the hotel room toward dusk, and could see no need to keep secrets. Seated in a bar, across the street from the Waldorf, John, Vince, Alvin Zipursky, and John Queenan described the day's events. As each investigator had presented his data, his totals to date had been listed on a blackboard; John had copied the figures on a note pad:

Cornell as yet had no six-month follow-ups, so the figures could not be counted officially, but Queenan had no sensitizations among 10 treated women—0/10—and, oddly, none either among 9 untreated women, i.e., 0/9 in the controls.

Liverpool had 0/27 in treated women and 9/29 in the controls.

Freda had 0/34 in treated women and 6/40 in the controls.

Baltimore had 0/9 in treated women and 3/9 in the controls.

Jennings had 0/22 in treated women and 3/16 in the controls.

Winnipeg had 0/4 in treated women and no controls.

Excluding Cornell and Winnipeg the combined totals were: 0/92 in treated and 21/94 in the controls.

In addition, there were some 100 other women, in all centers, who had been treated, but had not reached six-month follow-ups. None had become sensitized. The official results, alone, however— 0/92 against 21/94—went far beyond John's expectations and far beyond Ronnie Finn's expectations, and their hopes, of as recently as a year before. The anti-Rh gamma globulin appeared 100 percent successful. There had been no failures!

John was asked: "Do these figures have statistical significance?" "Statistical significance!" he ejaculated, "Why the P[robability]" value is tremendous!" Later, he added: "As the figures went up on the blackboard, we could see it was proven!"

The Waldorf session had provided one other enormous surprise. It came from Winnipeg.

"It's a bombshell!" exclaimed John.

Alvin Zipursky reported it.

"He's courageous!" said Bill, a hard man to impress, to himself.

Zipursky had explained that in more than 40 women, thus far, he had injected anti-Rh antibody, not at delivery, as everyone else was doing, but in small, divided, doses during pregnancy—as everyone else feared to do. As the first Rh specialist to begin using Kleihauer's technique to find fetal cells in pregnant mothers, Zipursky, like Zuelzer and Cohen, believed sensitization could occur before delivery. So he had decided to try to prevent it by giving 7S anti-Rh gamma globulin while the baby was in utero.

"Even if the antibody gets across the placenta," the intrepid Canadian said, "the quantities necessary to prevent immunization in the mother are many orders of magnitude less than those required to harm the infants." He adduced as proof the fact that none of the babies had been born with erythroblastosis. And none of the mothers, four of whom had reached six months postpartum, had become sensitized to the Rh factor.

On his notepad, John had jotted: "Dr. Zipursky. Broke through a barrier. Can give [7S in pregnancy]. No need for 19S."[7]

Bill heaved a sigh of relief.

John said: "If postpartum treatment fails to be 100 percent effective, then we can all fall back on treating the mothers beforehand!"

The older hands had been less impressed with this alternative than the younger ones. Even the 100 percent success of the postpartum injections well might be a mirage, for what ultimately mattered was not whether a woman harbored antibody in her blood six months after delivery. What mattered was whether she remained unimmunized, and produced no antibody the next time she became pregnant. That was the critical test. Yet, in all of the world, only six women—including John's sister-in-law, Kath—had thus far delivered a second child. There remained a remote, but real, possibility that the anti-Rh gamma globulin had repressed, but not wholly prevented, sensitization which would appear, perhaps more forcefully than usual the next time the women became pregnant. Perhaps the antibody even was helping to *mask* immunities—enhancing, yet hiding the sensitizations—that would crop up only later.

Only many more "safe" subsequent pregnancies in which "protected" mothers delivered disease-free babies would calm all fears.

Singher, if he had made a substantive judgment, kept it to himself, although he would make no bones about being bitter that the treasures of his secret meeting had been offered up to the press; *Medical World News* published them three weeks later, together with Judy Ramsey's tribute to Philip Levine.[8, 9] Long a doubter, Levine too declined to comment for the record on the new results, but leaving the meeting room he had turned to an out-of-town participant to remark: "Probably, it works."

For John, Vince, and Bill, at this moment of dramatic triumph, there was the need—from which John did not shirk—to take into account the February 1960 reference to Finn's passive-antibody prevention proposal that Clarke and Sheppard had just exhumed. "Finn can claim priority in terms of publication," John declared. The New York group would continue to feel, however, that they had arrived at the key concept at about the same time, and—what is much more certain—had done so independently. But for all their success, the fact of their not having been first increasingly cast the shadow of pain over the pleasure of their achievement.

Liverpool, informally at least, was as excited about New York's new data as New York had been about Liverpool's a month before. In a letter, John Woodrow wrote to John Gorman, saying, wryly: "I trust that a personal letter like this, after the series of official contacts through *Lancet*, will not be considered too highly irregular.

"I would like to congratulate Vincent, Bill, and yourself on your early results in the clinical trial, which are most exciting. . . ."[10]

The year 1965 provided the Rh workers two additional noteworthy events. After John went to the AABB in Miami later in the autumn to present their very latest data—still no sensitizations among treated women, with the numbers now rapidly rising—he and Carol Rutgers were wed. They left the United States for a honeymoon trip to Australia, to see his parents, and a jaunt to New Guinea, where John was to follow up his earlier G6PD researches. In Liverpool, meanwhile, Cyril Clarke had succeeded to the coveted chair of Professor—*the* Professor—of Medicine at the University of Liverpool Medical School.

The possibility of Rh prevention had been proven in women in the year then ending. But the two research teams still faced obstacles—and surprises.

# 27

## A Long Wait

AN ANGUISHING WAIT BEGAN. The clinical results continued to look good. But if you worried about them, as John and Vince did, they looked too good: Thus far, no protected woman had become sensitized. Inward doubts had to be carried onward, under outward show of confidence. Only a statistically significant number of unaffected second pregnancies in "protected" women could serve to lay all doubt to rest.

The mood of the moment may well have been accurately captured by Canada's redoubtable Rh expert of experts, Bruce Chown, with whom Zipursky was working in his prevention-during-pregnancy program. "I'm sure that you and John and Bill feel as we do," Chown wrote to Vince in the spring of 1966, "that we're far from understanding what the mechanism of 'apparent prevention' is. I hold my breath every now and then, wondering whether we can possibly be making matters worse rather than better."[1]

Ortho, to cash in on its gamble, had to act on the assumption that the method, even if not understood, nevertheless would prove successful. Little patent protection was available for a product that was a natural biologic substance, gamma globulin, so Ortho's preeminence in the marketplace would have to be built upon preeminent production, sales, and public relations—once the product could be offered for sale.

All this was a gamble: *If . . . If* it worked. *If* the government would license it for sale. It was a gamble in which the stakes—in cost and hopes—were rapidly rising.

Ortho submitted its New Drug Application (NDA), or licensing request, to the federal government in April. Approval of an NDA requires months, sometimes years, of investigation and bitter negotiation between drug company and government licensing agency. The licensing agency for serums, blood products, and vaccines was the Division of Biologics Standards (DBS) of the National Institutes of Health.

Speedy approval was out of the question. Among medical observers in Washington, DBS and especially its long-time director, Dr. Roderick Murray, had reputations for slow motion. The fact that an Rh prophylaxis represented an entirely *new* form of preventive treatment augured a wait that would be longer, not shorter, than usual—despite the promising field trials.

So new, in fact, was the prospect of using *AMIS* to prevent disease that quite basic problems had to be solved. Bill, for example, was taxed with the complex task of developing a way to quantify and express the material's potency per unit dose. Then there was the question of what to call it. Technically it was *hyperimmune human anti-Rh 7S gamma globulin,* or *Rh-immunoglobulin.* Neither of these descriptive designations was succinct enough to be remembered, nor specific enough to describe what it was supposed to do.

Ortho solved the naming problem by coining *RhoGAM,* a contraction based on the *Rho* form of anti-Rh antibody and *gam*ma globulin, for its registered trade name. But how describe, generically, the mode of action of an injection that prevented, or was a preventer of, sensitization to the Rh factor?

John Gorman, back from New Guinea, sat down with a pencil and a pad of paper one day to find a precise and graceful word to describe what the injections would do. Among words he considered to fill the blank "_____ immunization" were: *check, discourage, forbid, inhibition of, combat, suppress, quell, dam, quench, extinguish, eliminate, smother, stifle, eradicate, abolish,* and *blockade.* Perhaps indicative of his state of mind, as well as the preparation's purpose, the last three words in his list of one hundred were *elude, depress,* and *frustrate. AMIS* was tough to depict.

News reporters and headline writers felt the naming and describing problem even more acutely than did the scientists. Some of them, including the Author, chose to call it the *Rh vaccine*.*

John had returned from his honeymoon trip to Australia and New Guinea early in the spring, and had been back at work only a month or so when he was stricken with hepatitis—a possible aftermath of his visit to the jungles, or, what is also possible, a fall to the professional disease hazard of blood banking: hepatitis transmitted through contact with banked blood. He would be out of commission until midsummer.

Meanwhile, New York's squabble with Liverpool reached its zenith. By late January, Vince had 107 women past the six-month mark, and had incorporated the results, for which New York now claimed statistical significance, into a letter that appeared in the American publication *Science* on February 18: There were 0/48 sensitizations in the treated groups; 7/59 among the controls.[3]

In the letter, which John and Bill had also signed, Vince stated, erroneously, that New York and Liverpool had started their work "at the same time." He also said, of the clinical trials, "The positive trend of our results is now being confirmed by the results of others," including Liverpool.

Apparently it was only several months later that Clarke saw these statements, for in May he wrote *Science*'s editor, objecting to New York's "incorrect statement."[4]

"It was we," he said, "who first published preliminary results of our clinical trial, and the results of Freda, *et al.*, confirm the positive trend of *our* results."

An editor at *Science* wrote Vince to ask if he agreed that he had erred, and if he had, if he ought not acknowledge the error. "We most emphatically do not," Vince replied. "We are absolutely stunned at Clarke and Sheppard's uncalled for, petty indignation over a perfectly valid sentence, i.e., 'The positive trend of our results is now being confirmed by the results of others.' This sentence

---

* This admittedly violated one accepted usage of *vaccine*. The standard Dorland *Medical Dictionary* (Philadelphia: W. B. Saunders, 1951, 22nd edition), for example, characterizes *vaccine* as "any material for preventive inoculation," and *inoculation* as "introduction of a disease agent into a healthy individual to produce a mild form of the disease, followed by immunity"—a perfect description of the injections, except that immunity was being *prevented*, not produced. But a second, less restrictive meaning for *inoculation*, the "introduction" of serum and other substances into the body, accommodates it nicely. And a derivative definition for *protective inoculation* is an almost perfect description: "injection of an antiserum to protect against a disease." More elegantly, perhaps, *Time* coined "reverse vaccine" to describe it.[2]

states absolutely nothing at all as to who has rushed into print first with . . . preliminary and premature data with the use of the preparation we had discovered."[5]

*Science*'s editor decided not to publish Clarke's communication and admonished both Liverpool and New York: "The question of priority in this matter seems to have occupied several columns in *Lancet*, and we believe that transfer of the discussion to *Science* would merely enlarge the geographic coverage without resolving the question. We suggest that the question be resolved privately and that the solution be mentioned in the next papers published on the subject."[6]

The matter has never been so resolved.

Who first announced definite results possibly also will forever remain unresolved, for Clarke had conceded, in January 1966, that "evidence for protection is the absence of immune antibodies *six months after delivery* among the treated women. . . ."[7] (Emphasis added.) This would disqualify Liverpool's three- to six-month results, whose publication the previous August had so impressed John.[8] Perhaps for this reason, Clarke specified "preliminary" results in his unpublished letter to *Science*.[9] If the August paper is thus disqualified, it becomes impossible to pick out—in the welter of oral and written reports in succeeding months at the Waldorf and elsewhere—when and by whom a statistical proof was first presented.

Face-to-face relationships, fortunately, fared better. Bill and Clarke junketed through Europe to appear together at several Rh meetings in June, and in September both sides were represented in Sydney, Australia, when Philip Levine chaired an Rh session of the biennial Congress of the International Society of Blood Transfusion. The world totals had reached 0/244 in the treated group; 32/225 among untreated.

A week or so after these results were published, Wiener wrote a "Dear Vincent" letter saying: "Congratulations on your excellent results! At the same time I received McConnell's [recent] article, which I am reading. There is no doubt that your treatment will have to be used as a prophylactic for Rh sensitization.

"I note," Wiener continued, returning quickly to a theme still uppermost in his mind, "that McConnell uses anti-D instead of anti-Rh [nomenclature]. This marks him unfortunately as a CDE blood group mythologist. . . ."[10]

A few weeks later, Vince was asked by a blood study group to be "protagonist" in a discussion on "Prophylaxis of Erythroblastosis by

Immunization." The group had asked Fred Allen to take the negative side.[11]

Vince agreed. But the program chairman soon phoned to say that Allen had declined to be antagonist to the Rh vaccine—and no other opponent could be found. At about the same time, Wolf Zuelzer of Detroit, upon learning the current clinical trial results at the AABB in Miami, conceded that the Rh vaccine had proved to be effective and useful. The opposition had crumbled. Only DBS remained to be convinced.

There, the wheels of progress continued to turn excruciatingly slowly, and largely out of sight of Vince and John. They would only hear secondhand, through Ortho's contact men, when DBS wanted this or that new piece of data. One DBS demand was for a double blind clinical trial: The Rh vaccine to be injected into some women and a sham vaccine to be injected into others from unlabeled coded vials—so that neither patients nor doctors would know, until after the antibody studies were complete at six months postpartum, which women had received which injections. Such a clinical test hopefully would eliminate the influence of doctors' and patients' biased beliefs that the experimental preparation would—or would not—work.

Vince objected vehemently: "It is difficult to imagine how the clinical investigator or the mother's psychologic state could alter whether or not she makes an immune response."[12] But DBS insisted. Jennings, in California, volunteered to help Vince do the double blind study. More and more, the West Coast pathologist had come to play a leading role in promoting and advancing the clinical trials.

Medical journal and news reports now strongly hinted that the Rh vaccine was one of the important medical advances of the decade. Doctors and Rh-incompatible parents began to swamp Vince, John, and Bill with letters requesting advice and assistance.*

One family forwarded the autopsy report on their last child, a girl, who had been born dead. Would the vaccine help next time?

Because the mother was already sensitized, John had to reply No, it wouldn't. Amniocentesis might. And intrauterine transfusion.

Mercifully, there might be cathartic value in the writing, for some requests carried a medically unassuageable message of grief.

---

* Unknown to Vince and John, administrators at Columbia-Presbyterian were less impressed. A hospital public relations man later would recall being told to play them down, because they were getting too much publicity for an idea copied from England.

I am an Rh mother who lost her fourth child. The baby was induced early, at 7½ months. She lived 12 hours. . . . No one called my husband . . . and he didn't know till he called me that morning that we had lost our baby. . . .

As my religion does not approve of birth control, any help you could give us would be appreciated mentally as well as spiritually. . . . I would like to know more about my chances of delivering a normally healthy baby. We are not rich people but would go to all ends. . . .

[Signed] Rh mother in need of help.

There was little help that might be offered. For others, the best that might be done was not to arouse false hopes. A woman had written: "I heard you discuss Rh disease on the 'Today' program. My daughter-in-law would certainly appreciate any help you can offer. She is expecting her fifth Rh child. The last one had to be rushed to New York City for a blood change. The doctor she had would not take her again. . . ."

John answered: "I am sending some information on Rh to you rather than your daughter so that her hopes will not be raised for nothing. . . .Our new drug will unfortunately be of no use. . . ."

There were even confiding letters from presumed victims of Rh disease:

I am supposed to be an Rh cripple born in 1915 when precious little was known about this phenomenon, if it was even recognized, at the time, what ailed the baby.

It has been an ever-present millstone around my neck from birth because, while I was born of strong, healthy, fine English American farm parents, I just don't seem to coordinate neurally very well nor has muscle growth been comparable to my fellow humans.

A first child, born dead to my parents, was strangled in the umbilical cord and appeared very black. Two years later, when I was born, yellow jaundice set in and my urine ran brick red. I was so weak and listless they marvelled I lived out of it.

Sometimes help could be promised. John got a letter from an American foreign service officer stationed in Peru who had read in *Time* of the clinical trials. He wrote back:

The gg is an experimental drug of which only a limited number of vials have been manufactured. We would agree to release one vial to your obstetrician only if he can assure us that all the data that we need [from your wife] for our study will be obtained: blood samples during and for six months after pregnancy.

An obstetrician wrote to say he had enjoyed John's talk to a medical meeting in upstate New York. "Is there anything I can do at this late date to prevent sensitization of a twenty-seven-year-old patient of mine . . . who had had one child? At present she is not pregnant but would like to be. Is there any preventive method yet developed?"

Replied John:

> Your patient may well be a good candidate. . . .
> The material is only available for research trials at present, but it may be possible for her to be included. . . . I shall refer your letter to Ortho . . . [so that she] can be included in a local trial. Hopefully, at that time supplies may be much better. . . .

Persistence also paid off for some:

> Dear Dr. Gorman:
> I am still interested in being a volunteer in your Rh study and have also spoken to my obstetrician about it. . . .

> Dear Mrs. M———:
> I am glad that you are going to join our program. There is nothing to do right away until you become pregnant. . . .

> Dear Dr. Gorman:
> I would like to begin in your program as soon as it is convenient to you—and plan for a second pregnancy. . . .

Mrs. M——— was among the lucky few, for the vast majority of inquiries could not be accommodated. The vaccine could be used only in authorized clinical trials, so women who lived too far away from participating hospitals, or could not get admitted to them, simply were out of luck. Jennings would later recall "terrific pressures" that in most cases had to be withstood because of the strict governmental regulations under which the tests were being conducted.

In a few cases, *force majeure* prevailed. Once, when Jennings' phone rang, it was the Secretary of State in Washington, D. C., calling on behalf of the governor of Colorado, whose son, a GI in Thailand, and daughter-in-law were imminently expecting an Rh-incompatible baby. Ortho agreed to release a vial of the vaccine, through Jennings, and an emissary from the governor flew to Los Angeles from Colorado, picked up the vial, put it in his pocket, flew to Thailand, handed the vial to a doctor who met the plane, and clambered back aboard to continue his round-the-world flight back home.

Jennings later got a letter from President Lyndon Johnson's personal physician, whose daughter would soon deliver—and might need the injection. In response to this request, a vial was provided for the White House. When it was not the White House that asked, however, the answer most often was No—although the pressure was overwhelming.

By January, the world totals had jumped to 0/432 in protected women; 58/464 among untreated. Second pregnancies, slowly, were beginning to come in: In protected women the score stood at 0/36; in unprotected, 10/34—suggestive but not yet significant figures.

"If it weren't for the damned Pill," Vince complained one day, "we'd have had our answer months ago. But women just won't rush out to get pregnant again in order to give us the results we need!" For John, the feeling of helpless waiting was often excruciating. The more it seemed the vaccine was working, the more he worried it wouldn't. It seemed unbelievable that an idea born of their boyish enthusiasm could turn out so well.

"All along," he later would say, "we had the fear that the whole thing would collapse on us. When the second pregnancies began coming in we got especially fearful. Nancy Treacy, our technician, would call to say that she'd gotten a positive antibody reaction in a mother's blood—and we'd have fear. Then she'd call back later and say it was all right: The antibody was anti-Kell, or some other, unimportant blood factor, not anti-Rh—an artifact. Then we'd wait for the next one."

A specific cause for concern did occur. The ongoing Sing Sing trials yielded the first dread sign of enhancement that was traceable, without doubt, to the 7S anti-Rh gamma globulin fraction. Until now, it had been possible to believe that Liverpool's early enhancement had been due to their use of 19S rather than 7S. But Bill had prepared a series of ever-diminishing doses of pure anti-Rh 7S—down to .0001 ml of vaccine—which John and Vince injected into prisoners along with large amounts—6-10 ml—of Rh-positive red cells. Men who received 1 ml vaccine were protected. Men with .1 ml also were okay. But now, it turned out, of four men who received .01 ml one became sensitized, as did one who received .001 ml and two who received .0001 ml. Possibly, even with 7S, a great excess of antigen over antibody might enhance the risk of immunization.[13] Such an imbalance might cause enhancement in a woman—if too small an antibody dose were used, or the woman had too big a bleed.

Sing Sing, on these visits, seemed less bleak than it had at the start; before they were through, John and Vince would make more than seventy visits "Up River." It became their custom to stop for lunch on the return trip at a classy country restaurant alongside the highway. They would order steaks and double martinis. One week it would be Vince's turn to lift his glass over the elegantly-appointed table and propose a toast. "John," he would say, "research is hell!"

The following week, it would be John's turn: "Vince, research is hell!"

Fittingly, the definitive second pregnancy results came, finally, during a week in which John was scheduled to deliver a talk up-state at Albany Medical College, where Theobald Smith, the discoverer of *AMIS*, had received his medical training many years before. John felt able to brag just a bit, pointing out to an audience of professional public health workers that, outside of blood-banking, his own status was that of an amateur: He was an amateur in hematology, immunology, genetics, obstetrics, and public health and in all of the other disciplines through which the Rh problem now was being solved. "How sweet it is," he remarked, "to be invited to talk to professionals, because at the onset the professionals, the *Establishment*, were very strongly against this idea, saying: 'Don't bother with it; it won't work!'

"The subsequent delivery figures are now, I think, getting to the point of statistical significance: 0/42 in the protected group; 10/37 in the controls."[14]

# 28

## Supply Lines

THE CENTER of activity now shifted rapidly away from the Rh vaccine inventors to others more concerned with problems of supply and demand. Decision-making in Britain passed from Ronnie Finn and the Liverpool team to the Medical Research Council's working committee, the Ministry of Health, the National Blood Transfusion Service, and the Lister Institute—where experimental lots of the vaccine were being made.

Ortho, in the United States, was rushing to complete a huge new Rh vaccine processing plant at the rear of its headquarters building, and was actively centralizing and gathering unto itself control over work in progress. John, who would recall that at first he and Vince had taken part in key decisions and planning, now found, more and more, that they were being left out in the cold. "Licensing was a cloak-and-dagger operation with Ortho," he would later say. "Ortho didn't tell us anything beyond what we needed to know." Vince was even unaware of which federal licensing agency Ortho had applied to, believing it to be the Food and Drug Administration of HEW, which approved drugs, rather than DBS—which approved biologic products like gamma globulin.

Through Bill, Ortho issued its "approval" for publication of research papers which he, Vince, and John wrote.[1] The company hired a public relations man, who said to Vince and John: "As *RhoGAM* becomes a commercial reality, would you please let me know—in advance if at all possible—of any interview that you grant to the press?"[2]

This they declined to do. But, to their momentary annoyance, and future regret, they acquiesced to another directive that came from Singher. The World Health Organization (WHO) had called a parley, perhaps partly at Liverpool's prompting, to discuss how interested nations could make adequate supplies of Rh vaccine.

Ortho, actively seeking foreign markets, may not have viewed pleasurably the sudden upsurge of national pride in the manufacture of Rh vaccine, and may have feared that any sharing of information to which it was a party would be a one-way exchange, since its production methods were far in advance of others' and hence deserved to be regarded as trade secrets.

British experts had already been careless, or thoughtless enough, to publish some information Bill had told them that Ortho considered "confidential"; Singher vowed to safeguard whatever secrets remained.[3] He told John and Vince to decline invitations to the WHO meeting, which would be held in Geneva, Switzerland. And he rejected the meeting chairman's personal request that Bill Pollack be allowed to attend.[4, 5, 6] Singher's only concession was to allow Scotsman John Robertson to attend, representing New York. Robertson had started a clinical trial in Edinburgh using Ortho vaccine, after returning from his year's work with Vince, and he was close enough to developments in New York to present the latest publishable data in a favorable light. But he was far enough away from the manufacturing process not to know—or inadvertently disclose—trade secrets.

The problem of obtaining enough raw material to make the vaccine had grown to be a major cause of concern. The essential ingredient, 7S gamma globulin carrying a high level of anti-Rh antibody activity, could be obtained only from plasma or serum of Rh-negative individuals who had been strongly sensitized to the Rh factor. Unlike the ABO antibodies anti-A and anti-B, anti-Rh does not regularly exist naturally in Rh-negative individuals. It has to be made. Women sensitized "naturally" to the Rh factor by an Rh-positive fetus could be restimulated after they had passed childbearing age with a tiny amount of Rh-positive blood to become antibody producers. But there were only limited numbers of these women, and, hopefully, as use of the vaccine spread, their numbers would diminish.

Alternatively, human vaccine factories could be created in the bodies of Rh-negative persons—sterile or postmenopausal women or men—by injecting them with Rh-positive red cells. It is this procedure that was largely followed by the commercial blood suppliers who were Ortho's principal source of raw materials. A commercial supplier would begin by selecting one or two reliable, healthy Rh-positive donors whose blood had been used for a number of transfusions and had not caused hepatitis. He would harvest a pint or so of red cells from them and inject small amounts of it into a dozen or more Rh-negative donors in order—deliberately —to immunize them to the Rh factor. He would restimulate them periodically on a schedule designed to maximize their anti-Rh antibody production, and bleed them regularly for their antibody-rich plasma.

A recent technologic advance, *plasmapheresis*, increased enormously the productivity in human vaccine factories by permitting them to be bled as often as twice weekly. After a bleeding, the donor waits while the plasma is separated from the red cells by spinning the whole blood at high speed. Then the red cells are returned to the donor through a needle in a vein. According to Bill Pollack, the supplier pays his human vaccine factory at least $100 and perhaps $250 or more for his immunologic activity, his time, his pain, and a pint of his anti-Rh antibody-rich plasma. The supplier sells the plasma to Ortho at a markup.* Ortho might make 15 to 25 vials of vaccine from each pint of plasma.**

* Plasmapheresis operators in skid rows in the United States pay donors as little as $10 to $20 per pint; operators in Haiti, who are on record as having supplied some United States serum products purveyors, but not Ortho, paid $1.50. While no one paying these prices has yet conceded that he is producing raw material for Rh vaccine, there is every possibility that some have. Priming donors wth Rh-positive cells is quickly and easily accomplished, and an unscrupulous operator could do it without an unsophisticated plasma donor ever becoming aware that he now was producing a far more valuable gamma globulin, rich in anti-Rh antibodies.

** The donors faced two risks: If one later needed a blood transfusion and got a whole unit of incompatible Rh-positive blood, his high level of anti-Rh antibody could put him in jeopardy of a massive, perhaps fatal, transfusion reaction. These persons would be warned to avoid Rh-positive blood, and could be given identification cards so saying. More troublesome was the risk that a donor of the sensitizing Rh-positive red cells carried hepatitis, undetectable by available tests, which would be transmitted to the human factories. The only control for this danger, in the late 1960s, was careful selection of red-cell donors who lived clean lives away from known reservoirs of hepatitis, and who had previously donated blood that had been given to several recipients without causing hepatitis.

That this seemingly simple control was not always applied would soon become starkly clear. A New Jersey commercial blood supplier injected 49 Rh-negative donors with Rh-positive cells taken from three men to produce and harvest anti-Rh antibody.[7]

Ortho had the advantage of a long-established network of suppliers from whom it bought anti-Rh plasma and serum for making diagnostic reagents. Now it could pass the welcome word along to them that its orders would be increasing. In the United States there was no legal barrier to deliberate immunization of vaccine factories for plasmapheresing, or to paying them for it. Ortho's only—confounding—obstacle was government approval to sell the vaccine. But in Geneva, behind conference room doors at WHO headquarters, it quickly became clear that in other countries the supply problem was essentially different and more severe.

Present, in addition to Scotsman John Robertson representing Edinburgh *and* New York, were Ronnie Finn and Cyril Clarke from Liverpool, Chown from Winnipeg, Jörg Schneider from Freiburg, a hematologist from San Francisco, and immunologists and blood workers from Switzerland, Holland, Hungary, Czechoslovakia, and Russia.

The first order of business was to estimate how much Rh vaccine each country needed. Statistical projections ranged from about 550 doses for each million in the population each year—if, as in Liverpool, only women delivering their first, ABO-compatible, Rh-positive babies were treated—up to 3,000 doses annually per mil-

---

The company was supplying raw material for *RhoGAM*, according to Dr. Ronald Altman, director of the New Jersey Health Department's division of preventable disease; a hepatologist from the U.S. Center for Disease Control, Atlanta, Georgia, Dr. Charles Janeway, would confirm that this was the supplier's purpose.

Three of the 49 human factories got hepatitis within a month after the red-cell injections and 12 others showed signs of the disease. Since apparently none had been exposed to hepatitis in any other way, suspicion fell on the red-cell donors. One of them, the company said, was well-known to it, and appeared reliable when he came for blood-letting. But, it turned out, two weeks after his last visit he had been hospitalized with delirium tremens, superimposed on chronic alcoholism. Altman's epidemiologic report notes that "on admission, he was stuporous, dehydrated, and dirty and had body lice." He died the next day, with pneumonia and hepatic and renal disease. The second of the three red-cell donors had been a chronic alcoholic for seventeen years; he and the third donor had moderately diseased livers. Altman and his colleagues concluded that "the most likely source of the hepatitis virus was the blood of one or more of the[se] donors." [8]

The hepatitis victims' plasma was not used for vaccine, although Bill would say later that Ortho found it free of detectable hepatitis. Even if it had been used, there probably would have been no risk to vaccine recipients, since 7S gamma globulin, unlike red cells, probably will not carry hepatitis. But it seems odd, since relatively few red cells were needed, that truly "clean" individuals—not skid row drunks, who are constantly exposed to filth and hepatitis—were not bled to inoculate those individuals whose bodies were the factories in which the vaccine was made. "When you're giving blood repeatedly to people," Altman would say later, "you want to get the very best people as donors."

lion population if all Rh-negative mothers got it, regardless of the baby's blood type. An annual figure of 1,600 pregnancies—and doses—per million was projected as the need in the United States.[9] To protect all American women at risk, about 320,000 doses of vaccine would be required each year.

Calculating each dose at 1 ml of vaccine, the WHO conferees projected that 90 liters of Rh-positive plasma would be needed for each million in the population—15 human factories, or donors, per million if they were bled for a half-pint of plasma monthly. At this rate, full protection for the United States would require 2,500 to 3,000 steady donors—an enormous number! If, on the other hand, donors were bled weekly, 600 to 700 would suffice. At this rate, each donor would provide for 400 women annually, forestalling illness and/or death in up to 40 fetuses.

Ortho felt that in practice its productivity, in doses per donor, would outstrip the WHO projection once they got their government go-ahead—which event, a DBS spokesman said at the time, might be several years away.[10] Germany, on the other hand, faced exactly the opposite problem. Schneider, from Freiburg, said that there were no legal bars to marketing the vaccine. In fact, some vials were already being sold, making Germany first to have the vaccine available to the public, outside of experimental studies.

A half dozen German companies were attempting to produce Rh vaccine, Schneider related. But production was low—no more than a trickle. The problem was German law, which prohibited artificial stimulation of humans for antibody production. So the serum being used was being bought from the Swiss. German law—which was written to forbid the kind of "medical experimentation" that had been conducted in Nazi concentration camps during World War II—also forbade the use of prisoners for medical purposes. Schneider felt, however, that they might turn out to be the best vaccine source. "We hope this meeting will prompt a change in German law," he remarked. "Some prisoners are serving twenty-year sentences. Four or five volunteers could render a great service to medicine"—40 or 50 "good donors" would fill Germany's entire vaccine need.[11]

British law, unlike German, permitted artificial stimulation of antibody production. But it did not permit payment for blood or serum. Would a change be made to permit payments for the frequent, long plasmapheresing sessions needed to obtain serum for the Rh vaccine? "It's highly unlikely!" a British scientist said.

Standing firm on custom, law, and practice had, however, created a crisis. The British estimated that they could fill only 10 percent of their need for vaccine from the serum they could obtain from unpaid volunteer donors. Ortho was willing to supply Britain —and Singher would travel to London at one point for negotiations —but his offer would be rejected for reasons of national pride and, more important, refusal to allocate precious hard currency dollars to buy it.

The Canadians and Russians, unlike most of the others, favored the use of postmenopausal women who had become naturally sensitized by an Rh-incompatible pregnancy as vaccine factories. "So far, we've used only those who have had very sick or dead babies," Chown declared. He felt that payment for this special, frequent bloodletting was not unfair. "Through plasmapheresis we get half a liter of plasma a week from a good, robust donor. These women are emotionally set to be donors. For Canada, they are donors enough." The Russians carried feminism one step further. Moscow hematologist Dr. Maria Umnova explained that when the need came for deliberate stimulation of volunteers for antibody production, "*only* women, the old and sterile," would be used to produce the vaccine. "It will not come from men."[12]

Because at first the vaccine would be in short supply everywhere, the WHO conferees recommended that first priority be given to ABO-compatible mothers delivering their first Rh-incompatible infants.[13] Thus, all families might be assured at least two disease-free babies. In New York, stay-at-home John Gorman kept abreast of the Geneva talks by press, wireless, and postal dispatches. Prompted by a newsman, he offered a suggestion of his own for what women should do until the vaccine became available: "Advise them not to get pregnant!"

# 29

# Failure and Success

FAILURES finally came. Clarke found the first two, a few months after the Geneva meeting.[1]

The first occurred in a woman who appeared to have sustained a relatively large fetal bleed on the delivery table in giving birth to her first baby. She had been given a large, 5 ml dose of vaccine. It produced painful redness and swelling at the injection site—a rarely observed reaction.

The vaccine quickly cleared the fetal cells from the woman's circulation. But tests six months later showed that she nevertheless had become strongly sensitized to the Rh factor. Later, when she again became pregnant, she delivered a severely ill erythroblastic baby, which died.[2]

One possible explanation was that the woman had received more fetal red cells than the vaccine could cope with. However, Clarke and his colleagues advanced another theory: During her first pregnancy this young woman had been given an injection of gamma globulin as a prophylaxis against German measles, or *rubella*. Gamma globulin can itself be antigenic. Clarke speculated that the injection during pregnancy had immunized her to gamma globulin, and that when she was given the Rh vaccine, which is also gamma globulin, she had sustained an immune response that destroyed the vaccine before it could be of value; in so doing, it produced the severe local reaction seen at the vaccine injection site.

Liverpool's second failure, however, had not previously been given gamma globulin of any kind. She was a mother who had not been considered "high risk." She had been given a small, 1 ml vaccine injection. Blood tests showed her to be unsensitized. But four months after she again became pregnant she began producing anti-Rh antibody against her fetus, which later was delivered alive and, fortunately, only mildly erythroblastic. "No vaccine has ever proved 100 percent perfect," Clarke commented. "I'm slightly amazed, in fact, that no other failures have been reported in the United States or elsewhere before now."[3]

"It had to happen," lamented John, in New York. "One hundred percent was too good to be true.

"I'll be glad when it's all done," he added. "It makes me very nervous when I hear all this stuff coming out of England!"

But there was to be more. And the next case, while it occurred in the British Isles, was undeniably a failure of the American vaccine.

A clinical trial had been started in Ballinasloe in Galway County, Ireland, using the Ortho vaccine. The very first woman to have been given it now was reaching the end of her next pregnancy. When she delivered, on October 1, anti-Rh antibodies were found in her serum, and her baby was ill. She, too, had been given gamma globulin while pregnant, as a protection against rubella, strengthening the view that gamma globulin given during a pregnancy compromised Rh vaccine given at its end.

A second *RhoGAM* failure, the first in the United States, turned up on Long Island, New York, a week or so later. "Our over-all statistics can withstand one or two failures . . . at this point," John wrote to the clinicians in Ireland.[4] But inwardly, he was torn between relief that an unbelievable string of successes finally had been broken and fear that the whole game now might be jinxed.

Privately, Bill Pollack would gibe at John Gorman's gloomy reaction to the case failures and to the ego involvement that begot it, which, Bill felt, was unprofessional. "John was depressed," he would say, in his best professional tone. "I wasn't depressed or not depressed."

Ego involvement, however, was not without its rewards. To John now fell the good fortune of being the first to stumble onto the most dumbfounding and heart-warming episodes of the decade-long effort to develop an Rh vaccine. He was on the road, at a conference on Rh in Nashville, Tennessee. At dinner he was introduced to an invited guest at the conference, a shy, slight, middle-aged practicing obstetrician from St. Louis, Missouri. His name was Dr. Eugene Hamilton. John had never met him before, and he would turn out to be similarly a stranger to all other members of what John had begun to refer to as the "Rh college"—the group of clinicians and research workers all over the world whose interest in Rh transcended the usual barriers of nationality, university, and professional specialization.

Hamilton said he was well aware of the work in New York and Liverpool on Rh prevention. In fact, he said, while he had never contacted any of the experts—save Ortho, which had not re-plied—he had, himself, been making good use of a wholly homemade Rh vaccine in his clinical practice at St. Louis' St. Mary's Hospital. Not having the facilities to fractionate gamma globulin, he had been using raw plasma, plasmapheresed from the blood of Rh-negative women who had given birth to dead Rh-positive babies, and who therefore had high anti-Rh antibody titers. To guard against hepatitis, which could be transmitted by unprocessed plasma, he had used only a handful of donors, women whose habits were hygienic and whose health was carefully watched.

Hamilton told John that he had first started using these women's plasma to treat other, unsensitized Rh-negative women at delivery in April of 1962. Since then, working all by himself, he had injected 500 women with the vaccine. Of these, 74 had returned to the hospital to deliver 79 subsequent babies. No subsequent babies had been sick. None of their mothers had been jaundiced.[5]

What this meant was that Hamilton, without knowing it himself, and without anyone in the "Rh college" knowing about it, had an unchallengeable claim to be the first person ever to treat a woman with anti-Rh antibody—close to two years before anyone else dared to! It meant also that Hamilton had amassed far and away the largest clinical series of patients anywhere in the world! And most important, as of the moment, with more than fifty hospitals already testing the vaccine, Hamilton had fully half of all the sub-sequent pregnancy results in the entire world!

He had, he allowed, been pretty quiet about his results until now. He explained that he had known that he might need 70 to 80 second pregnancies to demonstrate statistically the merit in the vaccine injections.

"Unbelievable!" John exclaimed—and would continue to exclaim for weeks to come. When he rose to speak the next day, he said: "I think Dr. Hamilton made the understatement of all time when he said he had been a little quiet about his results.

"I think he is quite the greatest sleeper in medical history! I can tell you that it was the last thing I expected . . . to come down to Tennessee and find that there was a study [in the Midwest] *which was larger than the whole rest of the world put together, and we hadn't heard about it*! But the fantastic thing is that he has 100 percent success—and that's just wonderful!"[6]

Hamilton returned John's compliment, in comments that masterfully conceal the boundary between shyness and sly self-effacement. "I still feel somewhat like a justice of the peace who has been asked to sit with the Supreme Court, with Dr. Gorman and the other notables here," he said.[7] Liverpool had been his original spur: "I was impressed by the logic of Dr. Finn's early reports," he remarked, adding, diplomatically: "Probably Dr. Freda and Dr. Gorman are the moving factors in causing us to continue, because, when [once] we started, these gentlemen would obligingly come out with an essay of basic science studies which gave us [continuing] reason to believe this was a valid concept. And so, we would just stay on with it."

Disingenuous though he might have sounded, Hamilton had raised an enormous issue: Why do doctors read? Are medical journals, as he believed, instruction books in which doctors present their best techniques for others to use to benefit their patients? Or are they academic exercises, to be admired, but not imitated?

Most doctors in the English-speaking world had been exposed for years to reports on Liverpool's and New York's Rh prevention researches. The proposed therapeutic agent was easily available as serum or plasma, albeit not as 7S gamma globulin. A wide literature existed on the benefits and risks of gamma globulin and blood therapy. In the United States, at least, no law barred a doctor from obtaining and using anti-Rh serum or the Rh vaccine—as long as he did not buy or sell it across state lines. Yet, of all the doctors in the world, only Hamilton seems to have made a connection between what he read and doing something—now—for his patients.

John enthusiastically invited Hamilton to come to New York to participate in an Rh presentation that he and Vince were putting together for the forthcoming blood bank meeting. At it, John's fellows in the "Rh college" turned out to be amazed but less unequivocally enthused than he had been by Hamilton's homespun achievement.

"It's beautiful!" Vince exclaimed, as he added Hamilton's figures to the rest of the world's, doubling the totals. Vince also was appalled. Glancing toward Ronnie Finn, who had flown to New York for the AABB meeting, he said to Hamilton: "If you'd first called Ronnie Finn, and said you were going to use raw plasma, he'd have said, 'Stop! Stop!' "

Finn agreed. "Crude plasma has the distinct risk of transmitting serum hepatitis. I'd warn others," he said, "not to give it." Turning to a reporter, Finn urged that no story be written about Hamilton, or, that if it were, no mention be made of what he had used for his injections, so that no others would be tempted to repeat what he had done. The Rh vaccine was too close to success, he and Vince agreed, to risk any complications due to use of unrefined serum.

"Would you switch to *RhoGAM* when it becomes available?" Vince asked Hamilton.

"I think I might," Hamilton answered. "If it isn't too expensive. But if DBS continues to act with its usual alacrity, that may be a long time. Even now," he insisted, "any obstetrician working in a hospital with adequate blood-banking facilities can prepare his own.

"This idea just happened to pan out. But it shows there is always an opportunity for a man in practice to do some clinical investigation. If he follows his curiosity, he doesn't have to be in a big medical center and have an NIH grant to come up with something!"[8]

Said John: "You've got to admire Hamilton. He cut through a lot of crap."

News reports on Hamilton's remarkable coup appeared the same week, in November, as a progress report on Rh prevention that Vince, John, and Bill had written for the prestigious *New England Journal of Medicine*.[9] An editorial accompanying the *NEJM* report was written by Louis Diamond, who, thirty-five years earlier, had been the first to tie four sets of severe symptoms together as a single familial disease—erythroblastosis fetalis. Diamond, the developer of exchange transfusion, now hailed "the prevention of Rh sensitization" as a landmark in medical practice.

"A great step forward has been taken. In another generation . . . erythroblastosis and its treatment by exchange transfusion will be of historical value only."* [10]

---

* As of November 1967, when Diamond proclaimed the vaccine's success, neither of the two major United States obstetrics journals—*Obstetrics and Gynecology* and *The American Journal of Obstetrics and Gynecology*—had published an original report on the Liverpool or New York work in the 7½ years it had been underway. Neither, apparently, had the comparable British obstetrics journals.

In what would become the most authoritative American comment on the question of priorities, Diamond and the *New England Journal* ratified Vince, John, and Bill's formulation, saying that "as so often happens, two widely-separated groups of investigators conceived and developed the idea independently at about the same time."[11] But the standoff competition between Liverpool and New York—two rival World Champions, each crowned in his own country—would now be as nothing, compared to a startling intramural conflict that was bubbling to the surface in Britain.

The Liverpool team, as group investigator and author, had disbanded. All Liverpool Rh reports now came from one pen, or at most two or three, and the most important pronouncements henceforward would be found in lectures and papers by ex-team captain Cyril Clarke. First in May, before the Royal College of Physicians of London, then in October, in the *BMJ*, and finally, the following year, in *Scientific American*, he would raise an issue and, in the latter journal, stake a claim that would sow discord and quiet dismay in the Liverpool University department of medicine where he was chief.[12, 13]

The issue was: Who in Liverpool could take credit for having been first to propose using anti-Rh antibody to prevent Rh sensitization?

Ronnie Finn had always been represented as having been first to put forward the idea, and it had been assumed in the United States that he had conceived of it, undirected, while studying fetal cell populations in Rh-incompatible new mothers with the Kleihauer test. Clarke now proposed an entirely different, more deliberate version of the precipitating events.

Harking back to his butterfly studies with Sheppard and the similarity between the mimicry supergene and the Rh supergene, he says the problem was posed: "Could we somehow devise a protective system for unprotected Rh-negative mothers, that is, for cases where there is no ABO incompatibility between the mother and the fetus?

"For months," Clarke continues, "I puzzled over the problem with my colleagues Sheppard and Richard B. McConnell. One night my wife, who had taken a keen interest in our work, woke me from a sound sleep and said: 'Give them anti-Rh.' Now, nothing is more irritating to a physician than to be awakened in the middle of the night and told how to manage his medical affairs. In a huff, I replied, 'It's anti-Rh we are trying to *prevent* them from making,' and turned over and went to sleep again. In the clear light of morning, infuriatingly, the idea began to make sense. . . . I discussed the proposal with my colleagues, and we decided to test it."[14]

Clarke's account explicitly credits his wife, Féo Clarke, with first suggesting the correct antibody—anti-Rh—to use to prevent immunization. Clearly implicit is credit to Clarke himself, the team leader, for having deduced that something should be given to mimic ABO's protective effect.

What then was Finn's role, according to Clarke's account? In the article in *Scientific American*, Clarke first acknowledges Finn's presence and participation in describing the period *after* the formulation of the Rh prevention plan and the decision to test it in men: "We put Ronald Finn in charge of the [male volunteer] experiments."[15] Clarke ignores completely Finn's three years of rhesus research prior to the male volunteer studies. Clarke's other account of these events, in the *BMJ*, identifies no one individual as author of the key idea. He says: "Shortly after this 1958 paper"—by Clarke, Finn, McConnell, and Sheppard[16]—"it occurred to us that it might be possible to mimic the protection afforded by ABO incompatibility by giving the mother anti-Rh after delivery."[17]

Finn here is given credit for having "put forward . . . this idea . . . at a meeting of the Liverpool Medical Institution" in 1960, but he is not credited with having conceived it.[18]

A similar—and related—ferment brewed in New York. John and Vince had always said that their creative probing of the Rh problem began in 1960, and that the idea of employing the *AMIS* principle had sprung from John's reading of Florey's textbook—after which, with their plan fairly clearly in mind, they had met Bill Pollack, who decided to join forces with them. Bill now said that their initial meeting occurred in 1959—which, if true, would give New York parity if not priority in time over Liverpool. Bill also suggested that the *AMIS* proposal first arose in the talk he, John, and Vince had had in Vince's laboratory—an assertion which, if true, would give all three equal credit for the project's conception as well as for its execution.

Victory—the approval of the Rh vaccine for clinical use—when it finally came, came at about the same time in Britain and the

United States, though there were important differences. The British acted first, in January 1968. Physicians were notified by the Health Ministry that they could begin using the vaccine. But, because the raw material still remained in short supply, the Ministry advised that priority should be given to mothers with Rh-incompatible, ABO-compatible babies, who could be shown by Kleihauer blood test to have sustained fetal bleeds of 5 ml or over. Following a WHO interim recommendation, which British experts had helped write, only mothers delivering their first babies would be protected.[19] The collection of anti-Rh serum for vaccine manufacture and the administration of the vaccine programs would be in the hands of National Health Service blood centers in the various regions of Britain.

These programs already had run into problems. Liverpool bloodbanker Lehane, for example, who had met, with British blood, the wartime transfusion needs of wounded Allied fighting men and Axis prisoners, now was failing at the task of attracting British women to save other British women from the tragedy of Rh disease. He explained that the young ones refused to make regular trips to the blood bank for plasmapheresing; older women phoned in ill often enough to disrupt bloodletting schedules. Attempts were being made to set up panels of deliberately-immunized male volunteers as an alternative.* [20]

Similar problems existed elsewhere in Britain, but clinicians who could get the vaccine, and who were able to run the various tests to qualify patients for it, were free to go ahead and use it. Since the National Health Service was the supplier, the vaccine was free of charge.

In New York, on Friday morning, April 19, a Telex machine in the office of *Medical World News* whispered out a brief *Urgent Alert* from Washington: *"Division of Biologics Standards has just approved Rh vaccine."*

Vince was reached by phone a day or so later.

"Congratulations, Vince!"

"Wha-. What is it?"

"DBS approved *RhoGAM!*"

"That's good! That's very good." Vince's voice sounded evasive,

---

* A strategy which worked well in Ireland, where, Clarke later reported, Rh vaccine was plentiful and cheap. "This product could do well commercially," he explained, "due to great help from Guinness's brewery, where all the male plasma donors are employed. There is a widespread conviction that 'Guinness is good for you.' "[21]

strained, and far away. He had not heard, he said, and added: "I didn't expect anything to happen.

"It means more to Ortho than it does to John or me. We knew it worked a long time ago. It's not the same feeling as when we got our first big results. For us, the one that counted was the first Sing Sing study."

John, who had remained far less confident than Vince, also sounded far away. But he was not surprised by the news. "Ortho," he said, "wants to get all geared up before they announce the licensing approval. As far as I know, there isn't a supply problem; they've been stockpiling the stuff for months. But there may be problems of distribution and organization."

"How do you feel?"

"I'm actually trying to find something else to get started in, something important," he said. "Little tasks don't appeal to us any more—although a couple of years ago, I would have jumped into them."

A half hour later Vince phoned back to blurt out an unnecessary apology that explained why he had sounded evasive: He had known about the license approval, but Ortho had insisted nothing be said until they were prepared to meet full demand—and make their official announcement. Only when the company knew that the news was out did Singher write two identical letters of thanks to Vince and John saying, in part: "I would like to thank you and your staff on behalf of myself and the entire Ortho Research Foundation for your conscientious and steadfast effort to make *RhoGAM* a reality. Through your efforts, this important chapter in Rh hemolytic disease of the newborn can be written. We have been fortunate to have such a distinguished and dedicated group of investigators working with us on this project. . . . With kindest personal regards, [signed] Heron O. Singher."[22, 23]

The United States approval, unlike the British, had no strings attached, in the sense that all unsensitized Rh-incompatible women at risk, regardless of ABO status, number of previous pregnancies, or amount of fetal bleed could be treated. It would be up to Ortho— or its competitors—to meet the needs of the market, which theoretically might reach 25,000 vials monthly in the United States alone.

Ortho formally introduced *RhoGAM* as a product in June. Initially, the price charged hospital blood banks that ordered it was $64.80 a dose. This was cut to $46.60 in October, and then to $35.10 the following spring. The standard hospital charge for service, cross-matching, and injecting the vaccine would about double this amount. So, typically, the cost to a woman for protection against Rh sensitization and the threat of death for all her subsequent babies would be $75 each time she delivered.

# 30

# The Conquest of Rh Disease

WITHIN A YEAR or so the Rh vaccine had been injected into more than a half-million women. Vince, aboard a jet plane headed for the AABB's 1969 meeting in Houston, Texas—where he, John, and Bill were to receive the Association's Landsteiner Award, $500 each, from an award fund provided by Ortho—delivered the judgment: "The conquest of Rh disease is now a reality!"

Based on his own efforts in the Rh clinic that he had founded at Presbyterian Hospital, this seemed reasonable: With amniocentesis, early induction, and intrauterine transfusion he had reduced the disease's death toll in sensitized pregnancies from 30 percent to less than 9 percent in a decade.[1] More important, in Vince's hands at least, the Rh vaccine still had a perfect record: None of the 335 new mothers to whom he gave it, beginning in 1964, had become sensitized to the Rh factor or had delivered a baby with Rh hemolytic disease.

Results from Ortho's far-flung clinical trials with *RhoGAM* were only a little less impressive. Through January 1972, in 4,757 pregnancies in women whom Ortho continued to follow in clinical trials, the Rh vaccine thus far had proved to be 99.7 percent effective. Bill said: "The success rate is phenomenal!" Results reported from Britain and elsewhere were essentially similar.

John, who was attempting unsuccessfully to extricate himself from the tag end of the Rh problem, saw matters differently than did Vince and Ortho. The vaccine failures upset and obsessed him. His was the more conservative analysis of the data: If one woman in 100 becomes sensitized, John said, that means the vaccine is only 90 percent effective. Why? Because 90 of every 100 women will complete each at-risk pregnancy without becoming sensitized, even without vaccine. If the vaccine protects 9 of the remaining 10, that means the failure rate is 1 in 10, or 10 percent.

On the basis of an analysis that tends to accentuate the negative, John arrived at a vaccine failure rate of 10 percent based on the worldwide subsequent pregnancy returns available late in 1970.[2] What John failed to take into account was that a failure rate scored at the end of "subsequent" pregnancies must be divided by two, since two periods of risk are included: the first pregnancy and its delivery, and the second. Both Ortho and Liverpool failure rates, in fact, are very close to this figure of .5 percent—or, in John's view, 5 percent—per pregnancy.[3, 4] Alternatively stated, the vaccine is 99.5 percent, or 95 percent, effective per pregnancy.

Assuming that the higher 10 percent failure rate per pregnancy is correct  and assuming that every woman at risk gets the vaccine, a WHO Scientific Group on the Prevention of Rh Sensitization projected an eventual drop from 1.3 dead babies per 1,000 pregnancies each year to 0.13 deaths per thousand.[5] Applied to the United States, and assuming that four million completed pregnancies produce the roughly 3,500,000 babies who are born alive each year, then 100 percent utilization of a 90 percent effective vaccine would cut erythroblastosis deaths from 5,200 unborn and newborn babies a year to 520. Assuming the 95 percent efficacy of the Ortho and Liverpool trials, rather than the 90 percent of the WHO model, this would mean 260 deaths each year in the United States.

Even this figure could be high. While the period for which the WHO group calculated its baseline of 1.3 deaths per 1,000 pregnancies is not indicated, it must be an average of women who began bearing children in the mid-1960s or earlier. It thus may fail to take into account America's precipitous drop in family size. The number of children the average woman bears fell from 3.7 in 1957 to 2.1 in 1972.[6] Obviously, a disease that takes its major toll late, in large families, is going to be advantageously reduced when the average number of children each woman bears drops sharply. Ortho's birth control products could be having almost as significant an effect on erythroblastosis mortality as *RhoGAM*!

Even for women destined to become "vaccine failures," the question of *when* failure occurs is significant. As an example, there is the hypothetical woman who will become pregnant three times and who is destined to be a vaccine "failure." She will be naturally protected during her first pregnancy. If the vaccine given as it ends "protects," her second pregnancy too will be safe. If the vaccine given at its end fails, then only one pregnancy—her third—is jeopardized. This is a significant advantage, for it halves—from two to one—the number of afflicted pregnancies, and eliminates entirely a usually-more-severe second-afflicted pregnancy that might have occurred if, without the successful first vaccine injection, she became sensitized while delivering her first baby. A vaccine failure, *sensitization*, after this woman's or any woman's last pregnancy will, of course, have no obstetrical consequences.

Ortho uncovered one other relevant and provocative fact: The majority of women in whom failures occur have been given vaccine for the first time in a second or later pregnancy. This implies that the risk of vaccine failure increases with the number of pregnancies a woman has, and suggests also that virtually every woman who is protected with vaccine at the end of her first pregnancy will bear at least one more disease-free child.

Confronting these optimistic projections, there are, however, some important hedges:

Even with a vaccine that was 100 percent effective, erythroblastosis could not be eliminated overnight, for already sensitized women would continue to bear ill children. A statistician working for the city of New York, Alex Tytun, calculated that if all women at risk were given a 100 percent effective vaccine, only 1 percent of anticipated cases of the disease would be prevented in the first year, since most women would have been previously sensitized. By year two, 10 percent of cases would be prevented. Half would be prevented by the fifth year; 75 percent by the tenth year; and, the statistician concluded: "Hemolytic disease of the newborn should be almost eliminated in 20 or 25 years following the introduction of a comprehensive Rh vaccination program."[7]

In fact, comprehensive vaccination programs were not undertaken. In Britain, Ronnie Finn estimated, a year and a half after licensing, only 20 percent of women at risk were being treated—a situation that he bluntly branded "a national scandal."

Inadequate vaccine supplies, due at least in part to the ban on payments to plasma donors, appeared to be part of the problem, along with Health Ministry inertia and the absence in the British picture of an aggressive, profit-oriented private manufacturer. Because of raw material shortages, Finn had reversed his original objection to the use of raw anti-Rh antiserum. Its use, he said, would preserve a significant percentage of antibody that is lost during the extraction of 7S gamma globulin; unprocessed antiserum also would be cheaper. Eventually, coverage with the gamma globulin vaccine improved.

In the United States, Bill Pollack estimated, early in 1971, that just over 80 percent of new mothers at risk were being protected. A series of federal government surveys tended to confirm the accuracy of this estimate. Epidemiologist Dr. Richard Judelsohn of the Center for Disease Control (CDC), Atlanta, Georgia, said coverage was steadily rising. In urban and suburban areas, he said, coverage ranged from 85 percent to 90 percent of women at risk, and in some localities approached 100 percent. But in rural areas coverage was much lower, averaging 60 percent. One hospital in his sample in rural Georgia failed to provide vaccine to any of its patients.

Public health experts had asked themselves why a drug that was 100 percent safe and 99 percent effective was being given to only 80 percent of the women whom it might—enormously—benefit.*

Several barriers were discovered. The most important, according to health officers in the various states, was cost. "We have a large number of individuals who could not afford the $70 to $100 involved," said the public health chief of a Western state. Another state official said: "Our criteria for medical assistance eligibility leave many medically needy women with no resources with which to pay." Some states would not or could not help out: There's "no corner in our budget" for it, one official explained. To a lesser extent, health officers said, women were not being protected because they were unaware of the vaccine, or their need for it, and/or their

* A conflicting analysis suggests that 90 percent coverage of women at risk represents virtually full utilization. Dr. William Robertson of Children's Orthopedic Hospital and Medical Center, Seattle, Washington, reported that "an 88 percent utilization" rate was achieved in Seattle within months after the vaccine's commercial approval, "with nonacceptance by patients for bona fide reasons largely responsible for the 12 percent deficit."[8] Asked to specify "bona fide" reasons for patients to refuse it, he listed, in addition to cost: women who are Jehovah's Witnesses, and who reject such medication on religious grounds; women who undergo hysterectomy after delivery of their last child; and women who have decided, "Never any other kids!"

doctors, through ignorance or neglect, had failed to give it to them. A high New England public health official remarked: "Some physicians are resistant to anything new."

A remedial effort was launched by the March of Dimes. Its vice president for medical affairs, Dr. Virginia Apgar, urged Congress to include the Rh vaccine in legislation providing federal funds and assistance for vaccination campaigns.[9] Congress wrote Rh disease into its Communicable Disease Control Amendments of 1970, which were put into law that year.[10] The law authorizes federal grants to states for vaccination programs. Grants were to be administered by CDC. Epidemiologist Judelsohn began setting up an Rh vaccination service there late in 1970. It was his hope that CDC could begin making grants to states for vaccine in 1971, but the necessary federal appropriation was not forthcoming; in the spring of 1972, when he left CDC, it still had not arrived. Some funds were provided in the fiscal 1973 budget and the Health Appropriations Bill, but these were lost when President Richard Nixon, for other reasons, twice vetoed the Bill. Insiders at CDC were not sanguine that Rh would fare better in fiscal 1974.

As of early 1973, the federal government, at least temporarily, thus again had fumbled the ball on Rh, withholding minor sums for public health measures that well might have closed the gap between the high utilization levels already achieved by doctors, hospitals, and local health departments and optimal protection against the disease.

One other spur to full utilization seemed imminent: One or more legal suits by women who had failed to receive Rh vaccine following delivery, and who subsequently had delivered ill or dead babies, reportedly were close to resolution late in 1972, and it seemed to Rh experts that their chances for collecting significant damages were excellent. The resolution of one such case, in a mother's behalf, Judelsohn felt, "would be a strong hammer to hold over doctors' heads" to insure that all would get Rh vaccine.

Meanwhile, one new factor arose that threatened much of the previous progress: legalized abortion. It had long been suspected that both spontaneous and induced abortions could leak enough fetal blood into the mother to cause Rh sensitization. Vince established the incidence of such sensitizations as 3 to 4 percent of all abortions in Rh-negative women, with this risk rising from negligible at one month to 2 percent at two months and 9 percent at three months and beyond.[11]

There were grounds to suspect that at least some of the rare "first pregnancy" cases of erythroblastosis occurred in women who had been sensitized previously by spontaneous abortions that they themselves were unaware of or induced abortions that they had kept secret from their obstetricians.

The apparent rise in abortions following their legalization in New York State and elsewhere thus seemed to pose a new threat of large numbers of Rh sensitizations. Many abortion centers and abortionists provided Rh vaccine to their Rh-negative patients. Many did not. By studying patient charts in five hospitals, Judelsohn found in 1971 that only two out of three women at risk were given the vaccine. For Rh workers, the spectre of young women becoming sensitized by abortions before beginning their childbearing careers was especially disheartening, since if these women later became pregnant by Rh-positive husbands, even their very first babies could be afflicted.

Vince established that fetal bleeds from abortuses for the most part could be nullified by a fraction of the vaccine dose needed after full-term delivery. To provide such a dose, Ortho was working on a half-price mini-dose vial of vaccine specifically for abortions, as were other manufacturers. But despite Rh workers' strong concensus that it would be safe to give it to all Rh-negative abortion patients, the U. S. Food and Drug Administration, which has taken over licensing of serum products from DBS, which had been disbanded, was dragging its heels, much as DBS had. As of January 1973, no mini-dose had been approved.

Erythroblastosis was rapidly evolving from a clinical and research concern into a problem in preventive medicine. Hospital pediatrics departments already had noticed a decrease in the need for exchange transfusions for newborns. Yet the hope that Rh hemolytic disease would entirely vanish seemed for the moment remote. Already-sensitized mothers continued to conceive foredoomed babies. So did women who had failed to get the vaccine postpartum or postabortion, and women who had been inadvertently sensitized to the Rh factor by a mismatched Rh-incompatible blood transfusion; several hundred such sensitizations are estimated to occur in the United States each year. If the mistake is noticed quickly, multiple doses of Rh vaccine may prevent a woman from being sensitized by the Rh-positive blood with which she has been transfused. There also were a few true vaccine fail-

ures, which especially worried John Gorman.* A few of these failures could be shown to be due to massive fetal bleeds, in which the
Rh-positive cells simply overwhelmed the Rh-protective vaccine.
Immunity to gamma globulin seemed to nullify the vaccine in some
cases. And there was always the possibility—which John felt was
quite real—that in some cases sensitization did result from a bleed
that occurred well before delivery so that, as Zuelzer and Cohen
long ago had prophesied, vaccine injected at delivery was too late
to prevent it. "Flossie Cohen turned out to be right," John would
say. "We're only lucky that the number of cases she is right about
turns out to be so small!"

What, in perspective, had been achieved? At best, Rh hemolytic
disease of the newborn had been defeated. At least, it had been
reduced from a real menace in one United States marriage in eight
to a very rare, very preventible, and very treatable illness. In award
citations given to John and Vince, with $500 checks, by the Ma-
ternity Center Association of New York—the only such recognition,
besides the Landsteiner prize, that they had received by 1972—
they are lauded for "monumental contributions to medicine and
humanity, which will be measured in the saving of countless lives
and will stand among the great medical achievements in obstetrical
history."[16] Extended to include Bill Pollack and the Liverpool
workers, this praise does not seem exaggerated. In less weighty

---

* New therapies continued to be invented to chip away at the cases of erythroblastosis that continued to occur. Fetologist Jerold Lucey and others showed that the simple
expedient of exposing jaundiced babies to blue light would bleach away the toxic
yellow bilirubin. Blue light therapy complemented, and in some cases wholly replaced,
exchange transfusion.[12] Similar results, and apparently life salvage in some cases, were
reported by British clinicians who treated ill babies with barbiturates—which induce
an enzyme that detoxifies the lethal bilirubin in the blood. They planned to see
whether the unborn might also be so treated, by giving barbiturates to their mothers.[13]
For the unborn, Clarke and several colleagues had vigorously pursued a method—
reminiscent of Wiener's original "competition of antigens" plan—to reduce an already
sensitized mother's Rh antibody levels during pregnancy by plasmapheresing her
several times weekly. The aim was to remove the antibody-containing plasma, while
returning the red cells to her. The method failed to help.[14] Methods were sought to
improve the "open" intrauterine transfusion technique, to permit large infusions of Rh-
negative blood, beginning as early as the sixth month of gestation. Two Japanese obstetricians reported success in two severe cases in which they opened the mother's womb,
but, instead of pulling forth a fetal head or leg into which to transfuse blood, as Vince
and Karlis Adamsons had done, they drew up only the umbilical cord, through which
they performed an exchange transfusion with Rh-negative red cells. They then returned
the cord to the womb and resealed the womb. In both cases, liveborn babies were delivered several weeks later.[15]

language, *Time* magazine picked Rh "reverse vaccination" as one of the ten top medical achievements of the 1960s.[17]

In fact, despite countless press reports of "medical break-throughs," the resolution of a major disease problem is relatively rare. In the '60s, comparable inroads were made against only a few diseases: Polio and measles fell before relatively standard vaccines; rubella, which maims but usually does not kill, was being similarly restricted at the decade's end. An effective treatment was worked out for one extremely rare cancer, choriocarcinoma, which, perhaps significantly, is, like erythroblastosis, a feto-maternal disorder; the tumor, in the mother, is fetal tissue which, once destroyed, usually does not recur.

Artificial kidneys and transplantation, mostly of the kidneys, were developed to the point where a few thousand lives were extended each year—though neither cures nor preventives were found for the diseases they were designed to treat. Heart transplant, which was first accomplished in the same year the Rh vaccine was licensed, 1968, had by 1973 yielded only a few dozen one-year survivals, compared to 50,000 or more whole lifetimes already rescued by the Rh vaccine. The disproportionate acclaim accorded heart transplanters, compared to Rh vaccine inventors, is noteworthy.

Medical progress is, of course, more than lives saved. Cost and manpower savings—for example, reduction in the need for time-consuming full exchange transfusions—count as progress. A specific discovery's effect on medical theory and practice, as a whole, is important also. Thus, for example, amniocentesis, developed for Rh, has opened a whole new area of fetal diagnosis based on chemical and genetic analysis of the fluid and of fetal cells.

John Gorman pointed out that *AMIS* may have many other medical applications, one of which is the prevention of poison ivy. A person who has never been sensitized to poison ivy—that is, one who has never had it—might be kept exempt, even if subsequently exposed, by injection of anti-poison ivy antibody at the start of each growing season. Ronnie Finn had set out to pursue the proposition that it is *AMIS*, in pregnancy, that permits a mother to tolerate the antigenic intrusion into her body that is her fetus. If true, and if this mechanism could be isolated and controlled, the way would be open to solve the problem of graft rejection, which thus far has bedeviled work in organ transplantation. Bill Pollack, while at work on the Rh vaccine, made fundamental immunohematologic and immunochemical contributions to the understanding of the nature of the antigen-antibody reaction. Others would find in the Rh vaccine research reports clues and data for resolution of problems undreamt of in Liverpool and New York. Research reports and a new scientific literature began to appear based on it.

Even for a decade rich in medical progress, the conquest of Rh disease, through three essentially new techniques—one diagnostic, one therapeutic, and one prophylactic—must be rated a major triumph. The vaccine rates added honors for having been developed practically for pennies, during medical research's richest era. The United States government alone spent over ten billion dollars on medical research in the 1960s, not a nickel of which went to Vince and John's vaccine project until 1964—when the battle was essentially won. Estimates by John and Vince for New York and Julius Krevans for Liverpool and Baltimore suggest that through the decisive summer of 1965, total expenditures at these centers was under $500,000. Ortho has not revealed its costs to that point, but supposing that they double this amount, to $1 million, then the price for inventing a vaccine that will be good for all time is about what society pays today for lifetime care for a half dozen children irreparably brain-damaged by erythroblastosis.

Yet had it not been for Clarke and Sheppard's butterfly research grant from the Nuffield Foundation, John's almost flukey access to the New York City Health Research Council, and financial support from Ortho, the work might not have been accomplished. If new young researchers who dared to *Think Big!* about an Rh-preventive could hardly find seed money in the boom years of the 1960s, it takes little imagination to see that in research's lean years, the early 1970s, this work might well never be done. It is for the society that benefits from discoveries like an Rh vaccine to grapple with that fact. Ironically, having themselves become established men, Vince and John for a while had upwards of $50,000 annually in NIH and New York City grant monies with which to work. Then government support for research fell precipitously, and by 1971 they again were scrabbling to find money to pay a research technician's salary.

# 31

## Credit Where Due

FOR ALL principal participants in the Rh vaccine research, in Liverpool and in New York, the question of who is entitled to credit, and for what, remained, at decade's end, an issue of burning—often bitter—concern.

Does it matter? To the vaccine's direct beneficiaries—the families protected and the individuals live-born and healthy because of it—no doubt it matters little. What matters to them, whether or not they even are aware of the work, is that it was done, expertly, by whomever it was done. How many school children today know that the polio vaccine they are given was invented by Salk, not by Sabin, or Sabin, not Salk? Or know what it may spare them? Or care?

But there are other reasons for inquiring. Noteworthy achievement deserves an accurate accounting. It also *demands* it, for the participants' benefit, as well as for the benefit of the community—which has a stake in the recognition and reward of praiseworthy work. The commonweal depends on the accumulation of praiseworthy medical research, and if those who perform it do not receive appropriate recognition and praise, the best men of a generation will turn to other endeavors.

Even the younger Rh researchers, whose professional lives lie largely ahead, feel the issue keenly: What, in fact, have I achieved? They are now forty, or older, and as they and their progenitors have dramatically demonstrated, great research is done by green-horns, not by greybeards.*

Landsteiner was 32 when he discovered the ABO blood types.

Levine was 39 when he discovered a new red cell antigen in Mary Seno's blood.

Wiener was 33 when he showed that antibody against a rhesus monkey red cell antigen clumped 85 percent of white human bloods.

Ferguson was 31 when he linked *hydrops, icterus,* and *erythroblastosis* together as one disease.

Diamond was 30 when he added *congenital anemia* and elucidated the disease's clinical picture.

Nevanlinna was 31 when he showed that it is the last unaffected pregnancy that is—or is not—protected by ABO incompatibility.

Kleihauer was 30 when he published his test for fetal red cells in mother's blood.

Liley was 34 when he did his first intrauterine transfusion.

Ronnie Finn was 30 when he first presented his Rh prevention plan to the Liverpool Medical Institution.

John Gorman was 30 when he offered the *AMIS* proposal to the New York City Health Research Council.

Vince Freda was 34 when he submitted his and John's plan to NIH.

Bill Pollack was 35 when he made the first experimental batch of Rh vaccine.

For a doctor, age thirty arrives in or near his last year of specialty training. His learning and apprenticeship years are ending, and his elders' errors and shortcomings remain clear enough in his mind to invite correction. The demands of clinical practice and of administrative and pedagogic responsibility, which soon will burden all but the fortunate few, are momentarily in abeyance—and the way is open, briefly, for a bright and ambitious young man to challenge things as they are with bold research plans.

By age forty, all has changed: Routine and responsibility are the requirement of the day. All the Rh researchers have now reached that juncture, and so they well may wonder if their most creative years have passed.

At its best, research is arduous, time-consuming, and poorly compensated work. It is a gamble, with one's best years as ante. Few win a triumph as glorious as the Rh vaccine. And such success

---

* A researcher's *age* at the time he made his important contribution is here calculated by subtracting the year of his birth from the year in which he first announced his key finding or theory.

rarely strikes twice in one lifetime. Thus, for its inventors, the Rh vaccine, which came at the start of their careers, may also mark the zenith of their research achievements. So the question of just credit for what they have done cannot be one they approach with little concern. Most, certainly, would agree with Wiener when he said: "The problem may seem trivial to others, but to the individuals involved, the priority for discoveries they have made are of considerable importance."[1]

Scientists may not set out specifically to win recognition with their work, but when skill, fortune, and propitious circumstances conspire to favor their efforts, they can hardly be blamed for the wish that the cosmic forces would pause to certify what they have done. Rh research, perhaps because it progressed so quickly, was especially susceptible to rival claims and bitter enmity—witness Levine *vs.* Wiener, Wiener *vs.* Race. These poisonous animosities thrived on the obscurity of the record, as well as on active and passive attempts to subvert and obfuscate it. Levine, less shrill than Wiener and better protected by admirers and associates at Ortho, perhaps came out ahead in colleagues' eyes. But several of their colleagues, from three different countries—and each in a position to have some knowledge of the matter—say that the conflict cost both Wiener and Levine science's and society's richest reward, the Nobel Prize, for which they were, at least once, jointly nominated.

While none of the inventors of the Rh vaccine wants to discuss the possibility of such reward, their achievement is such that they could be forgiven silent dark wonderings on whether Nobel lightning will one day strike the "Rh college"—and, if so, which few of its stellar students will be caught in its glow. The Nobel limit is three recipients for any prize-winning achievement.

That the second, and perhaps last, generation of Rh researchers would be as dramatically productive as the first could hardly have been foretold when they began their labors over a decade ago. None is of a nature to have recorded day by day his ideas, plans, and accomplishments in a diary or journal. Thus, contemporary documentation is scant. Neither could it have been foretold that the same record of similar or identical discoveries and bitter rivalry that marked the start of Rh history also was to mark its end. Even these later events now are a decade gone, and factual recall, for all participants, has eroded. One may hope, therefore, that an analysis of these events and priorities, based on all documentation thus far available (1972), will help obviate, for Rh's second generation, the bitterness of conflicting, unresolved—and unresolvable—claims that continues to enmire the first.

Three issues remain outstanding. First: Who has priority for the Rh vaccine proposal, Liverpool or New York? Corollary: Did one group get the idea from another? Second: What is the relative value of their separate contributions—i.e., was one an also-ran? Finally: There is the provocative problem raised by Clarke in 1967—Did Féo and Cyril Clarke conceive of the Rh vaccine? Or did Ronald Finn?

Priority for the proposal that anti-Rh antibody passively administered at delivery might prevent Rh sensitization belongs to Liverpool, on the basis of all available evidence (see Chapter 16). Ronnie Finn's statement to the Liverpool Medical Institution in February 1960 that "a suitable antibody" might serve this purpose—a statement based on several years of intensive research—probably was made a month or so before John Gorman first met Vince Freda.[2, 3, 4] Were it not for the fact that Finn and McConnell recall that Finn specified "anti-Rh antibody" in his talk—though his text, which is extant, is nonspecific—one could conjecture that that decision was not made until later that year, by which time Vince and John might have arrived, via a different route, at the same suggestion.

The very latest that Liverpool's decision to use "anti-Rh" could have been made was July 1960, when Finn spoke to the British Genetical Society; the specification is in his text, which also is extant.[5] By then, Vince and John were deep into their creative dialogue, but there is no documentation, only memory, to say how far they had progressed (see Chapter 7). It is possible that they already *were* considering anti-Rh injections. But their first, rejected plan was to give 19S anti-Rh during pregnancy to compete with the mother's 7S anti-Rh—John's clonal competition theory. The significant conceptual evolution between the two drafts of John's New York City Health Research Council grant application, the first written in the autumn of 1960 and submitted in February 1961, the second written and submitted in May 1961, suggests that, contrary to memory, the conceptual stage of their work required months, rather than hours or weeks, to complete—and hence probably had not advanced to the final, *AMIS*, proposal by mid-July 1960. Thus, whether one relies wholly on written documentation, wholly on recall, or on both together, the priority for the idea of injecting anti-Rh antibody postpartum clearly belongs to Liverpool.

Both Ronnie Finn in Liverpool and Bill Pollack in New York have claimed that the key concept—the use of anti-Rh antibody—came up in 1959, or earlier. Based on the evidence, this is probably not true for Liverpool, and definitely not true for New York. The slow accumulation of Kleihauer test findings which led Finn to his proposal, and McConnell's recollection that he was hearing the idea for the first time at the Liverpool Medical Institution, in mid-February 1960, suggest that Finn had become aware of his idea only very shortly before.

In the case of New York, no documentation has come to light from John, Vince, or any other source that would even suggest that John and Vince had met in 1959, let alone that, together, they had met Bill. The sole untapped reservoir of documents that could further clarify the question of when their collaboration began is possessed by Ortho. Although asked repeatedly to produce any letters, memoranda, or notebooks that might establish a 1959 start for their collaboration, Bill has failed to do so. In fact, not only is his participation unlikely to date from 1959, it probably did not occur in 1960 either; only memory assigns it to even the latter year. Bill himself concedes that had he been aware of John and Vince's ideas in August 1960, when he attended the blood bank meeting in San Francisco at which Stern presented his provocative Rh experiments, he would not have failed to notice that they proved Vince and John's hypothesis. This he failed to do.

Vince wrote to Levine, apparently without prior introduction from Bill, late in 1960; Levine answered the letter on December 5.[6] It seems unlikely that Vince would write to Levine in this way if he had already undertaken a collaboration with one of Levine's junior associates. By February 1, John was off to Australia for a month. So unless the meeting took place in December or January, for which there is no positive evidence, it probably did not occur until after John's return on the last day of February 1961 (see Chapter 9). If, as John believes, his demonstration of his prothrombin machine to Ortho salesman John Nerres was the event that led to his first meeting with Bill, then the meeting did not take place until March or April, for in a letter to his parents dated March 8, John says that on that day he made the machine operative in the blood bank for the first time.

A related problem is whether Bill took part in the thinking that first led to the proposal that *AMIS* might be harnessed to prevent Rh sensitization. It is conceivable that he did. But here it is two memories against one: Vince and John say that John got the idea before the talk with Bill, from reading about *AMIS* in Florey's textbook. Certainly, if Bill did not meet John and Vince until after John's first grant application was filed in February, as available documentation strongly suggests, then the matter is certain: Bill was not in on the idea's inception.*

Similarly, it seems virtually certain, though it can never be absolutely proved, that when John and Vince formulated their proposal they were unaware of the Liverpool work. The only hint of it that had appeared in print before dateable proposals of their own is the single sentence by Finn in *Lancet*.[8] It neither specified which antibody would be used, nor that delivery would be in time, and so it would not have been much help to John and Vince even if they had seen it. Hence, Louis Diamond's judgement that the discovery occurred "independently" on both sides of the Atlantic seems valid.[9]

Vince and John are fortunate that their complete proposal, in Vince's rejected NIH grant, predates, albeit only by days, publication of the first Liverpool paper in the *British Medical Journal* (see Chapter 13).[10] This assures their claim to independent discovery, if not priority or parity of publication. They also are fortunate that someone edited the letter Finn wrote for publication in *Nature* late in 1960, deleting the specification "gamma globulin" as the vehicle for the anti-Rh antibody—which they then first proposed in print and, with Bill's participation, developed and tested.[11, 12, 13]

---

* The contrary view was fostered and encouraged by Ortho and by Philip Levine, who, approaching his seventieth birthday, now also remembered his own role as having been one of catalyst and booster of the Rh vaccine research. His view was important because he remained the world's single most respected authority on Rh; his words carried weight. In remarks to the AABB in 1969, reproduced here verbatim, Levine said:

I'd like to give you a little history of how the entire thing . . . was developed by Drs. Pollack, Gorman and Freda. It was an historical date in October of 1959 when Dr. Pollack gave a talk at [Columbia College of] P[hysicians] and S[urgeons] and for the first time met Drs. Freda and Gorman. After the lecture, in a long bull session, Dr. Pollack described his work on the preparation of anti-immunoglobulin sera, and in the course of this work . . . the group at Ortho . . . observed that in the presence of excess of antibody the primary response of antibody production was suppressed. . . .

This immediately excited the three workers who saw immediately the application to prevention of Rh hemolytic disease. . . . Dr. Freda suggested that Sing Sing would be an appropriate place—the prisoners at Sing Sing could be volunteers—to receive red cells with gamma globulin. Dr. Pollack immediately, ah, suggested that we—they—do not use plasma containing antibodies, but rather gamma globulin, which they knew was free of the dangers of hepatitis. After that history was made, and the rest of the story you know because then we went to Rh-negative women. . . . At the same time . . . the Liverpool school considered the same . . . program.[7]

Would either side have quit if the other had not existed? Probably not. New York, once started, encountered no major setbacks. Liverpool, having failed badly in its first experiment, had lived through its "finest hour," and was moving forward again by the time Ronnie Finn learned of John, Vince, and Bill's interest. Contrary to what Vince has said, there is no evidence that Liverpool quit, even temporarily. On the other hand, Clarke and Finn have been candid enough to say that at one key point they were waiting for New York data before plunging into clinical trials. Without those data, they might have plunged more slowly, but it is hard to believe that they would not have plunged at all. Both Finn and Clarke are determined, if cautious, men. Either group could have, and would have, gone it alone. It also seems clear, however, that cross-fertilization of ideas and competitiveness helped get both teams to the finish line sooner than either would have arrived there alone.

A key issue, which is as yet not wholly resolved, could significantly strengthen New York's claim to parity of achievement, if not priority of publication. That is the issue of which, if either, team proposed the correct *reason* for believing that the Rh vaccine would work. If Liverpool proposed first a workable treatment based on a correct rationale, that is one thing. If the treatment works, as it does, but for a different reason, that might be something else again. But if it turned out that New York proposed the right treatment, for the right reason, even though several months later, sense says that their claim for parity would be much advanced.

Liverpool proposed to prevent Rh sensitization by duplicating the ABO-protective mechanism through which a mother's natural anti-A or anti-B will destroy group A or B fetal cells that enter her bloodstream. They proposed using anti-Rh antibody to destroy Rh-positive fetal cells in the maternal bloodstream and/or coat them with antibody so their antigen sites would be blocked and they would be quickly and harmlessly removed.

New York, on the other hand, proposed to apply a pure immunologic principle, which works in a number of antigen-antibody systems completely unrelated to blood—the *AMIS* principle first elucidated by Theobald Smith.*

Experiments might help decide which principle was operative in

* How and why *AMIS* works remains unknown in 1972.

the Rh vaccine. Bill and Hans Hager confirmed that in rabbits, as in man, a 19S antibody *will* prevent sensitization by clearing antigenic red cells from the circulation. But the Rh vaccine is not 19S; it is 7S antibody. Bill showed that a 7S anti-red cell antibody could prevent sensitization 100 percent of the time without significantly decreasing survival time of the antigenic red cells in the bloodstream. Rapid removal of red cells, as Liverpool has believed, thus does not appear necessary for the prevention of sensitization.[14]

One key experiment, both sides seemed to agree, might resolve the problem: Suppose Liverpool is right, and cell clearance is the key mechanism. Then an antibody that "found" one antigen on a foreign red cell's surface, and through it, destroyed the cell, would keep the body's immune mechanism from making antibody against the antigen in question.[15,16] It would *also* keep the immune system from making antibody against any other antigens that the red cell happened to carry.

If New York's theory is correct, on the other hand, antibody specific to one antigen on an injected red cell would prevent immunization to that antigen alone. But it would not prevent sensitization to other antigens that that cell happened to carry. Bill demonstrated, in rabbits, that the New York theory is correct: Animals negative for rabbit blood factors A and F were injected with red cells that were A-positive and F-positive. Then the animals were injected with anti-A antibody. The anti-A, like anti-Rh in humans, protected all animals from becoming immunized to the rabbit A factor. But almost half the rabbits became immunized to the F factor. This demonstrated that a specific immunologic mechanism provided the protection, not the clearance or destruction of the red cells.[17]

Clarke concedes that the animal data support the New York interpretation, in the face of Stern's experiments upon which Liverpool relied.[18] The matter could finally be resolved, he suggests, by conducting an equivalent experiment in male volunteers, using anti-Rh antibody and red cells that carry the Rh factor plus some other red-cell antigen. Surprisingly, such an experiment has not yet been done. Meanwhile, Clarke glosses over the conflict, saying: "From the practical point of view, [Liverpool's] 'coating' versus [New York's] 'central inhibition' is a sterile controversy, since the two are not mutually exclusive."[19]

The New York investigators, who believe the two modes of action *are* mutually exclusive, and who believe *AMIS* is the sole correct explanation for the vaccine's success, might gain ground toward a final resolution of issues outstanding with Liverpool if they did the definitive experiment in human volunteers to see if it supported their view. If one of the two sides turns out to be right, and the other is wrong, the one that is right will have considerably strengthened its claim to credit for the Rh vaccine.

Finally, what of events at Liverpool? Did Cyril Clarke deliberately set out to find a prophylaxis for Rh disease, succeed, and then employ Ronald Finn to execute his ideas, as he says he did in *Scientific American* and other publications? Or did Finn, having been assigned to this general area of inquiry, and having assimilated important ideas about it from within and without his department, come alone upon the key concept through the inner activity of a solitary mind?

If there is value in elucidating the creative process in medicine— and it is the thesis of the present volume that there is—then it is critically important to know how, and under what circumstances, the creative leap occurs. Is it a mechanical task which could be assigned to a computer? Does it flow from deliberate administrative decisions—Let us conquer *X* disease—and a task force approach? Or is creativity in medicine an individual, irrational, intuitive process?

These need not be mutually exclusive pathways. But in assessing any single instance of medical creativity, it is critically important to know how—and by whom—it was accomplished.

Clarke and Finn have been extremely reluctant to discuss directly their divergent views, either within the Liverpool department of medicine or with outsiders. The other members of the former Liverpool team have been similarly hesitant. When asked to reconcile the various accounts of what transpired, one team member, John Woodrow, replied diplomatically that it seemed to him an impossible puzzle. An outside observer, he added, might stand a better chance of resolving it.

Analysis of the available early documents, from the period when success seemed a remote possibility, contributes a few clues: Finn, in his thesis, advances the prevention proposal in the third-person passive voice required in formal medical reports: "A possible method of preventing erythroblastosis is described. . . . A pilot experiment is described using Rh-negative male volunteers, etc. . . ."[20] It may—or it may not—be significant that Finn does not attribute these ideas to anyone other than himself, though he knew, of course, that Clarke, as his advisor, would read the thesis in evaluating his doctoral qualifications. It is perhaps noteworthy that one unrelated idea that figures in the thesis apparently stemmed from a face-to-face discussion with geneticist Sheppard, and this is attributed, in Finn's bibliography, to "personal conversation."[21]

The first presentations of the anti-Rh proposal are in papers—in February and July 1960—that list Finn as the sole author. In each instance, he introduces his prevention proposal in the first-person singular, then shifts back to the third person: "May I conclude on a highly speculative note . . . it might then be possible . . . [to] prevent . . . erythoblastosis."[22]

The first *BMJ* report in May 1961, based on Finn's thesis, backs into the problem in the third person; it is already a team report, with seven authors, that specifically credits neither Finn, Clarke, nor anyone else with the key idea of anti-Rh preventive injections. Finn's thesis, however, is cited as a source, and he is specifically credited for his study of ABO and Rh interaction in Liverpudlian women: "It therefore seems obvious," the report says, "that a way to prevent sensitization in an ABO-compatible mother would be to destroy the fetal cells rapidly by some other means. Since the cells are by definition Rh-positive, the injection of anti-Rh would be the first thing to try."[23] Subsequent *team* reports shed no further light on who gets credit for what; Clarke is sole author of the account that credits Mrs. Clarke with the key idea.[24]

The two accounts of *how* the ideas came are strikingly different. For Finn, it will be recalled, the creative leap came after hours and hours of peering at Kleihauer slides and months and months of mental rumination of the Rh-protective mechanisms he was studying; he thinks he had the "answer," that Rh sensitization could be actively prevented, unconsciously in mind for months before he became consciously aware of what he was thinking (see Chapter 16). Clarke would later recall the event as "one of those things when the light suddenly dawns."

What would be Finn's view of the issue? Late in 1969, when he had largely withdrawn from direct participation in the department of medicine, Finn would say that he had never discussed with Clarke the *Scientific American* paper—the one in which Clarke explicitly advances the Clarkes' claim—and would decline to comment on it directly. He expressed genuine gratitude to Clarke for sponsoring his thesis research and for moving forward, adroitly, a project that he alone could not have advanced to the clinical stage.

He gave the impression of being an astute academician who would not contradict his superior, and a gentleman who would not dispute a claim made in a lady's name.

Nevertheless, speaking in another context, Finn declared: "I think that I came on this idea of protective mechanisms by myself. As far as I know, the basic idea of emulating ABO incompatibility was entirely my own." It was in this vein that he referred to the discovery through several long conversations concerned with the early days of Liverpool's research.

Sheppard would recall first hearing the vaccine proposal in the Clarkes' drawing room: "Cyril Clarke made the suggestion of using anti-Rh to get rid of the rhesus antigen to mimic the ABO protection."

McConnell, who appears to have the warmest rapport of anyone in the department with both Clarke and Finn, says: "I, in my own mind, have always credited Ronnie Finn with the idea. Either the group thought it up or Ronnie thought of it. If any one person is to get credit for having thought of the idea, it is Ronnie." In an account that he wrote for the 1966 *Annual Review of Medicine*, McConnell declared: "Finn had been studying the role of ABO incompatibility between mother and fetus in protecting against Rh immunization, and he speculated that the protection conferred by naturally occurring maternal anti-A and B antibodies might be mimicked by injecting anti-Rh antibodies."[25]

Clarke, asked directly to reconcile the *Scientific American* account, in which Mrs. Clarke is credited with conceiving the idea, with his statement in the *BMJ* that "This idea was put forward by Finn," declared:[26, 27] "It's very hard . . . ," but never ended his sentence; it sounded as if he had started to say it would be hard, so many years later, to say for sure. Then he declared, with an unsaid *but*: "The actual idea of giving it [anti-Rh]—the idea was my wife's. She had the idea. But Ronald Finn put it forward. [In assigning credit] you have to go on what's in print. . . . But he [Finn] didn't think about it. . . ."

Can the matter be resolved? There is not the remotest possibility that Finn would or could have come up with an idea for preventing erythroblastosis had he not been assigned to study ABO and Rh by Clarke. Neither could his key thinking have been achieved without assistance and counsel by Clarke, Sheppard, McConnell, and perhaps others. Nor is there any doubt that Clarke's keen ability to sense a good idea—and pursue it—made possible trials in male volunteers, and ultimately, in women, that Finn alone might have achieved only much later, if at all. Thus, it would even be reasonable to see Clarke's assignment of a key role to his wife, Féo, as a clever method of preventing any one member of his team from gaining preeminent credit—so that credit would redound on the entire team, of which he was the chief.*

But for all the key support and participation of Clarke and the others, without which neither the idea nor the actuality of an Rh preventive would have come to fruition in Liverpool, this observer finds credible Finn's description of his creative advance from the study of fetal cells in maternal blood to the possibility of actively preventing sensitization by clearing maternal blood of fetal cells. It seems unlikely, moreover, that a deliberate effort was being made, from the outset, to control Rh hemolytic disease clinically, rather than just study it. The creative move here—Ronnie Finn's— appears to this observer to include, inexorably entwined, the feeling that sensitization somehow *could* be prevented, and the idea that destroying foreign red cells in the mother's blood was *how* it could be done.

Finn would later say that he came to his proposal in two steps: *First*, give the mothers a "suitable antibody" to destroy the intruding fetal red cells. *Second*, find that suitable antibody. His initial choice, he said later, had been antifetal hemoglobin. Clarke never explicitly credits Finn with the first, and more original step, but he does not ever explicitly credit Mrs. Clarke with it either. So Finn's claim to his first creative step has not been specifically challenged.

In Clarke's account, his wife is credited only with having picked *which* antibody to use—step two. Possibly, she did. Finn says he did. Sheppard credits neither the one nor the other, but rather Clarke himself, from whom he first heard the idea. This leaves McConnell as the sole remaining knowledgeable contemporary. He gives the nod to Finn, and it is perhaps noteworthy that the *Annual Review of Medicine* article, in which he commits himself to print with this view, was written in 1965—before the problem of credit had become visible as a controversy in Liverpool.[28] The present author finds most credible McConnell's assessment favoring Ronnie Finn as author of both steps of the creative process which first marked the beginning of the end for the menace of Rh hemolytic disease.

* An interpretation that I owe *my* wife, Veva.—D.R.Z.

# 32

## Last Words

CREATIVE THINKING is required for research progress. But, as Bill Pollack insists, research is not ideas alone. Experimental data are needed. And drive: a will and an ability to achieve. Plus a setting in which achievement is possible.

Painful proof of this appeared just after the Rh vaccine was licensed. A practicing pediatrician in Windsor, Ontario, in Canada, Dr. Edward Winbaum, surfaced with an abashed acknowledgement: Substantially before Vince, John, and Ronnie Finn, he had conceived of an Rh vaccine—and had failed to pursue it.[1]

Winbaum had been called one day in 1956 to minister to children who had been exposed to measles. He gave each child the standard protective injection: "anti-measles serum," that is, serum from a recent measles patient, which is rich in anti-measles antibody. This passive antibody injection, it was believed, might help protect the exposed youngsters from attacks by the measles virus (antigen), thereby preventing the disease and, incidentally, preventing the children from becoming actively immunized against it.

Late that night, Winbaum was summoned to the hospital to treat a newborn erythroblastic baby. Tired and irritated at having been called out of bed, his brain feverishly churned up the day's events. "In my mind," he says, "anti-measles serum was transposed to anti-Rh serum—and I became very excited!

317

"The thought of using anti-Rh antiserum during pregnancy [to prevent Rh sensitization] occurred to me, but was quickly dropped for obvious reasons. Then the thought occurred of using anti-Rh immediately after the cord was tied." The antibody would "neutralize" the sensitizing Rh-positive fetal red cells. Winbaum, like Nevanlinna before him, and Vince and Ronnie Finn later, reasoned, correctly, that if the first pregnancy is protected, then sensitization must occur after delivery.

"By now I became very enthused with the idea, and in my mind worked out steps that might be taken to prove or disprove its effectiveness . . . using male prisoners initially. . . .

"I must admit it was quite a while before I could fall asleep."

What was to be done? Winbaum tried to peddle his idea to the blood establishment, as John and Vince later also would do. He wrote Chown, whom he says never replied, and to one of Fred Allen's colleagues in Boston, Dr. Sidney Gellis, who showed his letter to Allen.

Only Gellis replied favorably, saying, in a letter that remains extant: "To the best of my knowledge no one has ever tried to passively immunize an Rh-negative mother with anti-Rh [antibody] given immediately after birth.

"It would probably work, and is a good suggestion. To prove its efficacy would be a bit of work. . . . Dr. Allen and I both will be glad to offer advice or help should you wish to try it out. I asked Dr. Allen why he wouldn't try it himself, and he answered that he has so many projects going that he has no time at present. He admitted that several of these are not as worthwhile as the one you have suggested."[2]

Winbaum dropped the project.

"I did not pursue it further because of the logistics involved in a busy pediatrician attempting to do this, singlehanded, with no staff nor laboratory available to follow it up and through," he says. "Also, the time involved in a lone individual obtaining enough cases to be convincing seemed to me to be insurmountable."

Winbaum had idea enough to have succeeded, and did not. John Gorman reached the same idea in conjunction with Vince, a doer, and Bill, who was able, willing, and equipped to achieve. Ronnie Finn, who had conceived essentially the same idea, had the rare good fortune of working under a chief willing to pursue an idea far outside his given province of internal medicine, gambling heavily on it with time, team talent, and his own reputation. They triumphed, where Winbaum, who had been unable to translate thought into action, failed. Says Allen, who had also failed to act on the idea: "In medicine, it isn't the guy who says you ought to do such and such, but the guy who *does* it who gets the credit!" His own long-lingering doubts now are firmly resolved. Of Liverpool and New York, he says: "Nobody believed their early reports. They were too fantastic!"

At the end of the saga, Louis Diamond finds special cause for exultation. "Rarely," he says, "has it been our good fortune to have a disease recognized, its cause clearly determined, its treatment successfully developed to a great extent, and then its prevention found—all in one generation."[3] So rapid has been the conquest that everyone who played an important role in it remains alive at the end to exult with Diamond—all, save one.

Only Ruth Darrow is dead. She died in 1956, the year that her only son, Alan—whose birthday she had observed each year—would have attained his manhood. Darrow's youngest daughter, Gail, is an attractive, engaging young woman of thirty-one; she has recently wed. Gail is completely healthy and shows no sign of her ordeal at birth except for two tiny scars over blood vessels where her mother had had simultaneously removed and infused the unusually large measures of blood that well may have been the margin of her survival.

John Ferguson, after forty years, still remembers his discovery that erythroblastosis is one disease as his most exciting research achievement. He no longer works as a pathologist, but instead practices geriatric psychiatry at Delaware State Hospital in Newcastle, where he makes his home.

Louis Diamond is now past the mandatory retirement age in Massachusetts, and has retired from Children's Hospital in Boston, where his heart remains, to the University of California's San Francisco Medical Center. He has set up a hematology research unit there. He pursues his studies in anemia, which led him originally to erythroblastosis.

Chicago immunologist Kurt Stern who, at Joliet prison, had showed that anti-Rh antibody would inhibit Rh sensitization—but who then failed to appreciate what he had shown—is retired in Israel, where he continues his research, at Bar-Ilan University in Ramat-Gan. In 1972, twelve years after he reported this result to the AABB, that organization honored him, with an award and a cash prize, for his Rh research and other fundamental discoveries. Asked how he could have come so close and yet missed the import of his own experiments, Stern laughed and replied: "The human brain, including that of the research worker, does not always think things out in a logical way." Stern, a gentleman, has staked no retroactive claims. What had been his feelings upon learning what others had made out of experiments very much like his own? "I had no misgivings at all," he says. "I wished them the best of luck!"

As chief of the Red Cross blood program, Nevanlinna, of Helsinki, has made Finland the first country in the world to protect every eligible woman with the vaccine based on his elucidation of ABO "protection." Full coverage began in May 1969.

Bevis, who in Manchester had invented amniotic diagnosis, has moved to Sheffield where he actively promotes the Rh vaccine program which, he hopes, will "put out of business" both amniocentesis and intrauterine transfusion. He says: "It's a bit medieval, don't you think, sticking needles into the fetus?" His comment may be just a bit disingenuous, given his current research interest. Bevis is trying to develop the so-called "test tube baby" technique—in which an ovum, removed surgically from a mother's body, would be fertilized in a laboratory dish and then returned to her womb

Dr. Stern (left) is honored for key discoveries on ABO-Rh interaction. American Association of Blood Bank President, Dr. William Battaile presents award at 1972 annual meeting. Said Stern afterward: "I am honest enough to admit my satisfaction on having been given 'official' recognition by my peers. And I was deeply moved by the sincere good wishes expressed by colleagues." (*Courtesy AABB.*)

several days later as a developing conceptus. The aim is to circumvent infertility due to blockage of a woman's fallopian tubes.

Ortho's man of iron, Heron Singher, who drove *RhoGAM* through to commercial success, was stricken by a stroke several months after the vaccine went on the market. He has not fully recovered, and has retired.

Hans Hager, Bill's young co-worker and confidant at Ortho, has followed in his mentor's footsteps. He has earned his Ph.D.; his thesis project was the animal experiments confirming the efficacy of *AMIS*. Hager is now Director of Diagnostic Immunochemistry at a major drug company not far from Ortho. It is solid, professional, well-paid work, but it leaves him occasionally nostalgic. He misses the enthusiastic, idealistic sense of achievement that he feels "fortunate" to have experienced, as an apprentice working with Bill on a project that "will save more lives than a hundred physicians will save in their lifetimes." Paraphrasing the late President John F. Kennedy, Hager says: "It may sound trite, but you've got to say: What can you do for the human race if you have the opportunity? If you *have* the opportunity to do something really worthwhile, you should be very thankful!"

In London, Race and Sanger have brought out a new, Fifth, Edition of their blood bible, *Blood Groups in Man*. In it, they delete, for the first time, the chapter, "Blood Groups and Disease," in which Race first stated his ABO protection theory—the main spur to Ronnie Finn's thinking. "We cut out the chapter because, except for Rh, we felt we weren't really competent to talk about disease, and we were beginning to feel less competent about Rh," Race modestly says. Soliciting no credit for themselves, in a sentence they refer readers interested in Rh prevention to the reports of Liverpool's "brilliant" achievement.[4]

In Detroit, Wolf Zuelzer stands by his original judgments. Recalling Vince's first, rejected grant application, which he reviewed, Zuelzer concedes that "NIH sometimes misses the boat. But," he adds, "if I had it to do all over again today, with the same grant and an equivalent situation, I'd make the same recommendations."

Zuelzer's co-worker, Flossie Cohen, perhaps more than anyone else, still is torn: She knows the Rh vaccine works. But her studies show that it shouldn't. She finds its success hard to believe.

Having fallen on lean times, the NIH now trumpets the Rh vaccine as an example of how federal support of basic research pays enormous dividends in health care! Asked how NIH can claim credit for work it refused to finance, an NIH booster justifies this claim on grounds that the Institutes supported Stern's work at Joliet prison during the 1950s![5, 6]

In New York City, the Health Research Council, which was first to support John and Vince—and provided them with $329,765 over a decade—barely survives budget-cutting operations.[7, 8, 9]

At the opposite end of the earth, in New Zealand, intrauterine therapy innovator Bill Liley continues his research on pregnancy and the prenatal patient, whom he discovered. A doctor-patient relationship has emerged. "We've built up a very good view of the baby in utero," he says. "They suck their thumbs. They have hiccups. They will jump when we hit them with a needle.

"By the time we've seen one in outline by opacifying the fluid around it; done a test of its fluid; pricked it and felt it hop at the end of the needle—then we're no strangers to that baby. We know it very well indeed. It's as much a patient to us as if it were lying in an incubator or on a cot. It so happens, it has its mother wrapped around it—instead of a blanket!"

John Gorman's brother and sister-in-law, Frank and Kath Gorman, have returned home to Australia, where they now have six Rh-positive children—all protected by Rh vaccine. Kath remains unsensitized to the Rh factor. "It came up afterwards," she says, "that anybody who produces a new thing like the Rh vaccine has to be willing and agreeable to let it be tested on a member of the immediate family. I didn't know then that I would be the guinea pig." Now, she and Frank are more than pleased that she was.

In St. Louis, do-it-yourself immunologist Dr. Eugene Hamilton has not yet switched to *RhoGAM*. His results continue to be excellent.

Ortho, having sold its first one million doses in a noncompetitive United States market, is now competing for Rh vaccine sales. By mid-1972, licenses had been granted to Cutter Laboratories, Inc., for *HypRho-D*, and Dow Chemical Co. for *Gamulin Rh*. Both products are comparable to Ortho's *RhoGAM* and are marketed at comparable prices. Lederele Laboratories' similar *Rho-Imune* was approved December 6, 1972. Also licensed, in 1971, was a vaccine produced by the Commonwealth of Massachusetts, one of only two states with fractionation facilities of its own. Massachusetts is providing the Rh vaccine to every Massachusetts mother in whom it is medically indicated, *free of charge*. Unpaid plasma donors provide the raw material. Massachusetts estimates its production cost (1971) at $6 a dose.

Most of the Sing Sing volunteers have been released, and each man has received from Vince a "diploma," tendered in recognition of his being "a special kind of man with a special kind of courage"—a man who is "willing to chance the unknowns of a medical research study in the hope that his efforts will benefit others." A few of the men who became immunized to the Rh factor during the Sing Sing trials now earn $50 or so each week selling their plasma for vaccine production.

Philip Levine and Alexander Wiener still have not received Nobel honors that many feel they richly deserve. They have waited longer after the Rh discoveries than their mentor, Karl Landsteiner, waited from the time he discovered the ABO blood groups until he got his Nobel Prize in 1930. Wiener, who has now reached the retirement age of 65, continues his serologic labors and research for the New York City Medical Examiner, and his private practice, while carrying on the struggle against "blood group mythologists" Race and Sanger and others whom he feels would misrepresent truth and deny him just remembrance. His many scientific achievements seem not to have brought him peace of mind.

Levine, who is now getting to be quite old, still goes to his lab at Ortho. With his wife, Hilda, he continues to attend important blood congresses at near and far ends of the earth, where he is welcomed as an honored guest and world authority on Rh. More and more he can see developments in both Liverpool and New York as having stemmed directly from his own ABO researches and from the encouragement and support he and Ortho lent to the venture. A bit ruefully, perhaps, he marvels at how close he himself had come to a solution to the problem of erythroblastosis on the very day he first isolated its cause: "Little did I think, in 1941, when I was discovering anti-Rh in the serum of most mothers of babies with hemolytic disease, that this antibody, this agent that was causing the disease, was the one substance also capable of preventing it."[10]

Among the principals, Bill Pollack and Cyril Clarke have been the most substantially rewarded. Clarke, who was *the* professor of his department and chief of Britain's largest institute for medical genetics, now is reaching retirement age—he is now professor *Emeritus* at Liverpool. He recently became foremost among his internist peers when they chose him to be President of the Royal College of Physicians for a term of office that he completes this year (1973). At home, on his suburban Birkenhead estate high over the Irish Sea, in two greenhouses, Clarke and his wife, Féo, and geneticist Philip Sheppard continue to breed—and study—the elegant swallowtail butterflies that first brought them together in fruitful endeavor.

Assessing the elements of their success, Clarke credits his choice of friends and the willingness of the Liverpool group to pursue an idea that was far outside their everyday purview. "I don't think all research has to be very high-powered," he says. "There's a lot to be learned by using your eyes and your intelligence."

"It does seem surprising," Clarke remarks, in another context, "that it has taken until the 1960s to produce such a basically childlike idea for the prevention of Rh hemolytic disease, particularly since work on the suppression of immunization by passively administered antibody was going on in animals. Perhaps it is that, because the 'establishment' frowns on dilettantism, we are frightened of leaving our watertight compartments, and yet there is a lot to be gained by exposing one's ignorance in other disciplines."[11]

What remains of the Rh vaccine research in Liverpool is being conducted by doughty John Woodrow, with Richard McConnell's help. McConnell especially savors the prize of their success for its having fallen not to research specialists, who pooh-poohed their ideas, but to amateurs—"lunchtime immunologists"—who spend most of their time treating runny noses and backaches.

Bill Pollack, like Cyril Clarke, is doing well in the world. He is now Vice President and Director of Diagnostics Research at Ortho and a member of the board of directors. In his demeanor there begins to be seen a confident sense of command that suggests that he is enjoying the rewards of corporate achievement. Bill affects disdain for the Rh vaccine, which he scoffs at as oddball immunology scarcely worthy of a professional immunologist's attention. "Vince thinks this is the best work he's ever done," Bill says. "But I don't consider it that—it's not to me. I'm not proud of it as an immunologist." Bill is presently attacking, with the full strength of his powerful mind, what he considers to be a far greater challenge—the immunology of cancer.

Neither Vince, John, nor Ronnie Finn has reaped capital or titular reward for his effort. In New York, in fact, officialdom at the Columbia-Presbyterian Medical Center has at times shown itself less than pleased by the publicity John and Vince received for their achievements.

Ronnie Finn, in Liverpool, has almost completely severed his ties to the university and its medical genetics institute, whose existence he helped make possible. His clinical practice is mostly at outlying hospitals. His research interest is artificial organs, transplantation, and the immunologic roadblocks that stand in their way.

In the dream chambers of his mind, Finn quietly pursues the observation, made earlier by Bill Pollack and others, that the Rh vaccine works *after* delivery because pregnancy decreases a woman's ability to respond to a new immunologic challenge, her fetus.

"The mechanism of this tolerance is quite unknown," Finn says. "But it's too good to be left at rhesus disease.

"Does the fetus transmit some tolerance-producing chemical into the mother? I would like to speculate that the solution to this problem may well suggest new approaches to human organ grafting. I would, indeed, predict that somewhere in this area is the clue to the discovery of the 'penicillin'—the wonder drug—of transplantation."

In New York, it is proving to be more difficult for John and Vince to graduate and separate themselves from the "Rh college." So *much* has been achieved that they find it hard to experience the achievement as theirs—and so enjoy it.

John, who has been appointed Clinical Professor of Pathology at Columbia, still lives suspended between the certainty of his ideas, racing far out in front of all facts, and nagging doubts that he fears, even now, will capsize those ideas, hopes, and even reality into ignominious disaster. Before they had injected a single test dose into a male volunteer, he was convinced—by Stern's uncomprehending inability, in 1961, to induce immunity in Rh-negative men injected with anti-Rh antibody and Rh-positive cells—that their *idea* would succeed. But when it was the *reality* of success with which he had to grapple, doubt and depression gained the upper hand. "I had a fear all along that the whole thing would just crash," he says. "The plug would be pulled, and it wouldn't work— the idea, the results were too good to be true."

Even after *RhoGAM* had been used clinically in tens of thousands of women, John still worried obsessively that the commercial lots of vaccine would lose the magic of Bill's experimental batches —and the whole thing would fail. Calculating that a significant number of these women would be into their second, presumably protected, pregnancies by 1970, John vowed: "If, by then, there is not any increase in failures, I'll finally feel safe."

Even now, with that date passed and no sign of danger, he is still trying to extricate himself from Rh by writing a book, which will not get finished, and—fortunately for the present record—by reliving the past decade's events in order finally to be relieved of them. Among his current endeavors is an attempt to come to grips with the problem of routine work in the blood bank, which he abhors, by developing a computer program that will operate blood banks.

John is also trying to elucidate the creative process in medical research. He sees an informative example in Levine's recognition that he had held the ultimate solution to Rh disease in his hand in 1940 when he first identified a test tube of anti-Rh antiserum as the disease's cause. Yet two decades were to pass before anyone realized that the cause might also be the cure.*

John feels that the key to more rapid advance is the confident belief—he says "knowledge"—that at any given moment there already exists in what is known and reported in the literature the outline of another "goody" awaiting recognition. There is no need for new laboratory research to find it, John says. "It's already out there, ahead of current knowledge, if you just cast your ideas out beyond what is known, to reach it."

John has been more successful than Vince in accepting Liverpool's priority, and has been heard to say: "Ronnie Finn invented the Rh vaccine." Vince, like his mentor, Wiener—whose Rh research he has helped cap with success—finds it hard to enjoy a success that he must share, across the water. In moments of agitation, when he rails against Liverpool and "Clarke's butterflies," his mood is hauntingly reminiscent of Wiener's railings against Race, Sanger, and Philip Levine.

"Vince shouts across the Atlantic," remarks John Robertson of Edinburgh, who maintains good relations with both sides. "Liverpool," he adds, "ignores what's going on in New York."

Vince forgets his disappointment by keeping inordinately busy—delivering babies and managing difficult Rh cases. In 1969 he relinquished directorship of his Rh clinic, but he continues to do amniotic "taps," intrauterine transfusions—and, alone among its inventors, regularly injects women with Rh vaccine.

He is continuing both his research and his teaching at Columbia,

---

* Levine said later that the key piece of information, which he lacked, was the "apparently correct interpretation" that the immunizing bleed occurred "during labor and the separation of the placenta."[12] This could have been deduced in 1940s from the then-known fact that first pregnancies are spared. Wiener once made the correct deduction as did Chicagoan Edith Potter.

and at the same time is setting up a private obstetrics practice across the Hudson near his home in northern New Jersey.

In the tiny laboratory where he and John held their earliest talks, Vince has added, alongside the autographed and inscribed photograph of Alexander S. Wiener, an inscribed, autographed photograph of the other great pillar of Rh, who long doubted the merit of his Rh vaccine proposal—Philip Levine.

Vince, like John, searches in memory for an experiential handle with which to reach and relive, for himself, what he has done. Intuitively, he has fixed on an anecdotal, evocative approach to the experience as a whole. His touchstone is the transformation of a tiny, impressionistic detail of their adventure into Established Writ.

All over the world, Vince says, obstetrics experts, and others, now declare authoritatively that "the anti-Rh injection must be given within 72 hours postpartum," and some specifically warn: "Do not administer it later than 72 hours after delivery."[13]

There is no evidence to show that the injection is not as effective in the second 72-hour period postpartum as in the first, and there is certainly no reason at all to think that given at, say, 96 hours postpartum, it would be a hazard.

The 72-hour—three-days—specification that appears on the *RhoGAM* label was arrived at, many years ago, half in deadly earnest, half in jest, during an early phase of the Sing Sing trials. John and Vince had both had fantasies and fears that their presence in the prison, on repeated occasions, might involve them in a prison break as hostages or foils.

Warden Denno at one point confirmed their fears, suggesting, Vince says, that they not appear at the prison gates too regularly, at short intervals of only 24 hours. So John suggested that they give the men the red cells first, then return *two days* later to inject the protective antibody. "Let's go whole hog," Vince, with gambler's largesse, had said: "Let's wait *three* days—72 hours."

And so "72 hours" was casually set. Since this was the interval reported from the trials at Sing Sing, it came to be decreed, for women, as *the* permissible interval between antigen exposure and antibody protection. Perhaps it is not strange that when Vince and John get together, which occurs less frequently these days, it is this relatively insignificant but personal reminiscence, rather than the cosmic fact of a disease defeated and untold tragedies averted, that gives them pause to chuckle.

# Notes

Abbreviations of medical journal titles are based on the *Index Medicus* of the National Library of Medicine, Bethesda, Maryland. The reference form is also based on *Index Medicus*; additional data—for the most part the month or calendar date of publication—are included where they are germane to the narrative. Senior authors' first names are given when they do not appear in the text.

## CHAPTER 1: BITTER BEGINNINGS

1. No full biography of Landsteiner has been written. A start toward one was made by the late Dr. George Mackenzie, who completed a rough draft of several chapters before his death. This manuscript is now (1972) held by the American Philosophical Society, Philadelphia, and may be consulted only by permission of Landsteiner's son, Dr. Ernest Landsteiner—who forbids it to be published, according to the Society's Executive Director, Dr. George Corner. Mackenzie's enormous collection of source material, the "Landsteiner-Mackenzie Papers," may be consulted at the Society's library.
   Dr. Corner has written a brief sketch of Landsteiner's later years in his *A History of the Rockefeller Institute* (New York: Rockefeller Institute, 1964, pp. 201–208). The fullest—and warmest—précis of his life is an obituary by a close and admiring colleague at Rockefeller, Nobelist Dr. Peyton Rous, in *Obituary Notices of Fellows of the Royal Society* 5:295–324, 1947. Several reminiscences by Landsteiner's disciples also have proved helpful in preparing the present account: Levine, P., *A Review of Landsteiner's Contribution to the Human Blood Groups*, Raritan, N. J.: Ortho, 1960, 23 pp. (Text of an address to the thirteenth annual meeting of the American Association of Blood Banks, San Francisco, August 23, 1960). Also: Wiener, A., *Current Medical Digest* 18:1–8, Aug., 1951; Wiener, A. (as told to J. D. Ratcliff), *Reader's Digest* (British Edition), May 1968, pp. 93–100; and Wiener, A., *N.Y. J. Med.* 69:2915–2935, 1969.

2. The Nobel Foundation does not reveal losers' names, and scientists are reluctant to be quoted about what they have heard, for fear of jinxing their own or others' chances. Nevertheless, five colleagues, from three nations have, unasked, volunteered the information that Wiener and Levine were jointly nominated for the prize. One colleague also said that he had been interviewed in connection with the nomination by a representative of the Nobel Committee for Medicine. Another, a Scandinavian, maintained close relations with the obstetrics department at the Royal Caroline Institute, which is responsible for selecting the winners. The five colleagues concur that Wiener and Levine's quarrel compromised their chance of winning. The nomination and the alleged contributory reason for its failure have been confirmed for the author by one of the principals. Family friends know the other as "the doctor who was nominated for the Nobel Prize."

3. Wiener, A., *op. cit.*, 1968.
4. Levine, P., *op. cit.*, 1960.

5. William Boyd to G. Mackenzie, December 18, 1943, "Landsteiner-Mackenzie Papers," *op. cit.*
6. Furth's views are cited because of his close association with Levine. His assessment of Landsteiner's temperament and personality is confirmed by many contributors to the "Landsteiner-Mackenzie Papers" at the American Philosophical Society Library. See Note 1.
7. Wiener, A., *op. cit.*, 1968.
8. Wiener, A., *op. cit.*, 1951. Wiener cherishes this account of the genesis of his relationship with Landsteiner, and retells it often. But he does not often mention that the telephone summons came from Levine. He omits it in the *Reader's Digest* but includes it here because this account reproduces comments Wiener made when he and Levine shared the platform when they were given Passano Awards for medical research in June 1951.
9. Arthur Coca, quoted in a memorandum by G. Mackenzie of conversation with Coca, November 21, 1946, "Landsteiner-Mackenzie Papers," *op. cit.*
10. *New York Daily News*, April 5, 1937, p. 4.
11. Quoted in Ramsey, Judy, *Medical World News*, October 1, 1965, pp. 63–70.
12. P. Levine to G. Mackenzie, October 12, 1944, "Landsteiner-Mackenzie Papers," *op. cit.*
13. Levine, P., *op. cit.*, 1960.
14. Landsteiner, K., and Wiener, A., *Proc. Soc. Exp. Biol. Med.* 43:223, January 1940.

CHAPTER 2: BAD BLOOD AND SICK BABIES

1. Hippocrates, cited by Ballantyne, J. W., *The Diseases and Deformities of the Foetus.* Edinburgh: Oliver and Boyd, 1892, Vol. 1.
2. Clifford, S., and Hertig, A., *New Eng. J. Med.* 207: 105–110, July 21, 1932.
3. *Ibid.*
4. Sacks, Milton, "Hemolytic Disease of the Fetus and Newborn." In: Eastman, Nicholson, *Obstetrics* (11th Ed.). New York: Appleton-Century-Crofts, 1956, p. 1058.
5. Ferguson, J., *Amer. J. Path.* 7: 277–297, May 1931.
6. *Ibid.*
7. *Ibid.*
8. Blackfan, K., *New Eng. J. Med.* 207: 111–112, July 21, 1932.
9. Diamond, L., Blackfan, K., and Baty, J., *J. Pediat.* 1: 269–309, September 1932.
10. Clifford, S., and Hertig, A., *op. cit.*
11. Diamond, L., Blackfan, K., and Baty, J., *op. cit.*
12. See Allen, F., and Diamond, L., *Erythroblastosis Fetalis.* Boston: Little, Brown [No date; 8th printing; Copyright 1957]. Chapter 2 (Historical Review).
13. See Diamond, L., *Pediatrics 41*: 1–4, 1968.
14. Diamond, L., Blackfan, K., and Baty, J., *op. cit.*
15. Darrow, R., and Chapin, J., *Amer. J. Dis. Child.* 73:257–278, 1957. Darrow provided a full report on Alan for the medical literature in this paper; he is Case 1 in Family "D."
16. R. Darrow to Clifford Grulee, June 1, 1946 [Draft].

17. Darrow's work is reviewed in a special number of the *Journal of the American Medical Women's Association*, Vol. 12, No. 8, August 1957.
18. Darrow, R., *Arch. Path.* 25:378–417, March 1938.
19. *Ibid.*
20. *Ibid.*
21. *Ibid.*
22. *Ibid.*
23. *Ibid.*
24. Joseph Brennemann to Herman Bundesen, May 20, 1938.

CHAPTER 3: MOTHERS AND DOCTORS

1. Anon., *25 Years of Service*. New York: Blood Transfusion Association [No date; no pagination].
2. Levine, P., and Stetson, R., *JAMA* 113:126–127, July 8, 1939.
3. Landsteiner, K., and Wiener, A., *Proc. Soc. Exp. Biol. Med.* 43:223, January 1940.
4. Wiener, A., and Peters, H., *Ann. Intern. Med.* 13:2306–2322, June 1940. This paper is the source for the four following paragraphs.
5. Burnham, L., *Amer. J. Obstet. Gynec.* 42:389–397, 1941.
6. Levine, P., Katzin, E., and Burnham, L., *Proc. Soc. Exp. Biol. Med.* 45:346–348, October 1940.
7. Levine, P., Katzin, E., and Burnham, L., *JAMA* 116:825–827, March 1, 1941.
8. Levine, P., and Katzin, E., *Proc. Soc. Exp. Biol. Med.* 45:343–346, October 1940.
9. Levine, P., Katzin, E., and Burnham, L., *JAMA*, *op. cit.* Cf. Addendum.
10. Burnham, *op. cit.*
11. Darrow, R., and Chapin, J., *Amer. J. Dis. Child.* 73:257–278, 1947. The birth of this child, and subsequent events, are described as Case 6, Family "D." This paper is deceptive in inferring that Darrow knew her blood type, and that of her husband and baby, and planned treatment for it accordingly. The fact that she was *misinformed*, and believed herself to be Rh-positive— so that Rh incompatibility could not figure in her family's difficulty—is to be found in the manuscript of this paper, which now (1972) is in the possession of Dr. Irene Shmigelsky of Chicago. It includes the following passage, which is crossed out in pencil, and does not appear in the paper as it was published in 1947: "In 1944, the mother's Rh status *which had been reported as Rh-positive* was reinvestigated by Dr. I[srael] Davidsohn of Chicago. She was found Rh-negative with all anti-Rh serums (humans) employed." (Emphasis added.) A colleague, Dr. Clementine Frankowski, of Whiting, Indiana, confirms that Darrow's later proposal to treat erythroblastic babies with desensitizing doses of Rh-positive blood in part grew out of her retrospective analysis of this case. Frankowski says that Darrow had not then conceived of, and was not attempting to apply, this therapy in the present case.

All quotes that follow in this chapter are from Darrow and Chapin's published report of the case, cited here.

CHAPTER 4: PROGRESS

1. Corner, George, *A History of the Rockefeller Institute.* New York: Rockefeller Institute Press, 1964, p. 208.

2. United States Department of Health, Education and Welfare, Public Health Service, Division of Biologics Standards, *Highlights of Research Progress 1967.* Bethesda: D.B.S. [No date], p. 13. [Offset]

3. Klein, Jerome, RhoGAM Rho (4) immune globulin (human) and Rh disease [News Release]. Raritan, N.J.: Ortho [No date], p. 1. [Mimeo].

4. Klein, Jerome, *The Story of Ortho Pharmaceutical Corporation and Ortho Diagnostics.* Raritan, N.J.: Ortho [No date], p. 3.

5. *New York Times,* July 25, 1971, Section 3.

6. *Ibid.*

7. In a reminiscence that may also pertain to Ortho, the medical vice president of a rival manufacturer, G. D. Searle, Inc., said, a decade later, that when birth control pills were first marketed about 1960, attitudes were "vastly different from those today. Contraception was not a word which was used freely, and use in the lay press was circumspect indeed. No major pharmaceutical manufacturer had ever dared to put its name on a 'contraceptive.' The individual reaction of a very large religious minority . . . could not be gauged. The possibility of losing overnight . . . a considerable portion of our hospital business, and a crippling number of the physician prescribers of our products was not to be dismissed lightly." (Winter, Irwin, *JAMA* 212:1067–1068, 1970.)

8. Wiener staked his claim to *priority of publication*—which may be different from *priority of discovery,* since what is discovered first may not be published first—on the paper he published with Landsteiner in January 1940. Levine stakes his claim on the Mary Seno case, which he and Stetson published in July 1939.

   Part of the controversy turns on whether Levine adequately described a new blood factor in his case report. In the blood bank bible, *Blood Groups in Man,* British serologist Dr. Robert Race and his wife, Dr. Ruth Sanger—who kept cordial relations with Levine, but who were detested by Wiener—said later that "had Levine and Stetson given a name to the blood group system which they had discovered, it, and not Rh, would have been found in the title of . . . a thousand other publications." (Race, R., and Sanger, R., *Blood Groups in Man* [5th Ed.]. Philadelphia: F. A. Davis, 1968, p. 171.) But this Levine had failed to do. To Wiener, for whom naming is an indivisible part of claiming, this disqualifies Levine.

   Wiener later found other faults which he said rendered Mary Seno "irrelevant" to the discovery of the Rh factor. He would brand as "discovery in retrospect" Levine's claim that Rh incompatibility played the decisive role in this case because it was only in 1940, using test serum that Wiener supplied, that Levine and a colleague, Eugene Katzin, attempted to show that this was so. Wiener would say: "It's easy to make a discovery after someone else has done it."

   Wiener stressed that Levine could not positively identify the antibody that killed Mrs. Seno's baby and caused her transfusion reaction as anti-Rh antibody because by the time she was retested in 1940 he could no longer demonstrate its presence in her serum—a fact which Levine later would concede. Wiener said this disqualified any claims based on Mary Seno. (Levine would say that the 19S anti-Rh antibody, which then-available tests could detect, had, normally and naturally, disappeared from her veins, while the 7S, which might have continued to be present would turn out not to be detectable by then-available techniques. Levine adduced as evidence that the instrumental antibody in the Mary Seno case had been anti-Rh antibody the demonstrable facts that: her red cells were Rh-negative; her compatible donors were Rh-negative; her incompatible donors were Rh-positive; and incompatibles and compatibles appeared in her donor pool in the 85-15 ratio that characterizes the division between Rh-positive and Rh-negative individuals in the population.)

Later, Wiener made much of a statement by Levine in 1941 that "in the great majority of [erythroblastosis] cases the blood factor involved has been shown to be either identical with or related to the *Rh (Rhesus) antigen first described by Landsteiner and Wiener*" (Levine, P., *et al.*, Amer. J. Obstet. Gynec. 42:925–937, December 1941). (Wiener's emphasis.)

Wiener further faults Levine for failing to produce a test serum others could use: "He didn't identify—classify—an antibody that others could use in their cases."

Not satisfied to assert his claim while attempting to demolish Levine's claim to prior publication, Wiener tried to establish a priority—or, at least, a parity—of discovery for himself. Levine's report on Mary Seno clearly indicates that he did the critical tests on her blood in 1937, then waited over a year to publish them. Wiener later said of his monkey-rabbit-human blood experiments that led to discovery of the Rh factor: "The findings were made in 1937" (Wiener, A., *New York J. Med.* 69:2915–2935, November 15, 1969, see p. 2921).

Wiener was asked by the author to document this assertion with contemporary lab notes, memoranda, or other documents, some of which he would claim to have saved. He declined to do so. While his lab records or Landsteiner's—which are extant—may one day confirm Wiener's assertion, it can be said that examination of Landsteiner's detailed annual reports to the Rockefeller Institute reveals no reference to discovery of the Rh factor in 1937 or 1938. But in the report dated April 13, 1940, covering the preceding twelve months, Landsteiner wrote: "In collaboration with . . . Wiener it has *now* been found that such [rabbit anti-rhesus] sera may also contain antibodies reacting with an unknown antigen, tentatively designated as Rh, present in human blood in about 80% of individuals." (Emphasis added.) (Landsteiner, K., Annual Report [s] to Rockefeller Institute for 1937, 1938, and 1939 [Mimeo]. "Landsteiner-Mackenzie Papers," American Philosophical Society Library, Philadelphia.) Landsteiner's antiserum production records, which are in the possession of Dr. Merrill Chase of Rockefeller University, show that Landsteiner first injected rhesus monkey red cells into rabbits to make anti-Rh antibody on November 28, 1939. Wiener, on his own, certainly produced anti-Rh antibody and discovered the human Rh factor earlier in 1939. Perhaps he achieved that in 1937, but his failure to adduce any supportive evidence argues against it.

What of Levine? He resisted Wiener's claim from the start, questioning the authenticity of the Landsteiner-Wiener rabbit anti-rhesus serum. This counterattack is foreshadowed even in the statement he made in 1941 that so delighted Wiener: "In the majority of [erythroblastosis] cases the blood factor involved has been shown to be either identical with *or related to* the Rh (Rhesus) antigen first described by Landsteiner and Wiener." (Emphasis added.) (Levine, P., *et al.*, *loc. cit.*)

Levine continued, in 1944: "Soon after the genesis of erythroblastosis was described and potent human anti-Rh antibodies became available (December, 1940), it was observed by Levine and Katzin that [Mary Seno's] blood was negative with anti-Rh serum and that her antibodies were anti-Rh in specificity. Accordingly, it may be stated that Landsteiner and Wiener in 1940 observed an agglutinable factor [antigen] in the blood of rhesus monkeys related to the factor in human blood *previously* described by Levine and Stetson. It is also significant that all subsequent observations which led finally to the description of the genesis of erythroblastosis were made exclusively with anti-Rh serums produced by mothers of affected infants. In contrast to the reactions of the experimental serum of Landsteiner and Wiener . . . human anti-Rh serums give distinct and well defined agglutination, so that there has been no need for the use of the[ir] experimental serum." (Emphasis added.) (Levine, P., *Arch. Path.* 37:83–90, 1944.)

Several years later Levine significantly advanced his counterattack. He announced that he had repeated the original Landsteiner-Wiener experiments in his own lab, and had discovered that what they had found with their rabbit anti-rhesus serum was not the Rh factor, the killer of babies, but another, harmless, tag-along blood factor which had nothing to do with erythroblastosis (Levine, P., *et al.*, *Science* 133:323–333, 1961).

Levine made the gratuitous suggestion that this benign blood factor discovered by Landsteiner and Wiener be renamed, to honor them, the *LW factor*. His analysis and suggestion, which some blood experts have accepted, retains for the deadly blood factor that Levine then would have discovered, in humans, the name Rh—and of course bolsters his claim to have been the first to find it.

The Wiener-Levine quarrel thus ends up a *reductio ad absurdum*.

9. Ramsey, Judy, *Medical World News*, October 1, 1965, pp. 63–70.
10. Allen, F., Diamond, L., and Vaughan, V., *Amer. J. Dis. Child.* 80:779–791, 1950.
11. Vaughan, V., Allen, F., and Diamond, L., *Pediatrics* 6:173–182, 1950.
12. Mollison, Patrick, and Walker, William, *Lancet* 1:429–433, March 1, 1952.
13. Freda, V., *Amer. J. Obstet. Gynec.* 92:341–374, June 1, 1965.

CHAPTER 5: CLUES IN PASSING

1. Unger, L., and Wiener, A., *Amer. J. Clin. Path.* 15:280–285, 1945.
2. Freda, V., *Amer. J. Obstet. Gynec.* 92:341–374, 1965. See Table 2.
3. Fisher, R., *Amer. Sci.* 35:95–102, 113, 1947.
4. *Ibid.*
5. I. M. Jaundiced (pseud.), *Lab. Digest* (St. Louis) October 1954.

6. Diamond, L., *Amer. J. Public Health 38*:645–651, 1948.
7. Levine, P., *J. Hered. 34*:71–80, March 1943.
8. Wiener, A., *Proc. Soc. Exp. Biol., Med. 58*:133–135, 1945.
9. Finn, R., *Brit. Med. J. 1*:1486–1490, May 27, 1961.
10. Unger, L., *Proc. Third Int. Cong. of Int. Soc. of Hemat.* New York: Grune & Stratton, 1951, pp. 190–196.
11. Carter, B., *Amer. J. Clin. Path. 17*:646–649, 1947.
12. Greenwalt, T., *Proc. Third Int. Cong. of Int. Soc. of Hemat., op. cit.,* pp. 197–205.
13. Unger, L., and Wiener, A., *op. cit.*
14. Darrow, R., *JAMA 127*:1146–1147, 1945. (Letter.)
15. The failures are catalogued in Allen, F., *New Eng. J. Med. 269*:1344–1349, 1963.
16. Editorial, *Brit. Med. J. 2*:1481–1482, 1950.
17. Allen, F., and Diamond L., *Erythroblastosis Fetalis.* Boston: Little, Brown [No date; 8th printing; Copyright 1957], p. 8.
18. A. Wiener to V. Freda, January 7, 1957; January 29, 1957; July 18, 1960; October 8, 1960.

CHAPTER 6: YOUTHFUL ALLIANCE

1. The [Melbourne] *Herald,* October 11, 1965.
2. Diamond, L., *Amer. J. Public Health 38*:645–651, 1948.
3. Gorman, John, "Review of Literature: Saline vs. Blocking A[nti] b[ody]," 4/6/60. [Unpublished notebook in the possession of Dr. John Gorman, Presbyterian Hospital, New York.]

CHAPTER 7: DIALOGUE

1. Freda, V., *Amer. J. Obstet. Gynec. 84*:1756–1777, December 1, 1962.
2. This experiment, in the context of the then-current climate of immunologic opinion, is reviewed in Burnet, M., *Sci. Amer. 204*:58–67, 1961.

CHAPTER 8: FIGHT FIRE WITH FIRE

1. Gladstone, G., and Abraham, E., "Biological factors in the production of antibodies," in: Florey, H., *General Pathology* (2nd Ed.), Philadelphia: W. B. Saunders, 1958. P. 703.
2. Smith, T., *J. Exp. Med. 11*:241–256, 1909.

CHAPTER 9: "EGO-PEDDLING"

1. J. G. Gorman to J. S. Gorman, August 16, 1960.
2. H. Taylor to V. Freda, September 20, 1960.
3. Freda, V. [Unsigned], E. F. Antepartum Clinic [outline of plan of operation]. [No date, Unpaged, Mimeo], 6 pages.
4. H. Taylor to V. Freda, January 3, 1961. Acknowledges receipt of "outline of your plans" referred to in Note 3 above.
5. P. Levine to V. Freda, December 5, 1960.
6. J. G. Gorman to J. S. Gorman, October 9, 1960.

7. New York City Department of Health, Health Research Council, *Application for Investigatorship.* John Grant Gorman, February 15, 1961, 8 pp., [Mimeo.].
8. H. Merritt to G. Mirick, February 14, 1961.
9. G. Mirick to J. G. Gorman, March 7, 1961.
10. J. G. Gorman to J. S. Gorman, March 8, 1961.

CHAPTER 10: STERN

1. Race, R. and Sanger R., *Blood Groups in Man* (1st Ed.), Oxford: Blackwell, 1950, p. 235.
2. Stern, K., Davidsohn, I., and Masaitis, L., *Amer. J. Clin. Path. 26*:833–843, 1956.
3. Stern, K., Goodman, H., and Berger, M., *J. Immun. 87*:189–198, August 1961.
4. Stern, K., and Berger, M., "Experimental isosensitization to hemoantigens in man" [Abstract]. *Program, 13th Annual Meeting American Association of Blood Banks*, San Francisco, August 21–26, 1960, p. 39.
5. *Ibid.*
6. Stern, K., Goodman, H., and Berger, M., *op cit.*

CHAPTER 11: NEEDLE IN THE WOMB

1. Vaughan, V., Allen, F., and Diamond, L., *Pediatrics 6*:173–182, 1950.
2. Mollison, P., and Walker, W., *Lancet 1*:429–433, 1952.
3. Armitage, P., and Mollison, P., *J. Obstet. Gynaec. Brit. Comm. 60*:605–618, 1953.
4. Eastman, N., *Obstetrics* (11th Ed.). New York: Appleton-Century-Crofts, 1956, p. 585.
5. Bevis, D., *Lancet 1*:395–398, 1952.
6. Bevis, D., *J. Obstet. Gynaec. Brit. Comm. 63*:68–75, 1956.
7. Walker, A., *J. Obstet. Gynaec. Brit. Comm. 72*:998–1000, 1965.
8. Walker, A., *Brit. Med. J. 2*:376–378, 1957.
9. Editorial, *Lancet 2*:303–304, 1958.
10. Editorial, *Lancet 2*:549–550, 1959.
11. Liley, A., *New Zeal. Med. J. 59*:581–586, December 1960.
12. Liley, A., *Amer. J. Obstet. Gynec. 82*:1359–1370, 1961.
13. *Ibid.*
14. *Ibid.*

CHAPTER 12: TIMING

1. Allen, F., and Diamond, L., *Erythroblastosis Fetalis*, Boston: Little, Brown [No date; 8th printing; Copyright 1957], p. 25.
2. *Ibid.*
3. Unger, L., and Wiener, A., *Amer. J. Clin. Path. 15*:280–285, 1945.
4. Potter, E., *Rh.* Chicago: Yearbook Publishers, 1948, pp. 121–122.
5. Unger, L., and Wiener, A., *op. cit.*

CHAPTER 13: FORWARD MOTION

1. P. Levine to V. Freda, April 4, 1961.
2. Foster Whitlock to V. Freda, May 11, 1961.
3. New York City Department of Health, Health Research Council, *Application for Research Contract*. Principal investigator, Donald McKay; co-investigator, John Gorman, May 10, 1961, 9 pp. [Mimeo]. Subsequently approved as HRC Grant No. U-1154.
4. G. Mirick to members of (grants) review committee, Health Research Council, May 11, 1961.
5. U.S. Department of Health, Education and Welfare, Public Health Service, National Institutes of Health. *Application for Research Grant. Application No. H6754*. Principal investigator, Vincent Freda; co-principal investigator, John Gorman. Signed and dated by V. Freda, May 15, 1961; signed and dated by Houston Merritt, May 26, 1961; original copy marked received at NIH, May 31, 1961. 26 pages [Offset]. Quotes in this and the following four paragraphs are from the grant application.


CHAPTER 14: BUTTERFLIES AND BLOOD

1. Finn, R., *et al.*, *Brit. Med. J.* 1:1486–1490, May 27, 1961.
2. Editorial, *Brit. Med. J.* 1:1519–1520, May 27, 1961.
3. Clarke, C., *Sci. Amer.* 219:46–52, 1968.
4. *Ibid.*
5. Clarke, C., *Brit. Med. J.* 4:7–12, 1967.
6. Clarke, C., and Sheppard, P., *Heredity* (London) 14:175–185, 1960.
7. Sheppard, P., *Amer. Naturalist* 87:283–294, 1953
8. Race, R., and Sanger, R., *Blood Groups in Man* (5th Ed.). Philadelphia: F. A. Davis, 1968, pp. 226–231 *et passim*.


CHAPTER 15: RONNIE FINN

1. Race, R., and Sanger, R., *Blood Groups in Man* (3rd Ed.). Oxford: Blackwell, 1958.
2. Finn, R., "Protective Mechanisms Against Rh Haemolytic Disease." Unpublished M.D. Thesis, Liverpool University, 1961., *Preface*, p. 1.
3. Levine, P., "Lecture to the Columbia University Seminar on Genetics and the Evolution of Man," *circa* 1955. The ABO findings from this talk, the text of which has not come to light, appear in: Levine, P., *Hum. Biol.* 30:14–28, February 1958.
4. Reepmaker, J., "ABO Antagonisme En Morbus Haemolyticus Neo-natorium." Thesis, The University of Leyden, 1955. Cited in: Levine, P., *op. cit.*, 1958.
5. Clarke, C., Finn, R., McConnell, ʀ., and Sheppard, P., *Int. Arch. Allerg.* 13:380, 1958.
6. Nevanlinna, H., *Ann. Med. Exp. Biol. Fenn.* (Suppl. 2) 31:1–80, 1953, p. 9.

7. Nevanlinna, H., and Vainio, T., *Vox Sang.* 1:26–36, 1956. Adapted from Table V.
8. Clarke, C., Finn, R., McConnell, R., and Sheppard, P., *op. cit.*, 1958.
9. Race, R., and Sanger, R., *op. cit.*, 1958, p. 315.


CHAPTER 16: "THEN THE PENNY DROPPED!"

1. Kleihauer, E., Braun, H., and Betke, K., *Klin. Wschr.* 35:637–638, June 15, 1957.
2. Zipursky, A., *et al.*, *Lancet* 1:451–452, February 28, 1959.
3. Finn, R., "Erythroblastosis." Talk delivered to the Liverpool Medical Institution, February 18, 1960, 4 pages [Typescript].
4. Finn, R., *Lancet* 1:526, March 5, 1960.


CHAPTER 17: SURPRISES

1. Finn, R., "Protective Factors in Erythroblastosis." Lecture to British Genetical Society, July 1960, 6 pages [Typescript].
2. Stern, K., and Berger, M., "Experimental isosensitization to hemoantigens in man [Abstract]. *Program, 13th Annual Meeting American Association of Blood Banks*, San Francisco, August 21–26, 1960, p. 39.
3. Stern was not the only one to perform an experiment of this type but miss its importance. Britain's leading expert on blood transfusion, Patrick Mollison, published in 1955 and in 1959, an experiment in which Rh-positive red cells were mixed with anti-Rh antibody and then injected back into the Rh-positive donor (Mollison, P., and Cutbush, M., *Lancet* 1:1290, 1955; Mollison, P., *Brit. Med. J.* 2:1035–1041, November 21, 1959). McConnell was familiar wtih these experiments, and would later recall that at some point he had mentioned them to Finn. Whether they served Finn as inspiration or confirmation is unclear, although the latter seems far more likely. Even if he saw them before reaching his own conclusion, it is clear that the interpretation was his own.
4. Finn, R., "Protective Mechanisms Against Rh Haemolytic Disease," Unpublished M.D. Thesis, Liverpool University, 1961, p. 171.
5. Finn, R., "Recent Thoughts on Rh Haemolytic Disease." Lecture to Columbia University Seminar on Genetics and the Evolution of Man, May 14, 1962, 15 pages [Typescript].
6. Finn, R., Clarke, C., McConnell, R., and Sheppard, P., "Transplacental passage of red cells in man." Letter to *Nature*, dated November 30, 1960, 4 pages [Typescript].
7. Finn, R., Clarke, C., Donohoe, W., McConnell, B., Sheppard, P., and Lehane, D., "Transplacental Passage of Red Cells in Man [letter]," *Nature* 190:922–923, June 3, 1961.
8. Gorman, J., Freda, V., and Pollack, W., "Intramuscular injection of a new experimental gamma$_2$ globulin preparation containing high levels of anti-Rh antibody as a means of preventing sensitization to Rh [Abstract]." *Program, IX Congresso de la Sociedad Internacional de Hematologia*, Mexico, D.F.,

1962. Published in *Proceedings of the International Society of Hematology* (9), New York: Grune & Stratton, 1963, pp. 545–549.

9. Finn, R., *op. cit.* 1962.

10. Finn, R., Clarke, C., McConnell, R., and Sheppard, P., *op. cit.*

11. Finn, R., "Erythroblastosis." Talk to the Liverpool Medical Institution, February 18, 1960, 4 pages [Typescript].

12. Nevanlinna, H., and Vaino, T., *Vox Sang.* 1:26–36, 1956.

13. Finn, R., *op. cit.* 1961, p. 165.

14. Finn, R., Clarke, C., McConnell, R., and Sheppard, P., *op. cit.*

15. Finn, R., Clarke, C., Donohoe, W., McConnell, B., Sheppard, P., and Lehane, D., *op. cit.*

16. Mollison, P., and Cutbush, M., *op. cit.*

17. Mollison, P., *op. cit.*

18. Finn, R., *et al.*, *Brit. Med. J.* 1:1486–1490, May 27, 1961.

19. Editorial, *Brit. Med. J.* 1:1519–1520, May 27, 1961.

20. R. Finn to K. Stern, August 25, 1961.

21. K. Stern to R. Finn, June 22, 1961.

CHAPTER 18: THE ROAD TO SING SING

1. J. G. Gorman to J. S. Gorman, June 25, 1961.

2. New York City Department of Health, Health Research Council, *Application for Research Contract*. Principal investigator, Donald McKay; co-investigator, John Gorman. May 10, 1961. 9 pages [Mimeo].

3. U.S. Department of Health, Education and Welfare, Public Health Service, National Institutes of Health, *Application for Research Grant, No. H. 6754*. Principal Investigator, Vincent Freda; co-principal investigator, John Gorman. Signed and dated by V. Freda, May 15, 1961; signed and dated by Houston Merritt, May 26, 1961; received at NIH, May 31, 1961. 26 pages [Offset].

4. *Ibid.*

5. V. Freda to Richard Rosenfield, August 16, 1961.

6. Uhr, J., and Baumann, J., *J. Exp. Med.* 113:935–957, May 1, 1961.

7. Smith, T., *J. Exp. Med.* 11:241–256, 1909.

8. Freda, V., Draft of an *Addendum* to U.S. Department of Health, Education and Welfare, Public Health Service, National Institutes of Health, *Application for Research Grant No. H. 6754*, *op. cit.*, August 9, 1961 [Typescript].

9. Stern, K., Goodman, H., and Berger, M., *J. Immun.* 87:189–198, August 1961.

10. Uhr, J., in: Uhr, J., and Landy, M. (eds.), *Immunologic Intervention* (Proceedings of an International Conference held at Brook Lodge, Augusta, Mich., April 26–28, 1971), New York: Academic Press, 1971, pp. 3–4.

11. J. G. Gorman to J. S. Gorman, September 2, 1961.

12. V. Freda to W. Denno, September 15, 1961.

13. W. Denno to V. Freda, September 21, 1961.

14. H. Kipp to W. Denno, October 6, 1961.

CHAPTER 19: ROADBLOCK

1. V. Freda to N. Eastman, January 24, 1962.
2. N. Eastman to V. Freda, February 25, 1962.
3. U.S. Department of Health, Education and Welfare, Public Health Service, National Institutes of Health, *Application for Research Grant, No. H6754.* Principal investigator, Vincent Freda; co-principal investigator, John Gorman. Signed and dated by V. Freda, May 15, 1961; signed and dated by Houston Merritt, May 26, 1961; received at NIH, May 31, 1961, 28 pages [Offset].
4. Zuelzer, W., "Report to Seventh M. & R. Pediatric Research Conference," Boston, November 21–22, 1952. In: Allen, F. (ed.), *Erythroblastosis Fetalis* (Report of the 7th M. & R. Conference). Columbus, Ohio: M. & R. Laboratories, 1954, p. 18.
5. Cohen, F., Zuelzer, W., and Evans, M., *Blood 15*:884–900, June 1960.
6. Uhr, J., and Baumann, J., *J. Exp. Med. 113*:935–957, 1961.
7. As dictated by Wolf Zuelzer to the author from official documents in his possession. Detroit, July 17, 1969.
8. *Ibid.*
9. *New York Times*, February 28, 1971.
10. Berendes, H., and Weiss, W., "The NIH Collaborative Study—A Progress Report." Paper presented to the Third International Conference on Congenital Malformations, The Hague, the Netherlands, September 7–13, 1969, 10 pages [Mimeo].
11. *Ibid.*
12. H. Berendes to author, August 13, 1970.

CHAPTER 20: FINN IN AMERICA

1. J. Krevans to V. McKusick, May 25, 1961.
2. Gorman, J., and Chandler, J., *Blood 23*:117–128, 1964.
3. J. G. Gorman to J. S. Gorman, November 8, 1961.
4. W. Pollack to V. Freda, November 29, 1961.
5. Freda, V., "Rh studies." Unpublished research notebook, entry dated December 19, 1961.
6. A. Wiener to Health Research Council of New York City Department of Health, January 27, 1962.
7. A. Wiener to V. Freda, February 12, 1962.
8. New York City Department of Health, Health Research Council. [Grants] review committee. Minutes, 1962.
9. *Columbia-Presbyterian Medical Center, Annual Report 1961.* New York: Columbia-Presbyterian Medical Center, 1962, p. 84.
10. W. Pollack to J. Gorman, February 13, 1962.
11. Cohen, C., and Allton, W., *Nature 193*:990–991, March 10, 1962.
12. Finn, R., *et al., Nature 193*:991–992, March 10, 1962.
13. James King to R. Finn, March 26, 1962.
14. J. Schneider to P. Levine, March 1, 1962.
15. P. Levine to J. Schneider, April 3, 1962.
16. *New York Post*, April 14, 1964.

17. A. Wiener to V. Freda, May 3, 1962.
18. Finn, R., "Recent Thoughts on Rh Hemolytic Disease." Lecture to the Columbia University Seminar on Genetics and the Evolution of Man, May 14, 1962, 15 pages [Typescript].
19. J. G. Gorman to R. Finn, June 6, 1962.
20. J. G. Gorman to J. S. Gorman, June 3, 1962.
21. J. G. Gorman to J. S. Gorman, June 17, 1962.


CHAPTER 21: SING SING


1. R. Finn to V. Freda and J. Gorman, June 23, 1962.
2. Gorman, J., Freda, V., and Pollack, W., "Intramuscular injection of new experimental gamma$_2$ globulin preparation containing high levels of anti-Rh antibody as means of preventing sensitization to Rh [Abstract]." *Program, IX Congresso de la Sociedad Internanacional de Hematologia*, Mexico, D.F., 1962. Published in: *Proc. of Int. Soc. of Hemat.* (9), Vol. 2. Mexico: University of Mexico, 1964, pp. 545–549.
3. Finn, R., *Lancet* 1:526, March 5, 1960.
4. Finn, R., "Protective Factors in Erythroblastosis." Lecture to the British Genetical Society, July 1960, 6 pages [Typescript].
5. *Proc. of Int. Soc. of Hemat., op. cit.*
6. Freda, V., and Gorman, J., *Bull. of the Sloane Hosp. for Women* 8:147–158, December 1962.
7. Finn, R., *Lancet, op. cit.*
8. Finn, R., *et al., Brit. Med. J.* 1:1486–1490, May 27, 1961.
9. Finn, R., *et al., Nature* 190:922–923, June 3, 1961.
10. Freda, V., and Gorman, J., *op. cit.*
11. J. G. Gorman to J. S. Gorman, February 17, 1963.
12. W. Denno to V. Freda, 1963.
13. Clarke, C., *et al., Brit. Med. J.* 1:979–984, April 13, 1963.
14. *Ibid.*
15. V. Freda to G. Mirick, April 11, 1963.
16. *New York Times*, April 18, 1963.
17. Associated Press dispatch, *Sacramento [Cal.] Bee*, April 18, 1963.
18. *Medical Tribune* [New York], April 29, 1963.
19. A. Ostwald to V. Freda, April 29, 1963.
20. V. Freda to A. Ostwald, May 7, 1963.
21. Allen, F., "Attempts at Prevention of Intrauterine Death in Erythroblastosis Fetalis." Tenth John G. Gibson II Lecture at the Columbia-Presbyterian Medical Center, April 25, 1963. Published as: Allen, F., *New Eng. J. Med.* 269:1344–1349, December 19, 1963.
22. Cited in V. Freda to T. Greenwalt, August 16, 1963.
23. Freda, V., Gorman, J., and Pollack, W., *Transfusion* 4:26–32; January-February 1964.
24. Cohen, F., Zuelzer, W., *et al., Blood* 23:621–646, May 1964.
25. *Ibid.*
26. *Ibid.*

27. H. Singher to V. Freda, February 25, 1963.
28. V. Freda to H. Singher, June 13, 1962.

CHAPTER 22: HEROIC HELP FOR THE FETUS

1. Liley, A., *Brit. Med. J.* 2:1107–1109, November 2, 1963.
2. Bevis did not publish these cases.
3. Allen, F., "Attempts at Prevention of Intrauterine Death in Erythroblastosis Fetalis." Tenth John Gibson II Lecture at the Columbia-Presbyterian Medical Center, April 25, 1963. Published as: Allen, F., *New Eng. J. Med.* 269:1344–1349, December 19, 1963.
4. V. Freda to Jerold Lucey, October 25, 1963.
5. *Medical World News*, January 1, 1965, p. 49.
6. Jackson, Benjamin, *Hospital Practice* 3:46–53, 1968.
7. Freda, V., *Hospital Practice* 2:54–63, 1967.
8. Adamsons, K., Freda, V., *et al.*, *Pediatrics* 35:848–855, 1965.
9. *Medical World News, op. cit.*
10. Liley, A., *op. cit.*
11. *Medical World News, op. cit.*
12. Lucey, J., and Butterfield, L. (eds.), *Intrauterine Transfusion and Erythroblastosis Fetalis.* Columbus, Ohio: Ross Laboratories, 1966. (Report of the 53rd Ross Conference on Pediatric Research, Aspen, Colorado, March 14–15, 1966), p. 11.
13. *Ibid.*, p. 14.
14. Quoted matter in this and the preceding paragraph is combined from *Medical World News, op. cit.*; from unpublished interview notes for this article; and from Ratcliff, J., "Conquest of Death Before Birth," *Reader's Digest*, April 1966, pp. 107–111.
15. Phibbs, Roderic, *et al.*, *Pediatrics* 47:689–696, 1971.
16. Oh, Williams, *et al.*, *Amer. J. Obstet. Gynec.* 110:330–335, 1971.

CHAPTER 23: PERIL

1. Cohen, F., and Zuelzer, W., *Vox Sang* 9:75–78 January-February 1964.
2. *Ibid.*
3. *Ibid.*
4. Medawar, P., and Sparrow, E., *J. Endocr.* 14:240, 1956.
5. W. Pollack to B. Chown, December 2, 1963.

CHAPTER 24: "KATH"

1. R. F. (Frank) Gorman to J. G. Gorman, February 13, 1964.
2. *Ibid.*
3. *The Times* (London), March 3, 1964.
4. R. F. Gorman to J. G. Gorman, March 5, 1964.
5. C. Clarke to J. G. Gorman, March 4, 1964.
6. R. Welch to J. G. Gorman, April 22, 1964.

CHAPTER 25: CLINICAL TRIALS

1. Finn is referring to Freda, V., Gorman, J., and Pollack, W., *Transfusion* 4:26–32, January-February 1964.
2. *Ibid.*
3. C. Clarke to J. G. Gorman, March 4, 1964.
4. Clarke, C., *et al., Brit. Med. J.* 1:1110, April 25, 1964.
5. Woodrow, J., *et al., Brit. Med. J.* 1:279–283, January 30, 1965.
6. J. Scudder to V. Freda, April 9, 1964.
7. V. Freda to J. Gorman, April 10, 1964.
8. J. G. Gorman to J. S. Gorman, May 19, 1964.
9. *Ibid.*
10. Gorman, J., Freda, V., and Pollack, W., *Proc. 10th Cong. Int. Soc. Blood Transf., Stockholm, 1964.* Basel: S. Karger, 1965, pp. 949–955.
11. Woodrow, J., *Proc. 10th Cong. Int. Soc. Blood Transf., Stockholm, 1964, op. cit.,* pp. 944–948.
12. *Medical World News,* January 1, 1965.
13. Woodrow, J., *et al., op. cit.*
14. Gorman, J., *et al.,* "Protection from Immunization in Rh-incompatible Pregnancies." Report to Section on Obstetrics and Gynecology of the New York Academy of Medicine, February 23, 1965. Published in: *Bull. N.Y. Acad. Med.* 42:458–473, June 1966. The statistics were updated in proof.
15. *Ibid.*
16. Cited in editorial, *Lancet* 1:1311–1312, June 19, 1965.
17. J. G. Gorman to C. Clarke, March 18, 1965.
18. Editorial, *Lancet* 1:1311–1312, June 19, 1965.
19. Gorman, J., Freda, V., and Pollack, W., *Lancet* 2:181, July 24, 1965.
20. Clarke, C., and Sheppard, P., *Lancet* 2:343, August 14, 1965.
21. *Ibid.*
22. *New York Herald Tribune,* August 7, 1965.
23. Gorman J., *et al., op. cit.*

CHAPTER 26: SECRET MEETING AT THE WALDORF

1. Freda, V., Gorman, J., and Pollack, W., *Lancet* 2:690, October 2, 1965. The typescript of this letter is dated September 9, 1965.
2. See *Medical World News,* October 1, 1965, p. 65.
3. Pollack, W., *Ann. N.Y. Acad. Sci.* 127:892–900, September 1, 1965. *N.B.:* The papers from this special symposium were published *before* the event, which took place September 10.
4. *Medical World News, op. cit.*
5. *Ibid.*
6. Freda, V., *et al., Ann. N.Y. Acad. Sci.* 127:909–925, September 1, 1965.
7. J. Gorman, memorandum, September 11, 1965.
8. Singher's reaction is described in J. Robertson to J. Gorman, October 19, 1965, and is based on a letter Robertson had just received from Singher.
9. *Medical World News, op. cit.,* pp. 31–33, 63–72.
10. J. Woodrow to J. Gorman, October 14, 1965.

CHAPTER 27: A LONG WAIT

1. B. Chown to V. Freda, April 4, 1966.
2. *Time*, December 26, 1969, p. 23.
3. Freda, V., Gorman, J., and Pollack, W., *Science* 151:828–830, February 18, 1966.
4. C. Clarke and P. Sheppard to Editor, *Science*, May 12, 1966.
5. V. Freda and J. Gorman to Robert Ormes, June 14, 1966.
6. R. Ormes to C. Clarke, June 16, 1966.
7. Clarke, C., *et al.*, *Brit. Med. J.* 1:213–214, January 22, 1966.
8. Clarke, C., and Sheppard, P., *Lancet* 2:343, August 14, 1965.
9. C. Clarke and P. Sheppard to Editor, *Science, op. cit.*
10. A. Wiener to V. Freda, October 14, 1966.
11. Richard Levere to V. Freda, October 3, 1966.
12. The fervor, which clearly is Vince's, was expressed later in: Pollack, W., Gorman, J., and Freda, V., "Prevention of Rh hemolytic disease." In: Brown, E., and Moore C. (eds.), *Progress in Hematology*, Vol. 6. New York: Grune & Stratton, 1969, pp. 121–147. This is the clearest and most concise of all the New York group's papers.
13. Gorman, J., *New York J. Med.* 68:1270–1277, 1968.
14. Gorman, J., "Rh Immunoglobulin as a Means of Prevention of Hemolytic Disease of the Newborn." Presented at the 51st annual meeting of the New York State Association of Public Health Laboratories, Albany, May 18, 1967 [Typescript].


CHAPTER 28: SUPPLY LINES

1. W. Pollack to J. Gorman, October 29, 1965.
2. Jerome Klein to V. Freda and J. Gorman, July 19, 1967.
3. P. Mollison to W. Pollack, November 23, 1966.
4. Howard Goodman to J. Gorman, February 3, 1967.
5. J. Gorman to H. Goodman, February 16, 1967.
6. H. Goodman to J. Gorman, February 28, 1967. Singher's dictum is implicit but not explicit in this correspondence.
7. Altman, R. and Marzinsky, P., *Morbidity and Mortality Weekly Report* 18:62–63, February 22, 1969. The events reported occurred in 1968.
8. *Ibid.*
9. *Medical World News*, June 2, 1967.
10. *Ibid.*
11. *Ibid.*
12. *Ibid.* N.B.: Some of the quoted material here appears only in the unedited typescript.
13. Chown, B., *et al.*, *Bull. WHO* 36:467–474, 1967.

CHAPTER 29: FAILURE AND SUCCESS

1. *Medical World News*, October 6, 1967, pp. 30–31.
2. Clarke, C., *et al.*, *Brit. Med. J.* 2:607–609, 1971.
3. *Medical World News*, *op. cit.*
4. J. Gorman to Niall Walsh, October 20, 1967.
5. Hamilton, E., Discussion, Symposium on the Rh Problem, Vanderbilt University, Nashville, Tenn., October 9–10, 1967 [Transcript]. The results of Hamilton's study were published as: Hamilton, E., *Obstet. Gynec.* 30:812–815, December 1967. Ironically, and perhaps appropriately, this is the first full report on the clinical use of Rh vaccine to appear in a major U.S. obstetrical journal.
6. Gorman, J., Remarks to Symposium on Rh, Nashville, Tenn., *op. cit.* [Transcript].
7. Hamilton, E., *op. cit.* (slightly abridged).
8. *Medical World News*, November 17, 1967, p. 44.
9. Freda, V., Gorman, J., and Pollack, W., *New Eng. J. Med.* 277:1022–1023, November 9, 1967.
10. Editorial, *New Eng. J. Med.* 277:1036–1037, November 9, 1967.
11. *Ibid.*
12. Clarke, C., "Prevention of Rh Hemolytic Disease." Lumleian Lecture delivered to the Royal College of Physicians of London, May 3, 1967. Published in: *Brit. Med. J.* 4:7–12, October 7, 1967.
13. Clarke, C., *Sci. Amer.* 219:46–52, November, 1968.
14. *Ibid.*
15. *Ibid.*
16. Clarke, C., Finn, R., McConnell, R., and Sheppard, P., *Int. Arch. Allerg.* 13:380, 1958.
17. Clarke, C., *Brit. Med. J.*, *op. cit.*
18. *Ibid.* One other account bears on the problem of who at Liverpool first suggested anti-Rh injections, but it must be labeled as wholly apocryphal, since the alleged inventor himself does not recall having made the suggestion. He is Philip Sheppard, who, it may be recalled, had spent an academic year (1954–1955) at Columbia University. He attended a meeting of the human genetics seminar—the same series at which Ronnie Finn would first meet John and Vince several years later—to hear Levine present his data on the total protection against Rh sensitization afforded by AB × O matings. Sheppard sat next to Dr. Richard Rosenfield, a highly regarded Rh expert, who was blood bank chief at nearby Mount Sinai Hospital. Rosenfield later would recall Levine insisting, on the basis of his inability to find Rh hemolytic disease in AB × O matings, that the A and B antigens, when present, provide 100 percent protection against Rh sensitization. The problem was that they are not always present. Levine failed to sell Rosenfield on this proposition, but, Rosenfield recollects, he *did sell* Sheppard, who immediately exclaimed: "If it will work with 19S ABO antibodies, it will work with 19S anti-Rh!"

Sheppard was quite excited by his idea, Rosenfield remembers, and enlarged upon it in the discussion period. Rosenfield himself was far less enthusiastic, arguing, he would later say, that there was not enough 19S anti-Rh antibody in even the best antiserum to do the job.

There is evidence, from his published papers, that Sheppard was thinking about ABO and Rh interaction at the time—and his alleged response to Levine's thinking was in keeping with what he knew (Sheppard, P., *Amer. Naturalist* 87:283–294, 1953).

When presented with Rosenfield's recollection, fifteen years later, Sheppard remembered the occasion but could not remember having made the suggestion. "It's gone, completely gone. To completely forget it, and then not remember it when someone made the same suggestion several years later—that's surprising! But I certainly can't even remember making the suggestion." If he made the suggestion, why might he have forgotten it? Sheppard laughed: "I had Rosenfield's expert view that it wouldn't work!"

19. Chown, B., *et al., Bull. WHO* 36:467–474, 1967.
20. Lehane, D., *Brit. J. Haemat.* 13:800. 1967. Cited in leading article, *Brit., Med. J.* 1:659–670, March 16, 1968.
21. Clarke, C., and McConnell, R., *Prevention of Rh-Hemolytic Disease.* Springfield: Charles C Thomas, 1972, p. 78.
22. H. Singher to J. Gorman, April 19, 1968.
23. H. Singher to V. Freda, April 19, 1968.

CHAPTER 30: THE CONQUEST OF RH DISEASE

1. Freda, V., *Amer. J. Obstet. Gynec.* 92:341–374, June 1, 1965, Table 4. These figures do not fully take into account the small but real added life salvage due to intrauterine transfusion, which began to be widely used only in 1964.
2. Gorman, J., *Clin. Obstet. Gynec.* 14:635–646, 1971.
3. *Ibid.*
4. Woodrow, J., *et al., Brit. Med. J.* 2:610–612, 1971.
5. WHO Scientific Group on the Prevention of Rh Sensitization, *Prevention of Rh Sensitization.* Geneva: *WHO Techn. Rep. Ser.*, 1971, No. 468.
6. *The New York Times*, December 5, 1972, p. 1.
7. Tytun, A., "Rh-Immunization Program" (Draft Copy). New York City Department of Health, Office of the Assistant Commissioner, November 21, 1968, 15 pages [Mimeo.].
8. *Medical World News*, May 26, 1971, p. 10.
9. Apgar, V., "Statement to the Senate Committee on Labor and Public Welfare," June 30, 1969. New York: National Foundation-March of Dimes, 5 pages [Mimeo].
10. Public Law 91–464.
11. Freda, V., *et al., Lancet* 2:147–148, 1970.
12. Behrman, Richard, and Hsia, D., *J. Pediat.* 75:718–726, 1969.
13. McMullin, G., *et al., Lancet* 2:949–952, 1970.
14. Clarke, C., *et al., Lancet* 1:793–798, 1970.
15. Furuya, N., and Yamauchi, H., *Proceedings of the Sixth World Congress of*

*Gynaecology and Obstetrics,* New York, April 12–18, 1970, Abstract No. 399.

16. Resnick, David, Two New York Physicians Win Medals for Developing Anti-Rh Immunoglobulin [News Release]. New York: Maternity Center Association, April 1968, 2 pages [Mimeo].

17. *Time,* December 26, 1969, p. 23.

CHAPTER 31: CREDIT WHERE DUE

1. *Medical World News,* October 1, 1965, p. 65.

2. Finn, R., "Erythroblastosis." Talk delivered to the Liverpool Medical Institute, February 18, 1960, 4 pages [Typescript].

3. Finn, R., *Lancet* 1:526, March 5, 1960.

4. The earliest contemporary record of the Gorman-Freda association is a memo by J. Gorman to himself, dated June 21, 1960, which contains a reminder to call "Freda." In the same memo, he writes: "Work out method of obtaining 19S gamma globulin. Who makes gamma globulin." This suggests that (1) he and Vince had not yet made contact with Bill Pollack at Ortho on that date and (2) that they had by then already discussed John's competition of antibodies plan for using 19S anti-Rh antibody to keep mothers from making the more dangerous 7S anti-Rh antibody.

5. Finn, R., "Protective Factors in Erythroblastosis." Lecture to the British Genetical Society, July 1960, 6 pages [Typescript].

6. P. Levine to V. Freda, December 5, 1960.

7. Levine, P., Introductory Remarks to the Karl Landsteiner Award Lectures at the American Association of Blood Banks 22nd Annual Meeting, Houston, November 19, 1969 [Transcript].

8. Finn, R., *Lancet, op. cit.*

9. Editorial, *New Eng. J. Med.* 277:1036–1037, November 9, 1967.

10. Finn, R., *et al., Brit. Med. J.* 1:1486–1490, May 27, 1961.

11. Finn, R., *et al.,* "Transplacental passage of red cells in man." Letter to *Nature,* dated November 30, 1960, 4 pages [Typescript].

12. Finn, R., *et al., Nature* 190:922–923, June 3, 1961.

13. Gorman, J., Freda, V., and Pollack, W., "Intramuscular injection of new experimental gamma$_2$-globulin preparation containing high levels of anti-Rh antibody as means of preventing sensitization to Rh [Abstract]." *Program, IX Congresso de la Sociedad Internacional de Hematologia,* Mexico, D.F., 1962. Published in: *Proceedings of the International Society of Hematology* (9). New York: Grune & Stratton, 1963, pp. 545–549.

14. Pollack, W., *et al., Transfusion* 8:134–145, May–June 1968.

15. *Ibid.*

16. Clarke, C., *Seminars Hemat.* 6:201–224, April 1969.

17. Pollack, W., *et al., op. cit.*

18. Clarke, C., *op. cit.*

19. *Ibid.*

20. Finn, R., Protective Mechanisms Against Rh Haemolytic Disease. Unpublished M.D. Thesis, Liverpool University, 1961.

21. *Ibid.*

22. Finn, R., *Erythroblastosis, op. cit.*, p. 4
23. Finn, R., *et al.*, *Brit. Med. J.*, *op. cit.*
24. Clarke, C., *Sci. Amer.* 219:46–52, 1968.
25. McConnell, R., *Ann. Rev. Med.* 17:291–306, 1966.
26. Clarke, C., *Sci. Amer.*, *op. cit.*
27. Clarke, C., *Brit. Med. J.* 4:7–12, October 7, 1967.
28. McConnell, R., *op. cit.*

CHAPTER 32: LAST WORDS

1. Winbaum, E., *Pediatrics* 42:214–215, 1968.
2. S. Gellis to E. Winbaum, August 23, 1957. Published in: *Pediatrics* 42:215, 1968.
3. Diamond, L., *Pediatrics* 41:1–4, 1968.
4. Race, R., and Sanger, R., *Blood Groups in Man* (5th ed.). Philadelphia: F. A. Davis, 1968, p. 224.
5. *San Francisco Chronicle*, December 25, 1970, p. 23.
6. Hugh Fudenberg to author, May 17, 1971; February 23, 1972.
7. Bazell, Robert, *Science* 173:1108–1110, 1971.
8. G. Mirick to author, April 16, 1969.
9. Lester Watson to D. McKay, August 3, 1961. Re: HRC Grant U-1154.
10. Levine, P., quoted in: Gorman, J., *The Role of the Laboratory in Rh Disease of the Newborn.* Philadelphia: Lea & Febiger, Chap. 1. In press. Levine made the remark at an Ortho symposium on Rh in 1969. As published by Ortho it is slightly different, and takes on a somewhat altered meaning. Cf., Levine, P., "The History of Rh and Hemolytic Disease of the Newborn." In: *RhoGAM One Year Later.* Raritan, N.J.: Ortho, 1969, p. 8.
11. Clarke, C., *Lancet* 2:1–7, 1968.
12. Levine, P., *RhoGAM, op. cit.*
13. *Emergency Medicine*, March 1970, pp. 67–68. The expert cited in this account is Dr. Edward Banner of the Mayo Graduate School. A similar warning is contained in the *RhoGAM* product information.

# Acknowledgments

ASSISTANCE IN USING the voluminous "Landsteiner-MacKenzie Papers" was graciously provided by American Philosophical Society Executive Director Dr. George Corner and Librarian Dr. Whitfield Bell, Jr. Brief recollections were offered by several members of Landsteiner's laboratory—Dr. Jacob Furth, Dr. Merrill Chase, Dr. James van der Scheer, Dr. Philip Levine—and by Dr. Alexander Wiener.

The elucidation of erythroblastosis at Harvard has been described by Dr. John Ferguson, Dr. James Baty, Dr. Steward Clifford, Dr. Arthur Hertig, and Dr. Louis Diamond, who helped clarify the history of exchange transfusion and other Rh events.

The few extant professional letters and manuscripts of Dr. Ruth Darrow are (1970) being kept by her former colleague and protégé, Dr. Irene Shmigelsky of Chicago, who kindly made them available for inspection and shared her personal recollection of her friendship and association with Dr. Darrow. Dr. Clementine Frankowski, Whiting, Indiana, and Dr. Josephine Chapin, Des Moines, Iowa, helped clear up puzzling and important facts about the birth and treatment of Ruth Darrow's daughter, Gail. Miss Gail Darrow (now Mrs. Tony Kaliss), and her elder sister, Virginia (now Mrs. Robin Oggins) have kindly shared their memories of their mother and her work. Mrs. Alice Darrow (the second Mrs. Chester Darrow) helpfully arranged these conversations. Dr. Lawrence Gartner contributed an astute retrospective postmortem diagnosis.

The early days of the Blood Transfusion Betterment Association and the part it played in the discovery and exegesis of the Rh factor have been evoked by Dr. Jacob Geiger and Dr. Peter Vogel of New York City. Dr. Lyman Burnham has sketched in the key moment when intragroup transfusions due to Rh were linked to erythroblastosis.

Dr. Philip Levine provided a few helpful comments on some relatively well-known and well-reported aspects of the early years of Rh research, and also contributed some observations concerning later events at the Ortho Research Foundation in Raritan, New Jersey. Miss Judy Ramsey, the author of a profile of Levine that appeared in *Medical World News*, lent her notes and impressions for this account. Mr. Steve Murata kindly lent a tape recording made of Levine's remarks on Rh to the American Association of Blood Banks twenty-second annual meeting in Houston, Texas, November 19, 1959. Thelma Rudnick, R.N. (now Mrs. Mort Weisinger) continues to remember Levine as the dedicated man of science who inspired her during her student days at Beth Israel Hospital, Newark.

Dr. Alexander Wiener granted one valuable interview in which he discussed his relationship with Dr. Vincent Freda and provided a plentitude of reprints and letters of reminiscence, as well as one key telephone interview on the early days of Rh. Regrettably, he would not consent to be interviewed about some of these matters except under conditions unacceptable to the author. Wiener claims to have contemporary letters, memoranda, documents, etc., from the period 1937–1942, but has declined to make them available; thus part of the record of those important days is missing.

Dr. Edith Potter (Mrs. Edith Meyer), now of Fort Myers, Florida, provided helpful historical perspective on the reception accorded Levine's theory of Rh and erythroblastosis when it was first published.

Dr. Fred H. Allen, Jr., has provided important perspective on the early history of exchange transfusion and on his own and others' efforts to deal in a fundamental way with erythroblastosis.

A glimpse of Dr. Vincent Freda at Presbyterian Hospital about 1960 has been provided by Dr. Sandra Grant. Dr. George McKay and Dr. John Ultman have provided key information on events relating to Dr. John Gorman in the same period. Dr. George Mirick, the Scientific Director of the Health Research Council of the City of New York, has kindly opened his files, permitting documentation of Dr. Gorman's several grant requests.

Dr. Kurt Stern has willingly shared what must be a painful account of his investigations of ABO-Rh interaction. Dr. Robert Race and Dr. Ruth Sanger cordially recalled their key roles in suggesting the correct explanation for ABO "protection."

Dr. Douglas Bevis has kindly recalled the promptings that led him to initiate fetal diagnosis with amniocentesis. Dr. Fred Stratton has confirmed his catalytic role in this endeavor. Dr. A. Harold Walker has graciously taken a day to exhibit the diagnostic system he perfected in Manchester, and Dr. John Robertson, Edinburgh, Scotland, has recalled his role in amniocentesis' early days.

A studied glimpse into the initiation of the Rh prevention project at Ortho has been provided by Dr. William Pollack. An informal appraisal of these events has come from his co-worker, Dr. Hans Hager. Mr. Glen Hill remembers well some of their early difficulties—and the steps he was able to take to help overcome them.

Light has been shed on the fruitful similarities between rhesus and swallowtails by Dr. Philip Sheppard, as well as by Dr. Cyril Clarke, who, with Mrs. Féo Clarke, kindly exhibited their elegant breeding collection of swallowtail butterflies.

Dr. Harri Nevanlinna has explained his Rh research in Helsinki in the period following World War II—and the startling discovery that grew out of it.

Dr. Jörg Schneider, a colleague and friend of Dr. Enno Kleihauer, has explained some of the circumstances surrounding the invention of the Kleihauer test as well as his own demarches against erythroblastosis based upon it.

Dr. Jonathan Uhr vividly recalled discussing antibody-mediated immunosuppression with Drs. John Gorman and Vincent Freda at a key juncture in their efforts.

Warden J. Leland Casscles of Sing Sing Prison (now Ossining Correctional Facility) has helped document the decision made by his predecessor, Warden Wilfred Denno, to permit testing at the prison; Dr. Harold Kipp has described the tests from his vantage point as senior prison physician.

Dr. Wolf Zuelzer and Dr. Flossie Cohen have discussed candidly their early, fervently-held belief that anti-Rh antibody injections postpartum could not prevent Rh sensitization. Dr. Zuelzer has provided a helpful postmortem on his evaluation of NIH Grant Application H.6754 of Dr. Vincent Freda. Mr. John Blamphin has provided helpful information in this regard, as have Dr. Heinze Berendes, chief of the Perinatal Research Project, and several of his associates.

Dr. Julius Krevans has elucidated Baltimore's extremely helpful role in Liverpool's research. Dr. John Woodrow provided a complementary account.

Miss Nancy Treacy has vividly recalled her trip to Sing Sing and other aspects of New York's male volunteer and clinical trials.

Dr. A. William Liley kindly explained, at great length and with much humor, his discovery of intrauterine blood transfusion. Dr. Douglas Bevis graciously shared his experiences with a less-successful technique. Dr. Jerold Lucey kindly permitted the author to attend part of the conference he organized in Stowe, Vermont, in the autumn of 1964 to inaugurate the new subspecialty of fetology.

Dr. Richard Francis (Frank) Gorman, and his wife, Kathryn, have vividly recalled the birth of their first son, Kieron Francis. Dr. John S. Gorman relived his role in this event.

Two early participants in the clinical trials, Dr. Elmer Jennings and Dr. John Queenan, willingly provided information about them.

Confirmation of the intended purpose and outcome of the hepatitis-interrupted plasmapheresis project in New Jersey came from Dr. Ronald Altman and Dr. Charles Janeway.

Dr. Eugene Hamilton related his remarkable story with remarkable modesty. Dr. Richard Rosenfield remembered a pregnant moment, long ago, that Dr. Philip Sheppard had long forgotten.

Dr. Richard Judelsohn has provided up-to-the-minute reports on the Rh vaccine as a public health challenge. Dr. Edward Winbaum graciously recounted his anguishing tale of an opportunity missed. Dr. Hugh Fudenberg graciously explained a cost/benefit estimate he had developed.

A few who have helped must remain anonymous, and a few I have failed to mention. I thank them, too!

—D. R. Z.

# Glossary

These definitions apply to the immunologic system and diseases described in this volume, and are not necessarily applicable to others.

*A-antigen.* A substance, or blood factor, on the surface of some individuals' red cells, that provokes an immune reaction from anti-A antibody.

*ABO blood groups.* *See* Human blood groups.

*ABO-compatible.* One person is ABO-compatible to another if his red cells do not carry A or B antigen that will provoke a reaction from antibodies in the other's serum.

*ABO-incompatible.* One person is ABO-incompatible to another if his red cells carry A and/or B antigen that will provoke an immune reaction if transfused into the other, due to the presence in the other's serum of anti-A and/or anti-B antibody.

*ABO protection.* The immunologic phenomenon through which a fetus that is ABO-incompatible with its mother as well as Rh-incompatible with her appears to be less in danger of erythroblastosis than one which is Rh-incompatible but ABO-compatible with her.

*Agglutinate* (verb). To bring together in an aggregate, or clump, as some antibodies do to red cells.

*Agglutination.* Immune reaction in which red cells carrying a specific antigen (for example, A) are stuck together in clumps, or aggregates, by the corresponding antibody (anti-A).

*AMIS.* *See* Antibody-medicated immunosuppression.

*Amniocentesis.* Passage of a hollow needle into the amniotic fluid that surrounds the fetus in the womb, and the removal of a specimen of the fluid. Analysis of the fluid specimen indicates the severity of the fetus' erythroblastosis.

*Anamnestic reaction.* A secondary immune reaction, which occurs after the individual's body has initially responded to a particular antigen. Anamnestic reactions generally require less antigen, occur more rapidly, and are stronger than initial immunizing reactions.

*Anemia.* A deficiency state of blood in which there are too few red cells or the red cells are of too poor quality to fulfill their oxygen-transporting function in the body.

*Anti-A antibody.* An antibody naturally present in individuals of groups O and B that will attack and destroy red cells of persons in groups A and AB.

*Anti-B antibody.* An antibody naturally present in individuals of groups O and A that will attack and destroy red cells of persons in groups B and AB.

*Antibody.*   A substance produced by the body in response to a specific foreign material, or antigen. An antibody acts, in an immune reaction, to defend the body by destroying or nullifying the antigen against which it is made.

*Antibody-mediated immune enhancement.*   The immunologic phenomenon in which injection of a tiny amount of passive antibody (anti-X), along with its corresponding antigen (X), increases the likelihood of an immune response, and leads to a more potent active immunization (anti-X antibody production) than injection of the antigen alone without the passive antibody.

*Antibody-mediated immunosuppression.*   The immunologic phenomenon in which injection of critically large amounts of passive antibody (anti-X), along with its corresponding antigen (X), prevents the antigen from provoking an active immune response. The individual thus is kept from making his own (anti-X) antibody against the antigen.

*Antigen.*   A substance on or in a red cell that is antagonistic to a human or other organism in such a way that it forms an antibody against it. The blood factors A, B, and Rh are antigens. Chemically, most antigens are proteins.

*Anti-Rh antibody.*   An antibody that may be formed in Rh-negative individuals, in response to antigenic challenge by the Rh factor, which will attack and destroy red cells of persons who are Rh-positive.

*Anti-Rh gamma globulin.*   *See* Rh vaccine.

*B antigen.*   A substance on the surface of some individuals' red cells that provokes an immune reaction from anti-B antibody.

*Bilirubin.*   A breakdown product of hemoglobin released when red cells are destroyed; it is made by the liver. Some forms of this bile pigment are highly toxic, and may stain and injure brain tissue (*kernicterus*), causing death.

*Blood factor.*   An inherited antigen present on the surface membrane of red cells of some individuals but not on others.

*Blood groups.*   *See* Human blood groups.

*CDE.*   Alternative nomenclature for the Rh blood group system.

*Cell clearance.*   The removal of incompatible red cells from the bloodstream.

*Clone.*   An aggregate of cells whose members are all descended from a single individual. An *immunologic clone* is a group of lymphocytes that all produce antibody against a single antigen.

*Compatibility.*   A person is compatible with another if his red cells can be transfused into him without provoking an immune reaction, or *transfusion reaction.*

*Congenital anemia.*   A relatively mild form of erythroblastosis fetalis.

This anemia in newborns usually results from the destruction of their red cells by anti-Rh antibodies from the mother.

*Double incompatibility.* A fetus' incompatibility with its mother in both the ABO and Rh blood group systems. A fetus that is group A, Rh-positive is doubly incompatible with a group O, Rh-negative mother. *See* ABO protection.

*Edema.* Swelling of body tissues due to fluid retention.

*Enhancement. See* Antibody-mediated immune enhancement.

*Erythroblast.* An immature red cell. It is identifiable under the microscope because, unlike adult red cells, it still retains a nucleus. Too rapid destruction of adult red cells leads to compensatory overproduction of immature ones; hence, the disease name, *erythroblastosis*, which signifies the presence of an excess of erythroblasts.

*Erythroblastosis fetalis.* Disease of fetal and early newborn life. Usually occurs when red cells from Rh-positive fetus cross the placenta and provoke immune response in Rh-negative mother. Her anti-Rh antibodies then enter fetus, destroying its red cells, and stimulating abnormally high production of immature red cells, or *erythroblasts*.

*Erythrocyte. See* Red blood cell.

*Exchange transfusion.* In newborn erythroblastic infants, total or near-total removal of the baby's Rh-positive blood, which is vulnerable to attack by maternal antibodies brought from the womb, and its simultaneous replacement with invulnerable Rh-negative blood.

*Fetal bleed.* Red cells from the fetus that leak across the placenta into the maternal circulation during pregnancy or during delivery of the baby and placenta.

*Fetology.* A medical subspecialty that centers on care and study of the unborn baby.

*Fractionation.* The separation of serum into its component parts through physical and chemical methods. In this process, the 7S and 19S gamma globulin *fractions* can be isolated.

*Gamma globulin* (GG). That part of the serum of which antibodies are made. The gamma globulin is separable into several parts on the basis of their molecular weight. Two of these parts are designated 7S and 19S.

*Genetics.* The biologic science that deals with heredity, and change and similarity between organisms through time.

*GG. See* Gamma globulin.

*Group. See* Human blood groups.

*Group A.* A person whose red cells carry the A antigen but not the B belongs to group A.

*Group AB.* A person whose red cells carry the A antigen and the B antigen belongs to group AB.

*Group B.*  A person whose red cells carry the B antigen but not the A belongs to group B.

*Group O.*  A person whose red cells carry neither the A antigen nor the B belongs to group O.

*Hematology.*  The medical specialty that focuses on diagnosis and treatment of blood disease and the study of blood.

*Hematopoiesis.*  The physiologic process of making new blood cells.

*Hemoglobin.*  The stuff of red cells, which gives them their color and which binds oxygen so that the cells can transport it from the lungs to all body tissues.

*Hemolysis.*  Destruction of a red cell by an agent that eats through its outer membrane, spilling the contents. Some antibodies are *hemolysins.*

*Hemolytic anemia.*  Anemia caused by the destruction of red cells. Antibody against an antigen on a red cell's surface may *hemolyze* the cell. Erythroblastosis fetalis is a hemolytic anemia.

*Human blood groups.*  Usually designates the four groups of individuals—A, B, O, and AB—identified by the ABO system discovered by Landsteiner. For clarity, other systems, like Rh, are said to define blood *types*, rather than groups. Each blood group or type is based on a blood factor, or *antigen*, that is present on its members' red cells.

*Hydrops.*  The most severe form of erythroblastosis fetalis, in which the baby is born waterlogged, swollen, and, usually, dead.

*Icterus.*  Yellowing of the skin. It occurs when excessive destruction of red cells leads to a backup of their breakdown products in the body.

*Icterus gravis neonatorum.*  A form of erythroblastosis found in newborns who are unable to excrete bilirubin and other breakdown products of fetal cells destroyed by anti-Rh antibody from the mother.

*Immune antibodies.*  Antibodies that result from immunities triggered by disease organisms or other extrinsic substances. For example, anti-Rh antibodies in a woman sensitized by a fetal bleed of Rh-positive red cells.

*Immune reaction.*  The self-protecting production of antibody against an antigen, and the antibody's interaction with the antigen. Also called *immune response.*

*Immunization.*  The formation by an individual of antibody against a particular antigen. Once the individual has reacted immunologically to a given antigen, he will respond, quickly, with antibody production whenever that antigen is again present. This individual thus is *immunized*, or has developed an *immunity*, to that antigen.

*Immunocompetent clone.*  A clone of lymphocytes that produces antibody that is able to attack the antigen against which it is directed.

*Immunogenic.* Pertains to a substance that will provoke an immune reaction; an antigen.

*Immunohematology.* Subspecialty of immunology that focuses on antigens and antibodies of blood.

*Immunoincompetent clone.* A clone of lymphocytes that produces antibody that tolerates the antigen against which it is directed.

*Immunologic tolerance.* An individual's acceptance of an antigen, either through failure to produce antibody against it, or through the production of antibody that fails to attack the antigen.

*Immunology.* The science that studies the immune reaction.

*Incompatibility.* A person is incompatible with another if his red cells will provoke an immune reaction, or *transfusion reaction*, when transfused into the other.

*Intragroup transfusion reaction.* Transfusion reaction occurring after recipient has been given ABO-compatible donor blood. The term is archaic, since most "intragroup reactions" now can be traced to incompatibility due to Rh or other blood group systems.

*Intrauterine transfusion.* A transfusion of red cells into an erythroblastic fetus, usually through a thin tube stuck through the mother's abdominal wall, uterus, and into the fetal abdominal cavity.

*In utero.* In the uterus, e.g., a fetus.

*In vitro.* In glass, i.e., in a test tube or lab vessel rather than in a living body (*in vivo*).

*Jaundice.* Yellowing of the skin. It occurs when excessive destruction of red cells leads to a backup of their breakdown products in the body.

*Kernicterus.* *See* Bilirubin.

*Kleihauer test.* A laboratory method for identifying fetal red cells present in a specimen of the mother's red cells. The hemoglobin of the adult cells is washed away, while the hemoglobin in the fetal cells remains.

*Liter.* Approximately one quart liquid measure.

*Lymphocyte.* A white blood cell that plays a role in antibody production.

*Lyze* (verb). To dissolve, as some antibodies do to red cells.

*Mimetic* (adjective). *See* Mimicry.

*Mimicry.* The protective genetic mechanism through which an animal, like a butterfly, that tastes good to a predator takes on the appearance of another, bad-tasting species—with the result that predators leave it alone.

*ml.* Milliliter. A thousandth of a liter. 5 ml = 1 teaspoonful; 30 ml = 1 ounce; 1 ml is approximately 1 cc of liquid.

*Natural antibodies.* Antibodies that result from immunities which arise spontaneously in the normal course of an individual's growth and development. For example, anti-A antibody in a group B individual.

*19S.*   A part of the gamma globulin in which antibodies may exist. The 19S gamma globulin molecule is relatively large, has five armlike appendages and will not pass through the placenta from mother to fetus.

*Obstetrics.*   The medical specialty dealing with pregnancy, labor, and delivery of babies. Abbreviated *OB.*

*Passive antibody.*   Antibody that has been injected into an individual, as contradistinct from *active antibody*, which is made by the individual's immune system in response to an antigenic challenge.

*Pathology.*   The science of disease and its causes. Pathologists conduct autopsies and render diagnoses on the basis of tests and analysis of specimens removed from patients. In American hospitals, a pathologist often runs the blood bank.

*Placenta.*   Tissue structure at the fetus' point of attachment to the uterine wall. It is richly endowed with blood vessels. Maternal and fetal circulations are separated by a very thin membrane, through which nourishment passes in to the fetus.

*Plasma.*   The clear liquid portion of blood after the red cells have been removed.

*Plasmapheresis.*   A technique used in blood banks in which a donor's blood is spun at a high speed so that the plasma separates from the red cells. The plasma is processed to recover its gamma globulin and other medically useful fractions, while the red cells are returned to the donor. This permits the donor to be bled for his plasma as often as twice a week, rather than once every six weeks, which is the rule if the red cells are not returned.

*Postpartum.*   After delivery of a baby.

*Protection.*   *See* ABO protection.

*Reagent.*   A chemical used to identify another chemical. Anti-A antibody, for example, is a reagent that identifies group A red cells by clumping them in a test tube.

*Red blood cells.*   Dish-shaped cells whose stuff, the hemoglobin, gives them their reddish color. Red cells carry oxygen from lungs to all body tissues. Red cell covering, or *membrane*, carries A, B, Rh, and other blood factors, or antigens.

*Resident.*   A doctor receiving advanced training in a medical specialty, usually in a hospital.

*Rh-compatible.*   One person is Rh-compatible with another if his red cells cannot provoke an immune reaction, due to anti-Rh antibodies, when transfused into the other. Individuals who are Rh-negative are Rh-compatible with everyone. Individuals who are

Rh-positive are Rh-compatible with other Rh-positive individuals.

*Rh factor.* An antigen found on the red cell membrane surface of about 85 percent of humans. It is named after a similar antigen on rhesus monkey red cells; its chemical composition is unknown. The Rh factor is responsible for erythroblastosis fetalis and some transfusion reactions.

*Rh hemolytic disease.* Disease of fetal and early newborn life. It occurs when red cells from an Rh-positive fetus cross the placenta and provoke an immune response in an Rh-negative mother. Her anti-Rh antibodies then enter the fetus, destroying its red cells, and stimulating abnormally high production of immature cells, or *erythroblasts.*

*Rh immunization.* The immunization of an Rh-negative individual to the Rh factor through deliberate or inadvertent transfusion of Rh-positive blood, or (in pregnant women) through transplacental passage of fetal Rh-positive red cells into the maternal circulation.

*Rh immunoglobulin.* *See* Rh vaccine.

*Rh-incompatible.* A person is Rh-incompatible with another if his red cells can provoke an immune reaction, due to anti-Rh antibodies, when transfused into the other. A person is Rh-incompatible with another only if he is Rh-positive and the other is Rh-negative.

*Rh-negative.* A person whose red cells do not carry the Rh factor is Rh-negative.

*Rh-positive.* A person whose red cells carry the Rh factor is Rh-positive.

*Rh vaccine.* Potent anti-Rh antibody, in the form of the 7S fraction of gamma globulin. The vaccine is administered to a woman unsensitized to the Rh factor when she delivers a baby in order to prevent her from developing an immunity to the Rh factor that could cause sickness or death in the next Rh-positive baby she conceives.

*RhoGAM.* Ortho's registered trade name for Rh vaccine.

*S.* Svedberg unit, a determinant of a substance's molecular weight.

*Sensitization.* *See* Immunization.

*Serology.* The subspecialty of immunology that deals with serum, and especially the antibodies it contains and their reactions with red cell antigens. Under this designation it is a dying occupation, as yesterday's serologist tends to be today's immunohematologist.

*Serum.* The clear, liquid part of blood which remains after the red cells and clotting elements have been removed.

*7S.* A part of the gamma globulin in which antibodies may exist. The 7S gamma globulin molecule is relatively small, has two armlike appendages, and will pass through the placenta from mother to fetus.

*Supergene.* A unit of inheritance that ties together several genes, and the individual traits that they determine, so that all are expressed together in the next generation.

*Titer.* The measure of an antibody's strength. An antibody with a low titer, 1:2, is less potent than one with a higher titer, 1:64, or 1:64,000.

*Tolerance. See* Immunologic tolerance.

*Transfusion reaction.* The destruction of incompatible donor blood in a transfusion recipient's bloodstream may quickly produce discomfort, anxiety, difficulty in breathing, rapid heartbeat, and other distressful symptoms. Kidney failure and death may follow.

*Uterus.* The female organ in which the young develops from just after conception to birth.

*Vaccine.* A substance introduced into the body to prevent disease immunologically.

# Index